MW00699680

The GRE Math Prep Book for Students Who Have Forgotten a Lot of Their High School Math

Robert Gerver, Ph.D.

Cover, artwork, and internal design: Michael Gerver
Reviewers: Linda Gerver, Julianne Marra

Copyright 2022
ISBN: 978-0-578-34772-1

Dedicated to
the most wonderful family anyone could ever wish for:
Linda, Julie, Jordan, Courtney, Michael, and Cameron

About the Author

Robert Gerver, Ph.D. received the Presidential Award for Excellence in Mathematics Teaching from President Ronald Reagan in 1988, and his Ph.D. from New York University in 1990. Since 1977, he has specialized in creating programs and strategies for students who struggle. He has authored 27 math books and numerous journal articles. His math research program, *Writing Math Research Papers*, received the 1997 Chevron Best Practices in Education Award as the premier high school mathematics course in the United States. Dr. Gerver taught at North Shore High School on Long Island for 40 years, and was inducted into the Long Island Math Educators Hall of Fame in 2016 and the New York State Math Educators Hall of Fame in 2017. He currently teaches at The Institute for Creative Problem Solving at State University of New York at Old Westbury, in a math research program for high school students from all over Long Island. Over the past 4+ decades he has tutored students for the SAT, GRE, ACT, and many state mathematics exit exams. He has spoken at hundreds of mathematics conferences from Maine to Hawaii, and regularly gives professional development seminars all over the country. He is also the drummer of Just Sixties, the longest running Sixties tribute band in the United States, which he founded in 1982.

Table of Contents

So, you don't have to love mathematics or major in it in college to appreciate it. As a mature young adult, just learn to respect how it's enriched your life! And having a better outlook and attitude will make your GRE Math study sessions more productive.

Where Do You Stand with Respect to the Math Portion of the GRE as of Now?

Has it been years since you took a math course? Have you forgotten many of the math skills you learned in middle and high school? Are you a good math student who just needs a refresher course on many of the things you learned earlier? Have you had trouble learning mathematics in the past? Are there certain topics that consistently give you trouble? If you are apprehensive about taking the GRE, you need systematic, scientific, targeted strategies to overcome this. GRE courses and tutors can get expensive, but with a sound plan, desire, motivation, and time you can tackle the math portion of the GRE on your own.

Remember that it would take a dozen textbooks to comprehensively cover all of the mathematics you have learned in your school career. This book's focus is to comb through the essentials, find the ones you need remediation with, refresh your memory, and help you relearn those skills. This book does not reteach every single skill you learned in your middle and high school math classes. It concentrates on skills that, in almost five decades of teaching and tutoring students, I have found need to be refreshed so GRE practice exams can be taken effectively and efficiently, without stops and starts to relearn forgotten skills. If you are floundering with (or guessing?!) the basic skills, you will have a tough time negotiating problems when the GRE raises the bar to trickier, deeper, and more convoluted problems. You need solid basics under your belt before you try to gauge your ability with GRE-type questions. Many students who improved their practice GRE scores don't realize that a great deal of the improvement came from polishing up on forgotten facts that impeded their initial success.

So, keep in mind that the focus of this book is *not* to give you simulated GRE exam questions. It is to relearn and strengthen the underlying skills you have forgotten that would have hampered your GRE practice exam sessions. Once you have all of the core concepts under your belt, you can tackle GRE practice exams with much more success and effectiveness. You can concentrate on the problems themselves, because you have relearned and mastered the prerequisite components.

Be Proactive:
Make Your GRE Preparation Purposeful and Productive

The concept behind this book is the result of decades of helping college students with GRE nuances and challenges. I consistently noticed that students had trouble recollecting skills necessary to solve GRE problems. Consequently, they stumbled and got problems incorrect based on the fact that they had forgotten many skills required on the GRE.

Most college students purchase GRE review books that are comprised of 6-10 sample GRE practice tests. If that is your first step, as you attempt the problems, you will get stuck at roadblocks because you forgot (or had never mastered) certain mathematical concepts. It becomes difficult to time your practice sessions because you are constantly interrupted by researching previously-learned material to refresh your memory at multiple junctures throughout your practice time. **The GRE Math Prep Book for Students Who Have Forgotten A Lot of Their High School Math** will help you avoid that. Complete the review of all strategies *before* attempting a practice GRE. Then, you will avoid many of the roadblocks that were going to impede your progress when you take a full sample GRE exam. You'll get more out of your practice GRE exams if you don't get bogged down in relearning material you have forgotten.

Consequently, it is best to study for your GRE Math section systematically. First, you must comb through all previously learned concepts to see what you remember well and what you have forgotten. This book can act as that "comb." It will refresh your memory, and reveal what you need help with. Each concept has a section called <u>Key Descriptors</u>, which gives you words and phrases you can use to do an Internet search or look through a math textbook's index. Those sources will be perfect if you need a more comprehensive review.

How long will it take you to complete this book? That depends on how many skills you know solidly and how many skills you need to brush-up on. This book is the perfect diagnostic tool to make sure you are ready for GRE practice tests.

The purpose of this book is to review material required for the GRE math sections, diagnose where you need help, give you some studying strategies, and to maximize the results you get when you start taking practice GRE exams. This book is designed to help you avoid stumbling blocks when you take practice GRE exams, by refreshing your memory on things you may have forgotten, and helping you to relearn concepts you may have not sufficiently mastered. It is not intended to mimic GRE questions--it is support and preparation for tackling GRE-type questions. Carefully read the section below, "A Well-Planned Study Calendar Makes a Huge Difference" to see how you can integrate this book into your preparation plans.

Planning your Preparation

Getting Familiar with the GRE Quantitative Reasoning Sections

What mathematics classes should you have completed to maximize success on the GRE? The GRE Quantitative Reasoning (mathematics) sections cover topics from middle school arithmetic, high school algebra, geometry, and probability and statistics, which you may have taken in high school or college.

The math topics included on the GRE are categorized as Arithmetic, Algebra, Geometry, and Data Analysis. Some questions require students to employ skills from more than one of these topics.

- **Arithmetic:** This topic includes integers, divisibility, factors, exponents, roots, percent, ratio and proportion, absolute value, decimals and fractions, order of operations, estimation, and more.

- **Algebra:** This topic includes functions, algebraic operations, solving linear and quadratic equations, inequalities, word problems, coordinate graphing, equations of lines, systems of equations, and more.

- **Geometry:** This topic includes triangles, circles, polygons, special right triangles, area, perimeter, volume, the Pythagorean theorem, and more.

- **Data Analysis:** This topic includes measures of central tendency like the mean, median, and mode, measures of dispersion such as the range, interquartile range, and standard deviation, box and whisker plots, scatterplots, frequency distributions, normal distributions, Venn diagrams, permutations and combinations, and more.

Surprisingly, the GRE does not test higher-level high school math topics; it actually concentrates on middle school and early high school math. But you'd be surprised how a problem with only a sixth-grade math prerequisite can be tricky and/or downright difficult!

The GRE is usually taken online. In certain locations, it is possible to take a paper test, but this is usually only offered three times a year; twice in the Fall and once in the Spring. The computer version is offered several times every week, at testing centers or with an at-home site. The paper and online versions vary. The online test consists of two mathematics sections with 20 questions each. You have 35 minutes to complete each section. The paper version consists of two mathematics sections with 25 questions each. You have 40 minutes to complete each section.

There are four types of questions in the two Quantitative Reasoning sections.

- **Multiple Choice questions that have one correct answer.** The letters for the answer choices you bubble in are written in ovals. There is only one correct answer for each of these questions.
- **Multiple Choice questions where more than one correct answer is possible.** The letters for the answer choices you bubble in are written in squares to hopefully remind you that there may be more than one correct answer. To get the question correct, you need to give all of the correct answers. These questions could possibly have only one correct answer.
- **Numeric Entry questions**. A numeric entry question requires you to write in a number for your answer--there are no choices as in multiple choice. The online GRE calculator actually has a Transfer Display key that will transfer your calculator display to the numeric entry box. This helps avoid transcribing errors.
- **Quantitative Comparison questions**. These questions ask you to compare two quantities.

This book includes samples of all of these types of questions so you can get used to them.

There is no penalty for guessing, so you should answer every question. You will need to keep your eye on the clock when you take the GRE to make sure you have time to fill in answers to problems you did not have time to complete.

Familiarize yourself with the website **ets.org/gre** to get detailed information about all of the GRE specifics on test structure, scoring, and reporting scores.

Now that you are more familiar with the test, let's concentrate on refreshing your mathematics skills. How can we start a productive, proactive journey to achieve our goals?

A Well-Planned Study Calendar Makes a Huge Difference

You do not want to wait until the last minute to study for your GRE. That is tantamount to "winging it," and by virtue of the fact that you are reading this book, you have a more mature outlook on your education than that. The last-minute method stinks—it removes the chance for you to diagnose areas in which you have difficulty, reflect on concepts that trouble you, and to let the new skills that you have learned simmer and become internalized into your mathematics problem-solving arsenal. As a result, it erodes ability and self-confidence.

The GRE Math Prep Book for Students Who Have Forgotten A Lot of Their High School Math prepares you to start taking timed, practice GRE exams. It serves as a bridge to taking practice exams. We recommend that you complete this book a month or two before the actual GRE. Then you can use that month or two to take 5-10 practice GRE exams. It is very effective if you can do one complete, timed GRE each week for 5-8 weeks before the exam. Do the practice exams in one sitting so you can simulate the exam as best as possible. You want to simulate the "fatigue factor" so that on "Test Day" you will be well acclimated to the testing situation. Yes, all of this takes time, but you need to prioritize and allocate the respective amount of time for all of your activities, and the degree of reward you want from each of them. You may decide to "backburner" some other activities as you prepare for your GRE, but if you start early enough, the weekly time input can be easily and prudently scheduled.

Rather than "hope" some available time "morphs" into your schedule each week for GRE preparation, it is best to set a time in advance and stick to it. So, on Monday, you might put into your calendar "take Math GRE next Sunday 7pm." This time could change each week. It will need to be flexible since you have a busy life!

This book also includes twenty-five short, 3-5-minute daily quizzes. You can take one per day, Monday-Friday, during the five weeks before the GRE. They are just little basic fact reminders to keep you sharp on some basic skills you need to have at your fingertips as the GRE test date approaches. They are all basic, quick checkups to keep you fresh on the little things you may have forgotten. Some quizzes may take you under a minute to complete. They also help diagnose concepts you may need to brush up on. The answers are in the back of the book.

Once you are finished with this book, you should get a book of sample practice GRE exams, and do as many as you can. That is where you will really hone the skills you reviewed in this book, and get a feel for the difficulty level of the actual GRE.

Earlier, shorter, and frequent study sessions are better than last minute cramming. The new skills need to be internalized so they can be retrieved and then applied in future problems. Below is an ideal timeline for people who want to be very proactive to ensure their GRE goals are met. Notice you should start studying at least three months in advance. If you start later than that, you can do a little extra studying each week.

- Start this book three months (or earlier) before the GRE, and finish it within 5 weeks.
- Take one timed, practice GRE per week for 5-8 weeks before the exam.
- Take one daily quiz per weekday for 5 weeks before the GRE.
- Throughout this process, get extra help on topics you still find difficult.

You always have to use balance and discretion to achieve your goals in all of your activities. Decide what priority you give to your GRE grade, and adjust the suggestions above to meet your needs and schedule. Think of how long and how often you allocate time as a part of your other endeavors--whether it be a sport, theatre, musical instrument, family obligation, volunteer time, a household chore, a school subject, club, or course, or a hobby. You do not wait until the last minute for the school play, your sports team, or your recital. Your GRE preparation deserves the same amount of pride and maturity.

Calculator Usage

The GRE online test gives you access to a "four-function" calculator. It has addition, subtraction, multiplication, division, square root, parentheses, +/-, and memory keys. It is much less sophisticated than the graphing calculator you may have used in high school or college. The online GRE calculator also has a Transfer Display key that will transfer your calculator display to the numeric entry box for numeric entry questions only.

About Tips and "Tricks"

You might encounter some written material or videos on the Internet that deal with GRE test-taking tips and tricks. Keep in mind that no tricks can substitute for knowing the mathematical content. Knowing the content is a prerequisite for the test. If you don't know that the sum of the angles of a triangle is 180 degrees, and a question requires knowing that fact, relying on a "trick" is not wise.

When You Take Your Actual GRE

Some people who struggle with a topic have test anxiety--they get nervous before and during tests. Being nervous on test day is counterproductive--it makes taking the test more difficult. Interestingly, if nervousness and worry in the weeks and months *before* the test make you study and get better prepared, that worry may have worked in your favor. Your best route is to make sure you had plenty of practice in frequent smaller snippets, rather than putting in eight hours the day before the test.

The night before the test, be sure to get a good night's sleep. On the morning of test day, have a good breakfast. Then, think of how you prepared in a mature, productive, timely fashion over the past 2-3 months and rest assured you are putting your best foot forward.

How Are the Strategies in This Book Presented?

This book is divided into six parts.

Part 1-Mapping Out a Math GRE Practice Plan

This is the part you are currently reading. It is all about a carefully engineered plan designed, field-tested, and revised, to maximize your GRE Math score.

Part 2-General Strategies for GRE Success

Part 2 of this book has some general studying and test-taking strategies with examples. They include suggestions about test taking, problem solving, recalling formulas, calculator use, reading diagrams, keeping a list of your personalized GRE tips, and more. It is a good idea to read this short section at several different junctures during the two months before your GRE, so you internalize them.

Part 3-Mathematical Topics Refresher

Part 3 addresses the mathematical topics you need to review so you are able to take practice GRE exams. This is the bulk of the book, and the part that will "bring back" many of the skills you may have forgotten. It is absolutely necessary you relearn these skills before attempting a practice GRE exam. The mathematical topics in Part 3 will be presented in this format:

Core Concept

The Core Concept title is the mathematical umbrella name of the strategies that will be covered. The Core Concepts are numbered 1 through 88. They are presented in a deliberate and sensible, but not a rigid, order--different students could have covered the strategies in their math courses in different orders. There are several related skills presented in each Core Concept. As you go through the book, you may decide to skip Core Concepts for which you are not in need of any review.

Introduction

The Introduction section introduces the material that will be covered for this individual strategy. It is where you will "self-relearn" the 'why' and 'how' of the material you may have forgotten.

Examples

The Examples give sample model problems covering the Core Concept. In many Core Concepts, there is more than one Example. Keep in mind that this book is a review/refresher of concepts you have already learned in middle school and high school. You are using this book (and possibly other sources) to self-relearn these topics. You can always use the Key Descriptors feature (explained below) to get more information on any specific topic.

Solutions

The Solutions to each Example is fully explained, right after each Example is stated. The model problems should be just enough to get you reacquainted with the concept in a time-efficient manner.

Fill in the Blanks

This section requires you to fill in blanks with the correct words. This strategy helps make sure you understand the concept being covered, and the vocabulary you will need as you practice doing GRE-level problems. When completed, the full-sentence paragraph serves as a nice summary of the Core Concept that was covered.

Basic Problem

The Basic Problem reviews the essence of the skill covered in the model problem. This level of problem is sometimes called a "routine" problem. The math portion of the GRE usually features problems that are more complex than the Basic Problem, but you need to check that you understand the basics before you tackle the more advanced problems.

Intermediate Problem

The Intermediate Problem offers an extension, or a "twist" on the basic concept presented. They are more difficult, and less routine, than the basic problems. Many intermediate problems are multi-step problems that can tap other skills besides the specific skill being addressed in the Core Concept.

Challenging Problem

The Challenging Problem is a more difficult question about the Core Concept presented. Keep in mind that, depending on their background, different people have different opinions on how "hard" a problem is. Many challenging problems are multi-step problems that can tap other skills besides the specific skill being addressed in the Core Concept.

Numeric Entry Problem

Numeric entry questions require you to enter a number. Numeric Entry problems are presented in this book so you can get used to the format. Here is a sample of the numeric entry rectangle you will see on the GRE.

Quantitative Comparison Problem

In this book, every odd-numbered Core Concept features a Quantitative Comparison problem, so you can get used to the format. Here is a sample:

Compare Quantity A and Quantity B, using the information below.

Quantity A	Quantity B
The GCF of 16 and 48.	**The LCM of 3 and 8.**

Select one of the following answers.

a) Quantity A is greater.
b) Quantity B is greater.
c) The two quantities are equal.
d) The relationship cannot be determined from the information given.

Multiple Choice with Multiple Answers Problem

A Multiple Choice with Multiple Answers Problem appears in each even-numbered Core Concept. Each problem of this type can have 1-4 correct answers, and you have to select _all_ correct answers to get the problem correct. On the GRE, the answer bubbles for these questions have squares around the letter choices, as opposed to ovals for the "regular" multiple choice problems. The Multiple Choice with Multiple Answers problems in this book have the letter choices surrounded by square brackets as opposed to parentheses. Here is a sample:

Which of the following expressions is equal to 7?

[a] $-|6 + 1|$ [b] $|8 - 1|$ [c] $|8| + |-1|$ [d] $|8| - |-1|$

Here there are two correct answers, [b] and [d]. In this book, every even-numbered Core Concept features a Multiple Choice with Multiple Answers problem, so you can get used to the format.

Key Descriptors

If you want to use a mathematics textbook or do an Internet search to get more review on a specific Core Concept, the Key Descriptors give you key terms and phrases you can use to do an online search or look through a textbook's index. Both types of sources will give you more examples, explanations, and practice problems. You also may run across a different skill embedded within a topic that you need review on, and you can use textbooks or online resources for that skill too.

Did You Know That?

The end of some of the Core Concepts features a Did You Know That? box. This is a collection of historical facts, fascinating facts, math problems with counter-intuitive answers, and other mathematically-recreational tidbits and surprises. Enjoy them!

Review/Renew

Starting with Core Concept 50, each Core Concept will add an additional feature called Review/Renew. This will review a Core Concept previously covered, and the number of the Core Concept being reviewed will be indicated.

Remember, this material is not brand new to you. You have previously encountered these skills, even if you have forgotten them or had never mastered them. You are really "self-relearning" as you complete this book.

You know how you never really "read" your math textbooks? You only really used them for homework problems. If you were ever absent, you probably did not read ahead in the book to learn what you missed. You wanted a knowledgeable teacher to lead you through it, and rightly so.

Now, you can get practice in reading to learn math, using this book. Use it as a self-tutorial. The focus and concentration required will help you read GRE problems more carefully, efficiently, critically and constructively. Reading math is not like reading the gossip or sports pages--it always requires re-reading passages.

Part 4-Daily Quizzes

Part 4-Daily Quizzes consists of twenty-five daily quizzes you will use to make sure you have the Core Concept skills at your fingertips. These are short reviews of facts that will keep you sharp. They take just a few minutes each to complete. As discussed previously, you can take one each weekday for the last five weeks before your GRE. It is much better to take one a day--just a few minutes' work--than cram a bunch in the weekend before the GRE. This way, if the quizzes help you diagnose an area you need help in, you have time to relearn and practice that skill.

The quiz questions are not necessarily GRE "style" questions. (You'll have plenty of those once you start taking practice GRE exams). The quiz questions are designed to help you use the prerequisite skills you recently refreshed. Having a sound foundation in these skills allows you to analyze and think mathematically as you tackle GRE questions.

The Core Concept number of each quiz question is printed next to the question, as shown below in a sample quiz question. The 'CC 58' in the lower right corner means that this skill is covered in Core Concept 58.

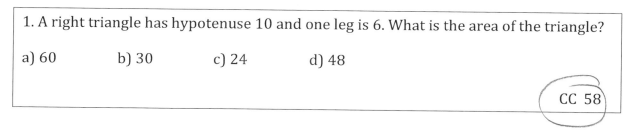

1. A right triangle has hypotenuse 10 and one leg is 6. What is the area of the triangle?

a) 60   b) 30   c) 24   d) 48

CC 58

If you have difficulty with a particular quiz question you can refer back to that Core Concept.

Part 5-Solutions to Core Concepts 1-88

Part 5-Solutions to Core Concepts 1-88 consists of worked-out solutions to all of the problems in Part 3. Additionally, the original problem is reprinted in the solution section so you don't have to bounce back and forth between pages to compare the solution to the original problem.

Part 6-Solutions to Quizzes 1-25

Part 6 includes answers to the 25 daily quizzes from Part 4, with cross references to the Core Concept each quiz question is based on.

'R' You Ready??!!

In this book, the **R's** have it. Completing this book will help you:

Refresh your mathematical memory.

Recall what skills you needed help with.

Relearn the skills at which you were proficient.

Rethink the concepts that traditionally gave you trouble.

Remember mathematical procedures you may have forgotten.

Review prerequisite steps necessary to tackle multi-step problems.

Rekindle an appreciation for the utility of mathematics.

Revisit all the basics necessary for prepping for GRE practice exams.

Reevaluate your outlook on succeeding on the GRE.

"Now I Get It!"

As you are reviewing the hundreds of skills presented in this book, you may sometimes react, "That makes so much sense! Why didn't they teach it that way?" The answer is, they probably did. Your mathematical background requires new concepts to "simmer"' a little bit before you internalize them, and you may have forgotten the derivation of the concept during this "simmering" period, and, of course, in the years you did not take a math course. Your increased mathematical readiness and maturity now allows you to revisit these old concepts that, in hindsight, might not look as daunting as they originally did. Relax--you have plenty of company in feeling this way!

PART 2

GENERAL STRATEGIES

General GRE Strategies and Suggestions

Before we get to the specific mathematical concepts, let's take a look at some general tips and strategies you can use as you get closer to taking your GRE exam.

1. You are going to start your own personal list of tips. This should be word-processed and saved on your computer. Every new fact or strategy you encounter should be written as 1-2 sentences in a bulleted list. The order is not important. If you get a practice problem incorrect in this book or while you are taking practice GRE exams, write down the fact you needed to know to do it correctly.

As you continue practicing, you may make an error that you had previously made and already addressed as a bulleted tip. In that case, add an asterisk next to that tip to show it has been a trouble spot twice. Add asterisks every time you have a problem with any specific tip. That serves as a barometer that will help you know what facts to focus on remembering.

The week before your GRE, you should review every single tip you wrote down. Many students I have helped over the years had over 100 tips on their list. Remember, the tips can be any fact or strategy that alerts you.

Let's say a problem had feet and inches in it, and you ignored the different units, and got the problem wrong. You could add a bulleted tip, "remember to underline units and make sure your answer is in the units that were asked for." Tips can also be basic mathematical facts, like, "The measures of interior angles of a quadrilateral add up to 360 degrees."

2. Each of the Core Concepts covered in this book has a fill-in the blanks paragraph summarizing the material. You might want to copy and paste these paragraphs as individual tips in your personal tips list.

3. Get a binder for all of the work you do in this book and your GRE practice book. If you are solely using a tablet, make a file of the notes you generate. Label the top of each page with the date and the pages in the book the work is from. Keep a copy of your personal tips list in the front of this binder.

4. When you study for *any* mathematics test, you must be generating paper. You don't study mathematics by thumbing through notes and textbook pages and merely *looking* at them--that is a very passive way to study. You need to be *writing*. Cover solutions to previously done problems and see if you can answer them. Determine if you are moving along at a good speed, or stopping to deliberate too much. These were problems that you had already seen, so if you don't progress at a good pace, you have an indication that you need help on that concept. This will generate paper, and, sometimes, lots of it. That is an *active* way to study mathematics.

5. Occasionally review Part 1 of this book, so you are reminded of the format of the test and what mathematical concepts are on it. The more comfortable you are with the scope and type of the questions, the less intimidating the studying and testing experience will be.

6. Do not rush or skim when you read mathematics problems. Often, one missed word can change the way you approach the problem. Skimming does not save appreciable time, but it does cause errors. Get in the habit of re-reading mathematics word problems--it is a very different reading style than when you are reading a magazine while waiting to get a haircut!

7. Take note of key words as you read problems. Underline them when you can. Often one or two words can make a huge difference, and focusing on those key words is important.

8. Be sure to finish reading the problem. Sometimes students get so wrapped up in solving an equation they forget to see what the question asked for. Here is an example:

> Two angles, with measures $40°$ and $2x°$, are complementary. Find the difference between the measures of the angles.

The angles being complementary means that their measures add up to $90°$. By solving the equation $2x + 40 = 90$, a student gets the answer $x = 25$. This appears as one of the multiple-choice answers. But notice that the question asked for the *difference* between the two angles. Since $2x = 50$, the two angles measure $40°$ and $50°$, which are indeed complementary. The difference between 40 and 50 is 10. So, the correct answer is $10°$ even though the solution to the equation was 25. Moral of the story--read the problem and make sure you finish it!

9. Notice in strategy 8 above that the answer to the equation, 25, was given as one of the multiple-choice answers. We call this a **distractor**. It might distract the person who is "off-guard" and did not read the problem entirely and finish it carefully. You might look at this an as unfair "entrapment" but it underscores how focused you need to be when studying for and taking your GRE.

10. When doing arithmetic calculations, don't be a "hero" by trying to do tougher calculations in your head. Use the calculator provided, and do your practice sessions with that type of calculator.

11. Always check your entries on the calculator's display after you punch the keys. Don't just look at your fingers pressing the keys. Countless errors have been made by students not noticing they had an incorrect calculator entry.

12. Know your 100 basic multiplication facts, from $1 \cdot 1 = 1$ through $10 \cdot 10 = 100$. They will be needed all over the test. You can make flash cards to practice them. If you are deliberating on what $9 \cdot 7$ is, you are wasting time. If you have gotten this far in school with somewhat sloppy multiplication facts, make this GRE study procedure the time you right the ship. Just a minute or two of practice each day will get it done. Try writing the facts with your eyes closed--it is a great way to internalize new material.

13. Think about the English part of the GRE. It is difficult to improve your reading level in just a day. Interestingly, in math, you *can* learn a single skill in minutes that unlocks the keys to a problem's solution. If you add that skill to your problem-solving arsenal, you may get to use it more than once on your GRE. If you didn't know how to find a percent of a number, and someone showed you at breakfast the morning of the GRE, you would have additional expertise with which to conquer problems. However, recall from Part 1 that starting your GRE studying months in advance was recommended so forgotten material can be identified, relearned, reviewed and internalized. So, we do not recommend last minute cramming under any circumstances!

 14. It is often said that problem solving strategies help you "figure out what to do when you don't know what do." There are several basic problem-solving strategies you might want to familiarize yourself with.

- guess and check (trial and error)
- make a table
- draw a diagram
- find a pattern
- solve a simpler, related problem
- make an organized list
- work backwards

You can find explanations and examples of these strategies online. These strategies allow you to take what you know and apply it to what you don't know. Everything you add to your problem-solving arsenal has the potential to help you solve a problem on your GRE.

15. For some multiple-choice questions, it is possible to use the answers to arrive at the correct answer. This, of course, depends on the problem. Let's take a look at an example.

Which is not a solution to $x^3 - 9x = 0$?

a) 3   b) -3   c) 9   d) 0

If you forgot how to solve this, you can empathize with the "use the answers" method of getting the answer even better. You can just substitute each of the multiple-choice answers into the equation to see which is not a solution. The correct answer is choice (c), since

$$9^3 - 9(9) \neq 0.$$

Notice that this strategy is not possible for the open-ended, numeric entry questions.

16. There are many required formulas --slope, equation of a line, midpoint formula, distance formula, quadratic formula, area of a sector, arc length, mean, permutations, combinations, area, circumference, and more. Think of all of the formulas you have learned in mathematics. A good way to memorize new mathematical formulas is to write them with your eyes closed, so you are hyper-focused on the formula only. You can also say them out loud as you write them. Doing this several times, on different days, takes only seconds and helps you internalize the formulas.

17. On the GRE, diagrams are reasonably done to scale unless you are specifically told that the diagram is NOT done to scale. You can use this fact to help explore your solution route. However, don't assume that angles are right angles just from the picture. Don't assume line segments are perpendicular from the diagram, but if they look that way, you might look for this in your solution. You will need to use facts presented in the problem statement to make conclusions about the geometric relationships in the diagram.

18. A picture is a thousand words. For geometrical problems for which a diagram is not provided, draw one. It will make the problem easier to solve.

19. The GRE math sections are composed of short answers--there is no partial credit and nobody is looking at your work. To get credit, you have to get the correct answer! If you do 90% of a problem correctly and then make one misstep and get the incorrect answer, you get no credit. This is the same amount of credit as the person who was lost and clueless on the same problem, and got it wrong. Does that seem unfair? Think of it this way. If you went into a hospital to have your appendix removed, and the doctor did an excellent job of removing your spleen, would you want to give partial credit?! Sometimes, you need to get the correct answer for credit.

20. Don't waste unnecessary time showing comprehensive work. Don't skip steps that might cross you up, but don't include every step you don't need to get the correct answer as if your teacher was giving partial credit. Strike the appropriate balance for *you*.

21. Watch out for problems that use two different units of measurement. If a problem gives dimensions in feet and inches, carefully note what units are required for the answer and make the conversions accordingly. For example:

> A bucket holds 150 cubic inches of water. It is used to fill
> a 2-foot high cylinder that measures 3 feet in diameter.
> How many buckets of water will be needed to fill the
> cylinder?

Don't worry about the exact solution now. You will need to find the volume of the cylinder, but it is best to find it in cubic inches, even though the dimensions are originally given in feet. You will encounter problems like this in this book and have a chance to test how carefully you are reading.

22. Get used to the format of the numeric entry questions. There is a box to fill in your answer. Sometimes, if the answer is a fraction, two rectangles are provided, one underneath the other, with a line in between them. The line has a technical name--it is called a **viniculum**. Every Core Concept in this book has a numeric entry problem so you'll get plenty of practice. Also remember that there is a Transfer Display key on the online GRE calculator that allows you to transfer the calculator's display directly to a numeric entry question's answer rectangle. Double check your numeric entry question entries. You do not want to enter what would have been a correct answer incorrectly and get no credit!

23. Be careful with Quantitative Comparison questions. Compute Quantity A and Quantity B separately first. Then compare them. When you see your first question like this, it may seem a little convoluted and even strange. Once you have seen repeated examples, the format will not be an issue. Every odd Core Concept in this book has a Quantitative Comparison question.

24. You should not get bogged down in excessive, crazy arithmetic when doing a problem. That was not the intent of the question. The question was designed to test your problem-solving ability, so usually the arithmetic portion of any question is comparatively simple. If you find yourself mired in doing tedious, excessive calculations, you are likely doing something incorrectly.

25. No problem on the GRE should take a long time to solve. You won't spend 6 minutes on one problem. If it is taking you that long, you are not using the most efficient solution and you are costing yourself valuable time you could have used to tackle problems you can succeed at.

26. Waiting for the last minute is a poor way to study. Some people claim, "I do my best work at the last minute, under pressure," and things like that. When you study adequately in advance, and learn a new fact, you have time to review it, let it simmer, internalize it, and use it again. If you just cram the night before the test, you sacrifice all of those opportunities to improve.

27. As you take notes during your GRE study sessions, follow a writing procedure that you should be using in every mathematics class you sit through. Have you ever looked at your notes while studying for a test and not understood them, or maybe not even remembered the concept being taught? Too often in mathematics classes, the teacher only writes arithmetic, algebraic, and geometric results on the board. The verbal reasons are usually not written down--they disappear into cyberspace. Consequently, your notes are not as valuable tools as they could be when looked at weeks or months later. So, write full sentence explanations for everything. Writing full sentence explanations forces you to understand the concept--or they serve as a barometer for when you don't understand. Did you ever hear a student in your math class say, "I know it when you do it" to the teacher? I always told my students who said that, that if you can't put it into a sentence, you need help.

28. You need to apportion your time with discretion. Don't leave any questions unanswered--guessing would give you a better chance to get the answer correct. Leaving a question out guarantees you no credit. If a problem looks really tough for you, you might be better off spending your time checking and reviewing previous problems that you were doubtful of, rather than spending precious minutes on a problem you really feel clueless on. How will you get used to this tactic? When you finish this book and start taking timed, practice GRE exams, you will have a chance to make decisions like these.

29. If you solve a problem, you might realize at the end that your solution is incorrect. This could be possible because it is not one of the multiple-choice answers, or for some other reason. If you look at your work and retrace your steps, you might find your error. However, too often, when you review your own work, you are "entrapped" by your error and retracing does not uncover the problem. It is always smart to do the problem over again *without looking at your previous solution*. Then you will not be influenced by your previous error.

30. When reading a word problem, pause after each sentence. Ask yourself if you understand it up to that point. If you don't, read the sentence over rather than going on to the next sentence. Read each sentence in this fashion. Subsequent sentences are clearer when the previous sentences are fully understood.

31. Most students skip the front matter and get right to the heart of their textbooks. This book represents the beginning of your Math GRE journey, and Parts 1 and 2 of this book are a very important piece. You need to know where we are going and how we will systematically and scientifically get there.

32. Your outlook and attitude count, too. College is expensive. You have purchased this book and will need another book of practice GRE exams. View these purchases as a cost-effective investment to make sure you reach your college goals. If you don't write in your GRE practice books, you can pass them along to siblings, friends, or even donate them to a charity. Many take used books.

33. If you are looking for help or more practice problems on a certain topic, do an Internet search. There are tons of practice problems online, and a great deal of videos that explain specific topics. Use the Key Descriptors in each Core Concept.

34. The Educational Testing Service website **www.ets.org/gre** has information on GRE specifics and all day-of-test logistics. It would be a good idea to get familiar with this site.

PART 3

MATHEMATICAL TOPICS REFRESHER: CORE CONCEPTS

05/30/22

CORE CONCEPT 1
Order on the Number Line

Introduction

As a toddler, you started counting. Remember repeating 1, 2, 3, 4, 5, etc., as a child? This set of numbers is appropriately called the set of **counting numbers**. It also has two other names, the **natural numbers**, or the **positive integers**. The set of **whole numbers** includes the positive integers and 0.

$$\{0, 1, 2, 3, 4, 5, ...\}$$

Early in elementary school, you were introduced to the number line, first using only the counting numbers, and then whole numbers.

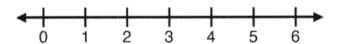

The set of negative integers is shown below.

$$\{...-6, -5, -4, -3, -2, -1, ...\}$$

Your experiences with numbers did not include negative integers like -1, -2, -3, 4, etc., until later in elementary school. Temperature, sea level, and stock prices are some scenarios in which you might have been introduced to negative numbers. Negative numbers appeared on the left side of 0.

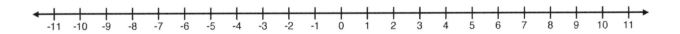

Note that the number 0 is neither positive nor negative, but the number 0 is even, since it leaves no remainder when divided by 2.

The number line never ends. It goes towards infinity in the right direction, and towards negative infinity in the left direction. Numbers on the left are less than numbers to their right. You can compare numbers on the number line using these four inequality symbols:

The symbol < means "less than." You can write 5 < 8.3.
The symbol > means "greater than." You can write 6.768 > -9.
The symbol ≤ means "less than or equal to." You can write 5 ≤ (2 + 3) or 5 ≤ 18.
The symbol ≥ means "greater than or equal to." You can write $1.5 ≥ 1\frac{1}{2}$ or 1.5 ≥ 1.111.

Also note that the symbol ≠ means "is not equal to" so you can think of this as an inequality symbol that does not tell you which number is greater.

Think carefully where decimals and fractions occur between the integers on a number line.

Examples

The following table has four columns, and one column is blank. For each row, compare the two quantities labelled *x* and *y* and insert a correct inequality sign.

Row Identification	x	Inequality Sign	y
a	7.4	>	-7.4
b	0.22	<	2.2
c	-14	<	(19 - 5)
d	46.1	>	46
e	46	>	45.9
f	-46	>	-46.1
g	-46	<	-45.9

Solutions

Row Identification	x	Inequality Sign	y
a	7.4	>	-7.4
b	0.22	<	2.2
c	-14	<	(19 - 5)
d	46.1	>	46
e	46	>	45.9
f	-46	>	-46.1
g	-46	<	-45.9

You can plot the points on the number line to visualize the solutions. In particular, notice how comparing two negative numbers requires you to critically rely on the number line. The answer to *d* is pretty clear since 46.1 is to the right of 46. Notice the placement of the numbers from rows *e*, *f*, and *g* on the number line:

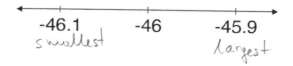

-46.1   -46   -45.9
smallest   largest

Fill in the Blanks

On the number line, if number *x* is to the left of number *y*, then the number *x* is _smaller_ than the number *y*. Any number to the left of 0 is _negative_, and any number to the right of 0 is _positive_, while _0_ itself is neither positive nor negative. The number line _never_ ends; it goes on infinitely in both directions.

Basic Problem

-9   0   5

Which of the following numbers is between 5 and -9?

a) -9.77   b) 5.001   c) -8.1   d) 6

Intermediate Problem

Which is a negative number between -7 and 3.3?

a) -7.006   b) 0   c) 3.2   d) -6

Challenging Problem

What is the greatest integer between -23.4 and -7.5?

a) -23   b) -24   c) -8   d) -7

Numeric Entry Problem

10 1 12 16 18 8
Which of the numbers in the set {7, -2, -15, -19, 15, 11} is farthest from -3?

3

15

Quantitative Comparison

Compare Quantity A and Quantity B, using the information below.

Quantity A	Quantity B
-79.11	**-79.0999**

Select one of the following answers.

a) Quantity A is greater.
b) Quantity B is greater.
c) The two quantities are equal.
d) The relationship cannot be determined from the information given.

Key Descriptors

counting numbers, inequalities, infinity, natural numbers, negative integers, number line, ordering real numbers, positive integers, whole numbers

DID YOU KNOW THAT?

11 + 2

"Eleven plus two" is an **anagram** of "twelve plus one" since they are phrases that use the exact same letters. They both equal 13.

12 + 1

Absolute Value

Introduction

When you think of the number line, you can think of the numeral itself (without the sign) being the distance the number is from 0, and the sign telling you in what direction to go from 0. For this reason, you can think of a signed number as a **directed distance**. The **absolute value** of a number is its distance from the origin, without regard for its direction. Two vertical bars surrounding a quantity are used to indicate absolute value. Let's look at how the notation works:

$$|7| = 7$$
$$|\text{-}13| = 13$$
$$|\text{-}2.32| = 2.32$$

Sometimes the absolute value is called the **magnitude** of the number.

Examples

For each row in the table, insert an equal sign (=) or an inequality sign (< or >) in the middle column to compare the two quantities x and y.

Row Identification	x	Inequality Sign	y
a	11 |-11|	>	-11
b	42.3 |-42.3|	=	42.3
c	7.5 |7.5|	=	|-7.5| 7.5
d	-33 -33	<	|33| 33
e	12¾ $\left\|-12\frac{3}{4}\right\|$	>	12
f	|66|	>	-66
g	4.1 |-4.1|	<	|-4.2| 4.2

Solution

Row Identification	x	Inequality Sign	y
a	$\|-11\|$	>	-11
b	$\|-42.3\|$	=	42.3
c	$\|7.5\|$	=	$\|-7.5\|$
d	-33	<	$\|33\|$
e	$\left\|-12\frac{3}{4}\right\|$	>	12
f	$\|66\|$	>	-66
g	$\|-4.1\|$	<	$\|-4.2\|$

Notice that in row *g*, while -4.1 > -4.2 from looking at the number line, taking the absolute values of these two numbers reversed the inequality sign.

Fill in the Blanks

The distance a signed number is from 0 on the number line is called its _absolute value_, which can also be called the _magnitude_ of the number. The absolute value of a number can never be _negative_, but it can be 0. A signed number can be viewed as a directed distance from the origin, and an absolute value can be viewed as an _undirected_ distance from the origin.

Basic Problem

If -19 is added to its absolute value, what is the sum? -19

a) 38   b) -38   c) 19   (d) 0

Intermediate Problem

Which of the following expressions has the smallest value?

(a) -$\|7 - 9\|$ b) $\|9 - 7\|$ c) $\|7 - 9\|$ d) $\|-2\|$
  -2   2   2   2

Challenging Problem

If $x = -2$ and $y = -7$, which of the following expressions is equal to -5?

a) $-|x + y|$ b) $|x - y|$ c) $|x| + |y|$ (d) $|x| - |y|$

Numeric Entry Problem

What is the absolute value of the difference between -132 and its absolute value?

$$\boxed{264}$$

Multiple Choice with Multiple Answers Problem

Which of the following expressions is equal to 7?

[a] $-|6 + 1|$ [b] $|8 - 1|$ [c] $|8| + |-1|$ [d] $|8| - |-1|$

Key Descriptors

absolute value, directed distance, magnitude of a number, signed numbers, undirected distance

DID YOU KNOW THAT?

A **perfect number** is equal to the sum of its proper factors.

The proper factors of 6 are 1, 2, and 3 and 1 + 2 + 3 = 6.

The proper factors of 28 are 1, 2, 4, 7, and 14, and 1 + 2 + 4 + 7 + 14 = 28.

Are there any odd perfect numbers?

This is an unsolved problem in mathematics that can be explained to a fourth grader!

CORE CONCEPT 3
Prime and Composite Numbers

Introduction

A **divisor** of an integer is an integer that divides into the number evenly (without a remainder). **Prime numbers** are positive integers that have exactly two divisors, the integer itself and 1. Note that with this definition, the number 1 is not a prime number. The smallest prime number, and the only even prime number, is 2. There are infinitely many prime numbers, starting with the first ten prime numbers shown below.

only divided by itself or 1.

$$\{2, 3, 5, 7, 11, 13, 17, 19, 23, 29, ...\}$$

Composite numbers are integers greater than or equal to 2 that are not prime. Composite numbers are positive integers that have more than two divisors. There are infinitely many composite numbers, starting with the first ten composite numbers shown below.

$$\{4, 6, 8, 9, 10, 12, 14, 15, 16, 18, ...\}$$

Notice that all even numbers except for 2 are composite numbers. Also note that 1 is neither prime nor composite. The numbers that can divide evenly into the composite numbers are called **factors**. For example, the factors of 20 are 1, 2, 4, 5, 10, and 20. The **prime factors** of 20 are the factors that are prime numbers. The prime factors of 20 are 2 and 5.

Example

What is the largest composite number that can be made by multiplying two different prime factors of 60?

2
3   *3 × 5 = 15*
5

Solution

The prime factors of 60 are 2, 3, and 5. The product found by multiplying the two largest, 3 and 5, is 15.

Fill in the Blanks

If a positive integer has exactly two divisors, it is called a _prime_ number. Positive integers with more than two factors are called _composite_ numbers. The only even prime number is _2_ and all other even positive numbers are _composites_. The number 1 is not _prime_ because it has only one factor, 1, and it is also not composite. There are _indefinitely_ many prime numbers.

Basic Problem

How many prime factors does the number 70 have? 1, 2, 70

a) 3   b) 4   c) 5   d) 2

Intermediate Problem

Find the <u>difference</u> between the <u>smallest and largest prime factors of 42.</u>

a) 40   b) 5   c) 6   d) 19   1, 2, 7, 42

5

Challenging Problem

What is the <u>smallest number whose prime factors are 2, 3, 5, and 7?</u>

a) 6   b) 210   c) 35   d) 30

Numeric Entry Problem

If the largest prime factor of 35 is divided by the smallest prime factor of 35, express the answer as a fraction.

1, 5, 7, 1

Quantitative Comparison Problem

Compare Quantity A and Quantity B, using the information below.

<u>Quantity A</u>   <u>Quantity B</u>

The largest composite number less than 10.   **The sum of the three smallest prime numbers.**

9   2,3,5 = 10

Select one of the following answers.

a) Quantity A is greater.
b) Quantity B is greater.
c) The two quantities are equal.
d) The relationship cannot be determined from the information given.

Key Descriptors

composite numbers, divisibility, divisor, even integers, factors, odd integers, prime numbers, prime factors

DID YOU KNOW THAT?

The number 0 is even. It is not positive or negative, and it does not have a reciprocal. There is no Roman numeral that represents 0.

CORE CONCEPT 4
Additive Inverses

Introduction

You first learned about negative numbers in elementary school. Temperature, sea level, and stock prices are some scenarios in which you might have been introduced to negative numbers. As you know from the number line, the number 0 separates the negative numbers from the positive numbers. If you add 0 to any number, the number remains the same; it "keeps its identity."

For this reason, 0 is called the **additive identity**. In middle school, you learned about the **additive inverse**, which is the **opposite** of a number. The sum of any number and its additive inverse is 0. You can find the additive inverse of any number by multiplying it by -1.

Examples

Fill in the following table in which y is the additive inverse of x.

Row Identification	x	Let y = The Additive Inverse of x	$x + y$
a	52	−52	
b	-7	7	
c	13.88	−13.88	
d	-0.341	0.341	
e	2	−2	
f	$|{-2}|$	−2	
g	-2	2	
h	$-17\frac{1}{4}$	$17\frac{1}{4}$	

0

Solutions

Row Identification	x	Let y = The Additive Inverse of x	x + y
a	52	-52	0
b	-7	7	0
c	13.88	-13.88	0
d	-0.341	0.341	0
e	2	-2	0
f	$\lvert -2 \rvert$	-2	0
g	-2	2	0
h	$-17\frac{1}{4}$	$17\frac{1}{4}$	0

Fill in the Blanks

The additive inverse of a number is also called its _opposite_. You can create the additive inverse of any number by _multiplying_ the number by _-1_. The sum of any number and its additive inverse is always _0_. The additive inverse of a positive number is _negative_ and the additive inverse of a negative number is _positive_. The number 0 is also called the _additive inverse_, and, interestingly, the additive inverse of 0 is _0_.

Basic Problem

The additive inverse of -8.1 is

a) -8.1   b) 0   c) -16.2   (d) 8.1

Intermediate Problem

The additive inverse of $\lvert -4 \rvert$ is
4

a) 4   (b) -4   c) 0   d) $\lvert 4 \rvert$

Challenging Problem

What is the additive inverse of $-|5 - 11|$?

-6

-6

(a) 6   b) -6   c) 0   d) 16

Numeric Entry Problem

What is the additive inverse of $-\frac{5}{7}$?

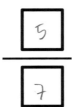

Multiple Choice with Multiple Answers Problem

Which two choices of the following represent the additive inverse of - 23?

[a] $-|-23|$ [b] $|-23|$ [c] $|-22| + |-1|$ [d] $|22| - |-1|$

Key Descriptors

additive identity, additive inverse, opposite of a number,

DID YOU KNOW THAT?

The product of
111,111,111 and **111,111,111**
is
12,345,678,987,654,321.
This product is a **palindrome**.
It reads the same forwards or backwards!

Multiplicative Inverses

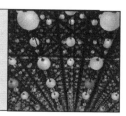

Introduction

The number 1 is called the **multiplicative identity** because when you multiply a number by 1, the number remains the same; it keeps its "identity." The **multiplicative inverse** of a number is its **reciprocal**. To find the reciprocal, you represent the number as a fraction and "flip" it. The **numerator** (top number of the fraction) and the **denominator** (bottom number of the fraction) are exchanged. The product of a non-zero number and its reciprocal is always 1, the multiplicative identity. Note that 0 does not have a reciprocal. There is no number that, when multiplied by 0, can possibly give the multiplicative identity 1.

Example

Find the product of 15 and its reciprocal.

Solution

The product is the answer to a multiplication problem so we have to multiply 15 by its reciprocal.

Express 15 as a fraction with denominator 1.

$$\frac{15}{1}$$

The numerator is 15 and the denominator is 1. "Flip" the fraction.

$$\frac{1}{15}$$

The reciprocal is $\frac{1}{15}$.

Multiply 15 by its reciprocal. Recall that when you multiply two fractions, you can just multiply the numerators and multiply the denominators.

$$\frac{15}{1} \cdot \frac{1}{15} = \frac{15}{15} = 1.$$

The product of 15 and its reciprocal is 1. The product of any non-zero number and its reciprocal is 1, and now you can see why this happens!

Fill in the Blanks

The reciprocal of a number is also called its __multiplicative inverse__. When a negative or positive number is multiplied by its reciprocal, the result is __1__, which is also called the __multiplicative identity__ To find a multiplicative inverse, express the number as a fraction and flip the __nominator__ and the __denominator__

Basic Problem

What is the multiplicative inverse of $\frac{15}{7}$?

(a) $\frac{7}{15}$ b) $-\frac{15}{7}$ c) $-\frac{7}{15}$ d) $\frac{15}{7}$

Intermediate Problem

What is the reciprocal of $\frac{1}{8}$?

a) $-\frac{1}{8}$ (b) 8   c) -8   d) 1

Challenging Problem

"opposite"

What is the additive inverse of the reciprocal of the only even prime number?

a) $\frac{1}{2}$ (b) $-\frac{1}{2}$ c) 2   d) -2 $2 \quad \frac{2}{1}$

Numeric Entry Problem

What is the reciprocal of the largest prime number less than 20?   19

$$\frac{1}{19}$$

Quantitative Comparison Problem

Compare Quantity A and Quantity B, using the information below.

Quantity A	Quantity B
opposite **The additive inverse of -3.** $-3 = 3$	**The multiplicative inverse of** $\frac{1}{3}$**.** $\frac{3}{1} = 3$

Select one of the following answers.

a) Quantity A is greater.
b) Quantity B is greater.
c) The two quantities are equal.
d) The relationship cannot be determined from the information given.

Key Descriptors

denominator, multiplicative inverse, multiplicative identity, numerator, product, reciprocal

DID YOU KNOW THAT?

The 10-digit number 1,274,953,680 uses all ten digits, and it is evenly divisible by all the integers from 1 through 16.

06/01

Undefined Fractions

Introduction

The **quotient** is the answer to a division problem. The horizontal line segment separating the numerator from the denominator of a fraction indicates division. For example, $\frac{6}{3} = 2$ since 6 divided by 3 is 2. You can check this by multiplying 2 by 3 to get the numerator 6. The quotient of two non-zero integers is called a **rational number**. You commonly think of rational numbers as fractions. Rational numbers can be positive or negative.

The denominator of a fraction cannot be zero. You can't divide by 0. A fraction with 0 as the denominator is said to be **undefined**. Imagine if you tried to check any answer to the equation "$\frac{6}{0} = ?$ ". There is no number that, when multiplied by 0, would give 6.

Example

For what value of x is the fraction $\frac{6}{x - 17}$ undefined?

Solution

The fraction is undefined if its denominator is equal to 0. Set the denominator equal to 0, and solve the equation.

$$x - 17 = 0$$
$$x = 17$$

The fraction is undefined when $x = 17$.

Fill in the Blanks

A rational number is the __quotient__ of two integers, and it can be expressed as a fraction. If the denominator of a fraction is equal to _0_ , we say the fraction is

__undefined__.

Basic Problem

What value of x would make the fraction $\frac{5x-10}{2x+14}$ undefined?

a) 2   b) 7   (c) -7   d) -2

$$2x + 14 = 0$$
$$2x = -14$$
$$x = -\frac{14}{2}$$
$$x = -7$$

Intermediate Problem

For what value of p is the fraction $\frac{p+31}{p-2}$ undefined?

a) -31   b) 31   (c) 2   d) -2

Challenging Problem

For what values of k is the fraction $\frac{k+1.7}{(2-k)(k+4)}$ undefined?

a) -2, 4   b) -1.7, 2, 4   (c) 2, -4   d) -1.7, 2

$$(2-k)(k+4) = 0$$

a) $\left(2-(-2)\right)\left(4+4\right)$
$\qquad 4 \qquad\quad 8$

b)

c) $(2-2)\ (-4+4)$
$\quad\ 0 \qquad\ 0$

Numeric Entry Problem

For what value of y is the fraction $\frac{y-3.2}{y-2.45}$ undefined?

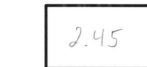

$$y - 2.45 = 0$$
$$y = 2.45$$

Multiple Choice with Multiple Answers Problem

Which of the following fractions are undefined when $x = 12$?

✓ [a] $\frac{5x-10}{2x-24}$ [b] $\frac{x-12}{2x+14}$ ✓ [c] $\frac{12x-12}{x-12}$ ✓ [d] $\frac{7x}{(x+2)(x-12)}$

$$(12+2)\ (12-12)$$
$$14 \quad\times\quad 0 \quad = 0$$

Key Descriptors

rational numbers, undefined fractions

CORE CONCEPT 7
Order of Operations

Introduction

If a mathematical expression has several operations in it, there is a correct sequence that must be followed to evaluate it. It is called the **order of operations**. This makes sure that an expression like $(13 + 3^2) - 4 \cdot 3 + 7$ has a unique value. (Otherwise, you could imagine different people working on different parts of it in a different order and getting different answers).

The rule is to do **P**arentheses and **E**xponents first, and then do **M**ultiplication and **D**ivision from left to right, and then **A**ddition and **S**ubtraction from left to right. The rule is sometimes abbreviated as **PEMDAS**, from the first letters of each of the operations. Be careful to note that you do multiplication and division from left to right, and that does not mean multiplication *before* division. You also add and subtract from left to right, not necessarily adding *before* subtracting.

Example

$$45 - 12 \div 4$$
$$45 - 3 = 42$$

Find the value of $45 - (11 + 1) \div 2^2$.

Solution

Work on the parentheses and exponents first.

$$45 - (11 + 1) \div 2^2$$

Note that 11 + 1 = 12 and 2^2 = 4. Rewrite the simplified expression.

$$45 - 12 \div 4$$

Multiply and divide in order from left to right. Note that $12 \div 4 = 3$.

$$45 - 3$$

Finally, subtract.

$$45 - 3 = 42, \text{ so } 45 - (11 + 1) \div 2^2 = 42.$$

Fill in the Blanks

The order of operations requires you to do _parenthesis_ and _exponents_ first.
Then, you _multiply_ and _divide_ in order from left to right. Finally, you
add and _subtract_ in order from left to right. A mnemonic (trick) for
remembering this is to use the initials _PEMDAS_.

Basic Problem

Find the value of $11 - (3^2 + 1) \div 2$.

$$9$$

$$11 - 10 \div 2$$
$$11 - 5 = 6$$

a) 0   b) 2   c) 1   (d) 6

Intermediate Problem

Evaluate the expression $3^3 + 15 \div (6 - 3) \cdot 2^2 - 1$.

$$27 + 15 \div 3 \cdot 4 - 1 =$$
$$27 + 5 \cdot 4 - 1 =$$
$$27 + 20 - 1 =$$
$$47 - 1 = 46$$

(a) 46   b) 55   c) 31   d) 42

Challenging Problem

What is the value of the expression $21 \div (3^2 - 2) + 2^3 - 4^2 + 3(5 \cdot 2)$?

$$21 \div 7 + 8 - 16 + 3 \cdot 10 =$$
$$3 + 8 - 16 + 30 =$$
$$11 - 16 + 30 =$$
$$-5 + 30 =$$
$$25$$

a) 23   b) 52   (c) 25   d) 16

Numeric Entry Problem

Express the value of the expression $7 \div (3 \cdot 23)$ as a fraction.

$$7 \div 69 =$$

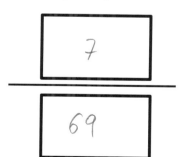

Quantitative Comparison Problem

Compare Quantity A and Quantity B, using the information below.

Quantity A	Quantity B
$\mathbf{30 - 4 \cdot 5 \div 2}$	$\mathbf{24 \div 4 + 2 + 10}$
30 − 20÷2 = 30 − 10 = 20	6 + 2 + 10 = 8 + 10 = 18

Select one of the following answers.

a) Quantity A is greater.
b) Quantity B is greater.
c) The two quantities are equal.
d) The relationship cannot be determined from the information given.

Key Descriptors

order of operations, PEMDAS

DID YOU KNOW THAT?

31 is prime.
331 is prime.
3,331 is prime.
33,331 is prime.
333,331 is prime.
3,333,331 is prime.
33,333,331 is prime.
333,333,331 IS NOT PRIME!
333,333,331 = 17 x 19,607,843.

CORE CONCEPT 8
Least Common Multiple

Introduction

The **least common multiple (LCM)** is the smallest positive integer that is a multiple of two or more given numbers. It is the smallest multiple the given numbers have *in common*. It is also called the **lowest common multiple**. This is used when adding or subtracting fractions (which will be reviewed later), and under those circumstances, is called the **lowest common denominator (LCD)**. Think of the positive multiples of 2:

$$\{2, 4, 6, 8, 10, 12...\}$$

Think of the multiples of 5:

$$\{5, 10, 15, 20, 25...\}$$

The smallest multiple they have in common is 10, so 10 is the LCM.

Example

Find the least common multiple of the numbers 2, 3, and 10.

2 4 6 8 10 12 14 16 18 20 22 24 26 28 30
3 6 9 12 15 18 21 24 27 30
10 20 30

Solution

There are several ways to do this, and perhaps the easiest way is to make a list of the multiples of each number, and look for a multiple that all three given numbers have in common.

The multiples of 2 are {2, 4, 6, 8, 10, 12, 14, 16, 18, 20, 22, 24, 26, 28, 30, 32...}.

The multiples of 3 are {3, 6, 9, 12, 15, 18, 21, 24, 27, 30, 33...}

The multiples of 5 are {5, 10, 15, 20, 25, 30, 35, 40...}

Notice that 30 is the lowest multiple of all three given numbers, so 30 is the LCM. If the lists start to get too long before you see a common multiple, there is a method that uses prime factors to find the LCM. You can look that up online and watch videos that show you how.

Fill in the Blanks

The smallest positive integer that is a multiple of two or more given positive integers is called the ~~lowest~~ *LEAST* common multiple , and this is abbreviated as LCM. To find an LCM, you can make a list of the multiples of each integer, and look for the smallest multiple that the lists have in common .

Basic Problem

Find the least common multiple for the numbers 12 and 15.

12 24 36 48 60
15 30 45 60

a) 3   b) 60   c) 30   d) 45

Intermediate Problem

What is the additive inverse of the least common multiple of 3, 5, and 10?

a) 30   b) $\frac{1}{30}$ c) -30   d) $-\frac{1}{30}$

3   6   9   12   15   18   21   24   27
5   10   15   20   25   30
10   20   30

30

Challenging Problem

What is the least common multiple of the three smallest prime numbers?

a) 30   b) 10   c) 105   d) 15

26 28 30 32 34 36 38
2 4 6 8 10 12 14 16 18 20 22 24
5 10 15 20 25 30 35 40
3 6 9 12 15 18 21 24 27 30

Numeric Entry Problem

What is the multiplicative inverse of the lowest common multiple of the smallest four natural numbers?

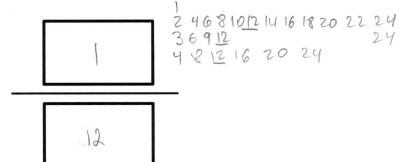

$$\frac{1}{12}$$

1
2 4 6 8 10 12 14 16 18 20 22 24
3 6 9 12   24
4 8 12 16 20 24

Multiple Choice with Multiple Answers Problem

Which of the following sets of numbers have a least common multiple of 60?

[a] {4, 15}   [b] {2, 30}   [c] {3, 4, 5}   [d] {5, 12}

handwritten:
4 8 12 16 20 24 28 32 36 40 44 48 52 56 60
15 30 45 60
3 6 9 12 15 18 21 24 27 30 33 36 39 42 45 48 51 54 57 60
5 10 15 20 25 30 35 40 45 50 55 60
12 24 36 48 60

Key Descriptors

least common multiple, lowest common denominator, lowest common multiple

DID YOU KNOW THAT?

In 2018, a FedEx employee, Jonathan Pace, found the largest known prime number. It is nearly one million digits long!

Greatest Common Factor

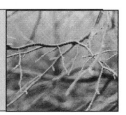

Introduction

An integer is a **factor** of a number if it divides into the number evenly. Divides 'evenly' means there is no remainder. The **greatest common factor (GCF)** of a set of integers is the largest positive integer that divides evenly into all of the integers. For example, the GCF of the set {12, 30, 42} is 6, because 6 is the largest positive integer that is a factor of all three of the integers in the set. The greatest common factor of *any* set of distinct prime numbers is 1.

Example

What is the greatest common factor of 16, 20, and 28? 2, 4

Solution

List *all* of the factors of each number. This is most efficiently done in **ascending order** (from smallest factor to largest factor).

> The factors of 16 are 1, 2, 4, 8, and 16.

> The factors of 20 are 1, 2, 4, 5, 10, 20.

> The factors of 28 are 1, 2, 4, 7, 14, 28.

The largest number in all three lists is 4, so 4 is the greatest common factor.

If the lists got too long, you can use **prime factors** (factors that are prime numbers) to find the GCF. You can look online for videos on how to do this.

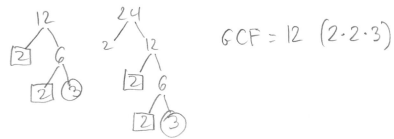

Fill in the Blanks

The _greatest common_ _factor_ of a set of integers is the _largest_ positive integer that divides _evenly_ into the original given numbers. Dividing evenly into an integer means that, after dividing, there is no _remainder_. If you had a set of twenty different prime numbers, their GCF would be _1_.

Basic Problem

What is the greatest common factor of the integers 15 and 30?

1 3 5 15
1 2 3 5 6 10 15

a) 5   b) 10   c) 15   d) 30

Intermediate Problem

You are given the numbers 7 and 11. Which of the following statements, I, II, III, are true?

I. The GCF is 7.
II. The LCM is 77.
III. Both numbers are prime.

a) I only   b) II and III only   c) III only   d) I, II, and III

Challenging Problem

integers greater than or equal to 2 that are not prime. Have more than two divisors.

Find the GCF of the four largest composite numbers less than 19.

14 15 16 18

a) 6   b) 3   c) 2   d) 1

14
2 7

15
3 5

16
2 8
2 4

18
2 9

Numeric Entry Problem

Find the sum of the GCF and LCM for the integers 3 and 7.

GCF 3
     7 = 1

LCM 3 6 9 12 15 18 21
     7 14 21   = 21

22

Quantitative Comparison Problem

Compare Quantity A and Quantity B, using the information below.

Quantity A	Quantity B
The GCF of 16 and 48.	**The LCM of 3 and 8.** 24

16

Select one of the following answers.

16 1 2 4 8 16
GCF 48 1 2 4 6 8 12 16

a) Quantity A is greater.
b) Quantity B is greater.   LCM 3 6 9 12 15 18 21 (24) 27 30 33 36 39 42
c) The two quantities are equal.   8 16 (24)
d) The relationship cannot be determined from the information given.

Key Descriptors

factor, GCF, greatest common factor, divisibility, evenly divisible, prime factor, quotient, remainder

DID YOU KNOW THAT?

A **twin prime pair** is a set of consecutive odd numbers that are prime, such as

$$\{3, 5\}, \{5, 7\}, \{11, 13\},$$
$$\{17, 19\}, \{29, 31\}, \{41, 43\}, \text{etc.}$$

It is not known if there are infinitely many twin prime pairs.

This is an unsolved problem in mathematics that can be explained to a fourth grader!

Improper Fractions and Mixed Numbers

Introduction

In Core Concept 5, you were reminded that the top number in a fraction is called the **numerator** and the bottom number is called the **denominator**. In elementary school, when you were first introduced to fractions as representing a part of a whole, the numerator was smaller than the denominator. If the numerator is greater than or equal to the denominator, the fraction is called an **improper fraction**. Here are some examples of improper fractions:

$$\left\{ \frac{7}{3}, \frac{13}{9}, \frac{8}{8} \right\}.$$

Positive improper fractions have a value greater than or equal to 1. If a fraction has an equivalent, non-zero numerator and denominator, it is equal to 1. A **mixed number** is a number that has an integer part and a fractional part. It represents a quantity *between* two integers on the number line. Here are some examples of mixed numbers:

$$\left\{ 2\frac{1}{3}, 11\frac{5}{9}, 20\frac{5}{8} \right\}.$$

Improper fractions can be expressed as mixed numbers, and mixed numbers can be represented as improper fractions.

Example 1

Express the improper fraction $\frac{23}{5}$ as a mixed number.

Solution 1

Divide the numerator by the denominator. That will give you the integer part of the mixed number. Be sure to keep track of the remainder.

$$23 \div 5 = 4 \text{ with a remainder of 3.}$$

$20 \div 5 = 4 \qquad + \quad 3$

The remainder is the numerator of the fractional part of the mixed number. The original denominator, 5, is the denominator of the fractional part of the mixed number. So $\frac{23}{5}$ expressed as a mixed number is $4\frac{3}{5}$.

Example 2

Convert the mixed number $7\frac{2}{9}$ to an improper fraction.

Solution 2

$7 \times 9 = 63 + = 65$

Multiply the integer part, 7, by the denominator, 9.

$$7 \cdot 9 = 63.$$

Add the numerator, 2, to this product, 63, to create the numerator.

$$63 + 2 = 65.$$

The denominator, 9, stays the same. When expressed as an improper fraction, $7\frac{2}{9}$ is $\frac{65}{9}$.

Fill in the Blanks

An improper fraction is a fraction that has its <u>numerator</u> greater than or equal to its <u>denominator</u>. Improper fractions can be expressed as <u>mixed</u> <u>numbers</u> which are numbers that have an integer part and a fractional part. If a fraction has an equivalent, non-zero numerator and denominator, it is equal to <u>1</u>.

Basic Problem

Express $6\frac{3}{7}$ as an improper fraction.

$6\frac{3}{7} = \frac{42+3}{7} = \frac{45}{7}$

a) $\frac{25}{7}$ b) $\frac{42}{7}$ c) $\frac{45}{7}$ d) $\frac{45}{3}$

Intermediate Problem

multiplicative inverse

If $4\frac{2}{3}$ is expressed as an improper fraction, what is its <u>reciprocal</u>? $\frac{14}{3}$

a) $\frac{11}{2}$ b) $\frac{3}{14}$ c) $-\frac{3}{14}$ d) $\frac{14}{3}$

Challenging Problem

Which of the following mixed numbers has a <u>prime numerator</u> when it is converted to an <u>improper fraction</u>?

(a) $2\frac{3}{5}$ b) $5\frac{3}{7}$ c) $10\frac{5}{6}$ d) $11\frac{5}{8}$

$\frac{13}{5}$ $\frac{38}{7}$ $\frac{65}{6}$ $\frac{93}{8}$

38, 65, 93 are composite numbers because they have multiple factors

Numeric Entry Problem

What is the value of $\left|-5\frac{3}{7}\right|$ when it is expressed as an <u>improper fraction</u>?

$\left|-\frac{38}{7}\right| =$

$\frac{38}{7}$

Multiple Choice with Multiple Answers Problem

Which of the following mixed numbers has a <u>composite number</u> for the <u>numerator</u> when converted to an improper fraction?

[a] $2\frac{5}{8}$ [b] $4\frac{2}{7}$ [c] $2\frac{3}{5}$ [d] $3\frac{2}{3}$

$\frac{21}{8}$ $\frac{30}{7}$ $\frac{13}{5}$ $\frac{11}{3}$

                                         prime   prime

Key Descriptors

converting improper fractions to mixed numbers, converting mixed numbers to improper fractions, improper fractions, mixed numbers

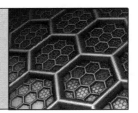

CORE CONCEPT 11
Simplifying Fractions

Introduction

The word **quotient** indicates division. A **rational number** is a number that can be expressed as the quotient of two integers. You commonly see rational numbers written as **fractions**. Rational numbers can have equivalent fraction and decimal representations. For instance, you probably remember that

$$\frac{1}{2} = 0.5 \text{ and } \frac{1}{4} = 0.25.$$

Two equivalent fractions can also have different representations. For example,

$$\frac{2}{4} = \frac{1}{2} \text{ and } \frac{6}{8} = \frac{3}{4}.$$

When the numerator and denominator have their GCF = 1, we say the fraction is in **simplest form**. Sometimes a fraction in simplest form is called a **reduced fraction**, but this term, while widely used, can be a bit misleading, since the simplified fraction is not *smaller* than the original fraction. All fractions have the ability to be put in simplest form if they are not in simplest form already.

Example

Express the fraction $\frac{24}{36}$ in simplest form.

Solution

Find the GCF of 24 and 36 by making lists of the factors of each:

Factors of 24: {1, 2, 3, 4, 6, 8, 12, 24}   Factors of 36: {1, 2, 3, 4, 6, 12, 18, 36}.

The GCF is 12. Divide the numerator and denominator by the GCF. You can cross out the 24 and 36 and replace them with the quotient after you divide by the GCF.

$$\frac{\cancel{24}^{2}}{\cancel{36}_{3}}$$

The simplest form of $\frac{24}{36}$ is $\frac{2}{3}$.

Note that if you do not divide by the GCF, but divide numerator and denominator by *any* common factor, you will just have to repeat the procedure so it may take a few steps to get the fraction into simplest form.

Fill in the Blanks

When a fraction is expressed in ___quotient___ form, the GCF of the ___numerator___ and the ___denominator___ is equal to ___1___. If a fraction is not in simplest form, you can simplify it by dividing the numerator and the denominator by the ___greatest___ common factor.

Basic Problem

Express the fraction $\frac{12}{48}$ in simplest form.

1 2 3 4 6 12
1 2 3 4 6 8 12

a) $\frac{1}{4}$ b) $\frac{1}{2}$ c) $\frac{6}{24}$ d) $\frac{3}{12}$ $\frac{1}{4}$

Intermediate Problem

Which of the following fractions is in simplest form?

a) $\frac{19}{95}$ b) $\frac{32}{60}$ c) $\frac{18}{30}$ d) $\frac{41}{60}$

5

Challenging Problem

$$\frac{51}{60} \times \frac{60}{51} = 1$$

Express the multiplicative inverse of $\frac{51}{60}$ in simplest form. $\frac{60}{51}$

a) $\frac{60}{51}$ b) $-\frac{51}{60}$ c) $-\frac{60}{51}$ d) $\frac{20}{17}$

Numeric Entry Problem

"inverse"

*mixed number is a
number + fraction*

Express the reciprocal of $\frac{42}{60}$ as a mixed number in simplest form.

$$\frac{60}{42}$$

$$1\frac{18}{42} = 1\frac{3}{7}$$

$$\boxed{1\ \frac{3}{7}}$$

18 | 1 2 3 6 9 18
12 | 2 3 6

Quantitative Comparison Problem

Compare Quantity A and Quantity B, using the information below.

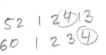

Quantity A	Quantity B

The denominator of the fraction $\frac{52}{60}$ $\frac{13}{15}$ **when it is written in simplest form.** 15

The numerator of the improper fraction, in simplest form, that is equivalent to the mixed number $5\frac{1}{3}$. $\frac{16}{3}$ 16

Select one of the following answers.

a) Quantity A is greater.
b) Quantity B is greater.
c) The two quantities are equal.
d) The relationship cannot be determined from the information given.

Key Descriptors

equivalent fractions, fractions, quotient, rational number, reducing fractions, reducing rational numbers, simplest form of a fraction, simplifying fractions, simplifying rational numbers

Multiplying Numerical Fractions

Introduction

When you want to multiply two fractions, you can just multiply the numerators to get the numerator of the product, then multiply the denominators to get the denominator of the product. You can, at any juncture, simplify the fractions to make your work easier. If you have to multiply mixed numbers, change them to improper fractions first, simplify if you can, and then multiply the numerators and the denominators.

Example 1

Find the product of $\frac{10}{35}$ and $\frac{14}{25}$.

Solution 1

You could multiply 10 by 14 to get the numerator of the product and multiply 21 by 25 to get the denominator of the product. However, if you simplify first, you can make the computations easier. First, you can simplify either or both of the fractions. Notice that $\frac{10}{35}$ can be simplified, using common factor 5, to $\frac{2}{7}$. Now the problem simplifies to:

$$\frac{2}{7} \cdot \frac{14}{25}$$

You can simplify further by looking *diagonally* at the 7 and the 14. They have common factor 7. Cross out the 7 and the 14 as you divide both by 7 and write the quotient for each.

$$\frac{2}{\cancel{7}} \cdot \frac{\cancel{14}^{2}}{25}$$

You can also look diagonally at the 2 and the 25, but they do not have a common factor that will simplify the fraction.

Multiply the numerators and multiply the denominators. The product is $\frac{4}{25}$.

Example 2

Find $\frac{2}{3}$ of 42. $\frac{2}{3} \cdot \frac{42}{1} = \frac{2}{1} \cdot \frac{14}{1} = 28$

Solution 2

Use multiplication and place the denominator 1 under the 42 to make a multiplication of fractions problem. Simplify using common factor 3 and solve:

$$\frac{2}{\underset{1}{\cancel{3}}} \cdot \frac{\overset{14}{\cancel{42}}}{1} = 28$$

The product is 28, so $\frac{2}{3}$ of 42 is 28.

Fill in the Blanks

If you are asked to find the __product__, you need to multiply. When multiplying two fractions, it is a good idea to __simplify__ first to make the computations easier. If you have to multiply mixed numbers, change each mixed number to an __improper fraction__ first and then use the multiplying fractions procedure.

Basic Problem

What is the product if $3\frac{1}{7}$ is multiplied by $3\frac{1}{2}$? $\frac{\overset{11}{\cancel{22}}}{7} \cdot \frac{7}{\cancel{2}} = 11$

a) $9\frac{1}{14}$ b) $3\frac{1}{14}$ c) $\frac{44}{49}$ d) 11   (circled)

Intermediate Problem

What is $\frac{2}{3}$ of 210? $\frac{2}{\cancel{3}} \cdot \frac{\overset{70}{\cancel{210}}}{1} = 140$

a) 140   (circled)   b) 70   c) 315   d) 21

Challenging Problem

What is $\frac{5}{6}$ of the product of $2\frac{1}{2}$ and 12?

a) $2\frac{1}{12}$ b) 10   c) 25   d) 30

$$\frac{5}{2} \cdot \frac{\cancel{12}^{6}}{1} = \frac{30}{1}$$

$$\frac{5}{\cancel{6}} \cdot \frac{\cancel{30}^{5}}{1} = 25$$

Numeric Entry Problem

What is $\frac{2}{3}$ of $\frac{15}{22}$?

$$\frac{\cancel{2}}{3} \cdot \frac{\cancel{15}^{5}}{\cancel{22}_{11}} = \frac{5}{11}$$

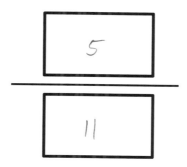

$$\frac{5}{11}$$

Multiple Choice with Multiple Answers Problem

Which of the following problems has an answer equivalent to $\frac{1}{2}$?

[a] $\frac{1}{3} \cdot \frac{\cancel{6}^{2}}{7} = \frac{2}{7}$ [b] $\frac{2}{\cancel{4}} \cdot \frac{\cancel{10}^{5}}{5} = 1$ [c] $\frac{15}{\cancel{7}} \cdot \frac{\cancel{7}}{30}_{2} = \frac{1}{2}$ [d] $\frac{22}{\cancel{8}}^{2} \cdot \frac{\cancel{6}^{3}}{11}_{1} = \frac{6}{4}$

Key Descriptors

multiplying fractions, multiplying mixed numbers, product

Keep change flip

CORE CONCEPT 13
Dividing Numerical Fractions

Introduction

You've probably seen division problems like "2135 divided by 5" written three ways:

dividend

$$2,135 \div 5 \quad \text{or} \quad 5\overline{)2,135} \quad \text{or} \quad \frac{2,135}{5}$$

divisor

In division examples like these, 2,135 is called the **dividend** and 5 is called the **divisor**. The answer to a division problem is called the **quotient**.

Division is the inverse operation of multiplication. This means that you can convert any division of fractions problem into a multiplication of fractions problem, and you already know how to multiply fractions. You might remember learning the phrase "keep-change-flip" to help you remember how to divide fractions.

The division problem $\frac{14}{25} \div \frac{2}{15}$ can be converted to a multiplication problem that has the same answer, using the process nicknamed "keep-change-flip." *Keep* the dividend as is. *Change* the division sign to a multiplication sign. Then *flip* (use the reciprocal) of the divisor (the second number) to create the following:

$$\frac{14}{25} \cdot \frac{15}{2}$$

Simplify and multiply to get the answer $\frac{21}{5}$, which can be converted to the mixed number $4\frac{1}{5}$. If you need to divide mixed numbers, change them to improper fractions first.

Example

Find the quotient when $\frac{2}{3}$ is divided by $\frac{7}{9}$.

Solution

The division problem $\frac{2}{3} \div \frac{7}{9}$ can be converted to the multiplication problem

$$\frac{2}{3} \cdot \frac{9}{7}.$$

Simplify using the common factor 3:

$$\frac{2}{\cancel{9}_1} \cdot \frac{\cancel{9}^3}{7}.$$

Multiply. The answer, $\frac{2}{3}$, is the quotient desired.

Fill in the Blanks

In the equation $x \div y = b$, x is called the _dividend_ y is called the _divisor_ and b is called the _quotient_. If x and y are fractions, you can change the problem to a multiplication of fractions problem by using the _reciprocal_ of the divisor, which is the second fraction. If x and y are mixed numbers, they need to be changed to _improper_ fractions first.

Basic Problem

$$\frac{5}{8} \div \frac{3}{4} = \frac{5}{\cancel{8}_2} \cdot \frac{\cancel{4}^1}{3} = \frac{5}{6}$$

a) $\frac{15}{32}$　　　b) $\frac{15}{16}$　　　c) $\frac{5}{6}$　　　d) $\frac{5}{24}$

Intermediate Problem

Cameron needs to divide $7\frac{1}{3}$ cups of antifreeze equally into 11 test tubes for a chemistry experiment. How many cups of antifreeze should go into each test tube?

a) $\frac{2}{3}$　　　b) $\frac{1}{33}$　　　c) $\frac{3}{2}$　　　d) $\frac{7}{33}$

$$\frac{22}{3} \div 11$$

$$\frac{\cancel{22}^2}{3} \cdot \frac{1}{\cancel{11}_1} = \frac{2}{3}$$

$$x \div \frac{12}{55} = \frac{5}{3}$$

Challenging Problem

The quotient of two fractions is $\frac{5}{3}$. The divisor is $\frac{12}{55}$. What is the dividend?

a) $\frac{275}{36}$ b) $\frac{4}{11}$ c) $\frac{36}{275}$ d) $\frac{12}{55}$

$$\frac{12}{55} \div \frac{5}{3} =$$

$$\frac{12}{55} \cdot \frac{3}{5} = \frac{36}{275}$$

Numeric Entry Problem

Find the quotient when $\frac{42}{45}$ is divided by $\frac{7}{20}$. Express your answer as an <u>improper fraction</u> in simplest form.

$$\frac{42}{45} \div \frac{7}{20} =$$

$$\frac{42}{45} \cdot \frac{20}{7} = \frac{24}{9} = \frac{8}{3}$$

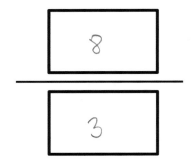

Quantitative Comparison Problem

Compare Quantity A and Quantity B, using the information below.

<u>Quantity A</u>   <u>Quantity B</u>

The reciprocal of $\frac{4}{11}$.

$$\frac{11}{4} = 2\frac{3}{4}$$

The product of $\frac{4}{11}$ and its reciprocal.

$$\frac{4}{11} \div \frac{11}{4} = 1$$

Select one of the following answers.

a) Quantity A is greater.
b) Quantity B is greater.
c) The two quantities are equal.
d) The relationship cannot be determined from the information given.

Key Descriptors

dividend, dividing fractions, dividing mixed numbers, divisor, quotient of two fractions

Adding and Subtracting Numerical Fractions

Introduction

The answer to an addition problem is called the **sum**. The answer to a subtraction problem is called the **difference**. You may recall focusing heavily on the denominator when adding or subtracting fractions. Adding and subtracting fractions with the same denominator ("like" denominators) is pretty intuitive; the answer uses the same denominator, and the numerators are added or subtracted, as indicated by the sign.

$$\frac{11}{23} - \frac{6}{23} = \frac{5}{23} \qquad \text{and} \qquad \frac{8}{9} + \frac{3}{9} = \frac{11}{9} = 1\frac{2}{9}.$$

Mixed numbers do not have to be changed to improper fractions for addition and subtraction; you can add or subtract the fractions and integer parts separately. When the denominators are different, you need to use the LCM to do the problem.

Example 1

Find the sum of $\frac{2}{9}$ and $\frac{4}{15}$.

Solution 1

Notice the two different denominators. Adding thirds and fifths is somewhat analogous to adding apple and oranges. We need to find the **lowest common denominator (LCD)**, which is a number that is the least common multiple of 9 and 15. The LCM is 45.

We need to change each fraction to an equivalent fraction with denominator 45. We accomplish this by multiplying by 1 in a fractional form convenient to get the desired denominator. First, we multiply $\frac{2}{9}$ by 1 in the form $\frac{5}{5}$ to give us an equivalent fraction with denominator 45.

$$\frac{2}{9} \cdot \frac{5}{5} = \frac{10}{45}.$$

Next, we multiply $\frac{4}{15}$ by 1 in the form $\frac{3}{3}$ to give us an equivalent fraction with denominator 45.

$$\frac{4}{15} \cdot \frac{3}{3} = \frac{12}{45}.$$

We add the numerators and keep the denominator.

$$\frac{10}{45} + \frac{12}{45} = \frac{22}{45}.$$

The correct sum is $\frac{22}{45}$.

Example 2

Subtract $3\frac{1}{4}$ from $21\frac{7}{8}$.

Solution 2

First write the problem vertically since it involves mixed numbers.

$$21\frac{7}{8} \qquad 21\frac{7}{8} - 3\frac{2}{8}$$

$$-3\frac{1 \cdot 2 = 2}{4 \cdot 2 = 8}$$

Then use the LCM 8 to get common denominators for the fraction parts.

$$21\frac{7}{8}$$

$$-3\frac{2}{8}$$

$$18\frac{5}{8}$$

Subtract the integers and subtract the fractions separately. The correct answer is $18\frac{5}{8}$.

If you need help with more complicated problems, use resources such as Internet videos, Internet examples and written information, and math textbooks. There are many model problems you can try in all of these sources, and they include worked-out solutions.

You can also ask your math teacher for help.

Fill in the Blanks

When you are asked to find the _sum_, you add, and when you are asked to find the difference, you _subtract_. If the denominators are the same, the process is simpler than if the denominators are different. When the denominators are different, you need to find the _lowest common denominator_ which is the LCM for the denominators. Then you multiply the fractions by 1, where 1 is written in fractional form, engineered by you to yield the common denominator. This common denominator is also used in the answer, and the _numerators_ can then be added or subtracted as indicated.

Basic Problem

Linda is mixing $7\frac{1}{2}$ cubic yards of mulch with $6\frac{1}{4}$ cubic yards of topsoil to create a mixture. How many cubic yards are in the mixture?

a) $13\frac{7}{8}$ b) $1\frac{1}{4}$ c) $13\frac{2}{6}$ d) $13\frac{3}{4}$

$$\frac{15}{2}_{\cdot 2} + \frac{25}{4} = \frac{30}{4} + \frac{25}{4} = \frac{55}{4} = 13\frac{3}{4}$$

Intermediate Problem

$$\frac{9}{16} + \frac{13}{24} = \frac{27}{48} + \frac{26}{48} = \frac{53}{48} = 1\frac{5}{48}$$

a) $1\frac{7}{48}$ b) $\frac{11}{20}$ c) $\frac{11}{24}$ d) $1\frac{5}{48}$

Challenging Problem

$$15 - 2\frac{5}{8} = \frac{15}{1} - \frac{21}{8} = \frac{120}{8} - \frac{21}{8} = \frac{99}{8} = 12\frac{3}{8}$$

a) $13\frac{5}{8}$ b) $12\frac{3}{8}$ c) $13\frac{3}{8}$ d) $12\frac{5}{8}$

Numeric Entry Problem

Find the difference between the sum and the product of $\frac{1}{2}$ and $\frac{1}{4}$.

sum
$$\frac{1}{2}+\frac{1}{4}=\frac{2}{4}+\frac{1}{4}=\frac{3}{4}$$

pro
$$\frac{1}{2}\times\frac{1}{4}=\frac{1}{8}$$

$$\frac{3}{4}-\frac{1}{8}=\frac{6}{8}-\frac{1}{8}=\frac{5}{8}$$

$$\frac{5}{8}$$

Multiple Choice with Multiple Answers Problem

Which of the following problems has an answer greater than 1?

[a] $\frac{2}{3}+\frac{1}{3}=\frac{2}{3}$ ✓[b] $\frac{11}{7}-\frac{1}{5}=$ ✓[c] $\frac{6}{7}+\frac{3}{7}=\frac{9}{7}$ [d] $\frac{7}{8}-\frac{3}{4}=$

$$\frac{55}{35}-\frac{7}{35}=\frac{48}{35}$$

$$\frac{7}{8}-\frac{6}{8}=\frac{1}{8}$$

Key Descriptors

adding fractions, common denominators, difference, LCD, lowest common denominator, subtracting fractions, sum

DID YOU KNOW THAT?

When these four fractions are incorrectly simplified as shown, the result is, surprisingly, the correct answer!

$$\frac{16}{64}=\frac{1\cancel{6}}{\cancel{6}4} \qquad \frac{26}{65}=\frac{2\cancel{6}}{\cancel{6}5}$$

$$\frac{49}{98}=\frac{4\cancel{9}}{\cancel{9}8} \qquad \frac{19}{95}=\frac{1\cancel{9}}{\cancel{9}5}$$

Equivalent Fractions and Decimals

Introduction

You have seen decimals since elementary school.

Decimals can be used to represent all rational numbers. When the denominator of a fraction is a power of 10 (like 10, 100, 1000, etc.), its representation as a decimal is straightforward.

$$\frac{7}{10} = 0.7 \quad \text{tens}$$

$$\frac{41}{100} = 0.41 \quad \text{hundreds}$$

$$\frac{139}{1000} = 0.139 \quad \text{thousands}$$

Likewise, decimals can be represented as fractions. The number of decimal places tells you the denominator. For example,

Four decimal places (ten-thousandths):	$0.1573 = \frac{1573}{10,000}$
Three decimal places (thousandths):	$0.749 = \frac{749}{1000}$
Two decimal places (hundredths):	$0.23 = \frac{23}{100}$
One decimal place (tenths):	$0.3 = \frac{3}{10}$

Some decimals **terminate**, which means they end after a finite number of decimal places. Look at the following set of terminating decimals:

$$\{1.2345, 123.9888888, 0.7, 6.0001, 41.904\}$$

Decimals that do not terminate are **nonterminating** decimals. **Repeating decimals** represent rational numbers that do not terminate—they have infinitely many decimal places, and a group of digits that repeats. The following decimal has a repeating pattern of 45123 endlessly.

$$324.4512345123451234512345123\ldots$$

Repeating decimals can be represented with a horizontal bar, called an **overbar**, on top of the digit pattern that repeats.

$$324.4512345123451234512345123\ldots = 324.\overline{45123}$$

If that pattern changed down the line, the nonterminating decimal would not be a repeating decimal, it would represent an **irrational number**.

Keep in mind that every rational number, even fractions without denominators that are powers of 10, can be represented as a decimal. These fractions can be converted to decimals using long division or a calculator.

Example 1

Convert $\frac{5}{16}$ to an equivalent decimal.

Solution 1

Use your calculator and divide:

$$5 \div 16 =$$

The display should read 0.3125. So $\frac{5}{16} = 0.3125$. If you were using long division, you would set up the problem like this:

$$16\overline{)5.0000}$$

If you are using a calculator, make sure you enter the numbers in the correct order!

Example 2

In the following table, some fractions are given and need to be converted to equivalent decimals. Additionally, decimals are given and need to be converted into equivalent *simplified* fractions. Remember to simplify the fractions!

Row Identification	Fraction	Decimal
a	$\frac{3}{8}$	.375
b	$\frac{75}{100}$ $\frac{15}{20}$ $\frac{3}{4}$	0.75
c	$\frac{9}{100}$	0.09
d	$\frac{2}{3}$	$.\overline{6}$
e	$\frac{531}{999}$	$\overline{.531}$
f	$\frac{8}{10} = \frac{4}{5}$	0.8
g	$\frac{18}{1000} = \frac{9}{500}$	0.018

Solution 2

Row Identification	Fraction	Decimal	Notes on Solution
a	$\frac{3}{8}$	0.375	$0.375 = \frac{375}{1000}$
b	$\frac{3}{4}$	0.75	$0.75 = \frac{75}{100} = \frac{3}{4}$
c	$\frac{9}{100}$	0.09	$\frac{9}{100}$ is already in simplest form
d	$\frac{2}{3}$	$0.\overline{6}$	This is a repeating decimal.
e	$\frac{531}{999}$	$0.\overline{531}$	Another repeating decimal
f	$\frac{4}{5}$	0.8	$0.8 = \frac{8}{10} = \frac{4}{5}$
g	$\frac{9}{500}$	0.018	$0.018 = \frac{18}{1000} = \frac{9}{500}$

Fill in the Blanks

If you want to convert a fraction to an equivalent decimal, __divide__ the __numerator__ by the __denominator__. A decimal that ends after a finite number of places is called a __terminating__ decimal and a decimal that repeats a group of digits in the same order, endlessly, is called a __nonterminating__ decimal. Some non-terminating decimals do have patterns, like 0.12112111211112111112111112..., but since the pattern is not repeating, these decimals represent __irrational__ numbers.

Basic Problem

What is $\frac{5}{8}$ expressed as an equivalent decimal?

1.3   (b) 0.625   c) 62.5   d) 0.013

Intermediate Problem

Which decimal is equivalent to $\frac{53}{99}$?

a) $0.5\overline{3}$ b) 0.53   (c) $0.\overline{53}$ d) 0.535353

Challenging Problem

A fraction that is equivalent to a repeating decimal is being created. The numerator is the largest prime number less than 10. The denominator is the smallest composite number greater than 16. How many digits are in the pattern that repeats?   16

(a) 1   b) 2   c) 3   d) 4 $\frac{7}{15}$

Numeric Entry Problem

What digit is in the 13th decimal place of the decimal $0.\overline{53142}$? 5 3 1 4 2 5 3 1

[1]

Quantitative Comparison Problem

Compare Quantity A and Quantity B, using the information below.

Quantity A   Quantity B

$$\frac{53}{99}$$.$\overline{53}$ $$\frac{35}{66}$$.$5\overline{30}$

Select one of the following answers.

a) Quantity A is greater.
b) Quantity B is greater.
c) The two quantities are equal.
d) The relationship cannot be determined from the information given.

Key Descriptors

changing a fraction to a decimal, irrational numbers, non-terminating decimals, rational numbers, repeating decimals, terminating decimals

DID YOU KNOW THAT?

An integer is evenly divisible by 3 if the sum of all of its digits is evenly divisible by 3.

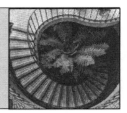

CORE CONCEPT 16
Rounding Decimals

Introduction

Decimals are often rounded because the degree of accuracy necessary for the given application depends on the specific situation. Cutting wood for a garage shelf does not require as much precision as installing fuel lines for a rocket engine. You'd never worry about a hundredth of a pint of orange juice but you might want to be very accurate if you were adding a hundredth of a pint of liquid nitrogen as part of a chemistry experiment.

When you round off a decimal, you create a new number that is not exactly equal to the original, it is an **approximation**. When you are asked to round a decimal, the instructions can refer to the number of places to round off to, or they could refer to the **place value** desired in the approximation.

Recall that a decimal is a special fraction that uses powers of 10 as their denominators.

Example

Round 12.6791 to the nearest hundredth.

12.68

Solution

Note that the instructions to this problem could have read "round to two decimal places" and the solution would still be the same.

Write the given number.

12.6791

Rounding to the nearest hundredth requires the answer to have two decimal places. Underline the digits that have the number of places desired in the approximation.

12.**67**91

Circle the number to the immediate right of the underlined numbers, and draw an arrow pointing to the number on its left. That is the number that will be rounded.

$$12.67\overset{\frown}{\underline{67}}\circled{9}1$$

If the circled number is 5, 6, 7, 8, or 9, increase the number to its left by 1, and drop the remaining decimal digits to the right of the underlined places. If the circled number is 0, 1, 2, 3, or 4, leave the number on its left unchanged, and drop the remaining decimal digits to the right of the underlined places.

You can use the symbol ≈ to indicate that the original number and the rounded number are *approximately* equal. Rounded to the nearest hundredth,

$$12.6791 \approx 12.68.$$

Be sure you remember the place values of the decimal places, and how to interpret the overbar notation for repeating decimals.

Fill in the Blanks

A decimal with one decimal place can be written as a fraction with denominator __10__. A decimal with __2__ decimal places can be written as a fraction with denominator 100. A decimal with four decimal places can be written as a fraction with denominator __10,000__. When a given decimal is rounded, the new rounded number is __not__ equal to the given number, it is an __approximation__ of the given number.

Basic Problem

Round 98.055 to the nearest tenth.   98.1

a) 98.16   b) 98.1   c) 98.06   d) 98

Intermediate Problem

Michael rounds the number 12.62684 to the nearest tenth and Courtney rounds it to the nearest thousandth. What is the sum of their rounded approximations?

a) 25.227   b) 25.226   c) 0.027   d) 0.026

12.6 + 12.627 =

Challenging Problem

6.78178 6.7818
T HThTT

Round 6.$\overline{781}$ to the nearest ten-thousandth.

a) 6.78178   b) 6.78   c) 6.7818   d) 6.782

Numeric Entry Problem

8.666   8.67

Round 8.$\overline{6}$ to the nearest hundredth.

8.67

Multiple Choice with Multiple Answers Problem

Which of the following decimals, when rounded to the nearest hundredth, is 23.74?

[a] 23.737   [b] 23.$\overline{74}$ 74   [c] 23.$\overline{73}$7   [d] 23.7455

Key Descriptors

decimal place value, rounding decimals,

DID YOU KNOW THAT?

An integer is divisible by 11 if you alternately add and subtract its digits from left to right or right to left, and your answer is divisible by 11. This is called "Casting Out Elevens."

OONAHill

Interpreting Percent

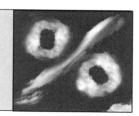

Introduction

The word **percent** means 'out of 100.' It is interesting that you can view the percent sign itself, %, as being made up of two 0's and a 1. Very often we compare numbers to 100, especially in school. If you receive a 91% on a test, you immediately know you did very well, but if you get a fractional score, say out of 28, like, $\frac{22}{28}$, you do not get a quick intuitive feel for how well you did. You'd probably convert it to a decimal and then a percent to determine how well you did, because fractions, decimals, and percents are closely related. You already have reviewed equivalent fractions and decimals.

Example 1

Express the decimal 0.73 as an equivalent percent.

Solution 1

Since percent means out of 100, and the decimal 0.73 representing the fraction $\frac{73}{100}$ is already "out of 100", the decimal

$$0.73 = 73\%.$$

If you just moved the decimal point in 0.73 two spaces to the right, you would have done the conversion without even writing the fraction. So let's make this our rule. *To convert a decimal to a percent, move the decimal two spaces to the right and add a percent sign.*

Example 2

Express 12% as an equivalent decimal.

12 %

$\frac{12}{100}$

.12

Solution 2

We can convert 12% to the fraction $\frac{12}{100}$ which, as a decimal, is 0.12, We can just reverse the rule we set up in Example 1. *To convert a percent to a decimal, move the decimal point two spaces to the left and drop the percent sign.*

Note that the "simplified" version of $\frac{12}{100}$, which is $\frac{3}{25}$, is not as easy to intuitively interpret as 12%.

Fill in the Blanks

Percent means "out of __100__." You can think of a percent as a fraction whose __denominator__ is 100. These fractions can be converted directly to decimals. To change a percent to an equivalent decimal, you move the decimal point two places to the __left__, and drop the __%__ sign. To change a decimal to an equivalent percent, move the decimal point __2__ places to the __right__, and add a percent sign.

Basic Problem

Which of the following is equivalent to 0.23?

a) $\frac{0.23}{100}$ (b) 23%   c) 0.23%   d) 2.3%

Intermediate Problem

Which of the following, I, II, III, represent numbers that are equivalent to <u>45%</u>?

   I.   0.45   II. $\frac{9}{20} \cdot \frac{5}{5} = \frac{45}{100} = 0.45$ III. $\frac{45}{100}$%

a) I only   (b) I and II only   c) II only   (d) I, II, and III

Challenging Problem

Which of the following represents $\frac{13}{250}$ as an equivalent percent?

a) 5.2%   (b) 0.052%   c) 52%   d) 520%

$$\frac{13}{250} \cdot \frac{^{\cdot 4}}{^{\cdot 4}} = \frac{52}{1000}$$

Numeric Entry Problem

Express 70% as a fraction in simplest form.

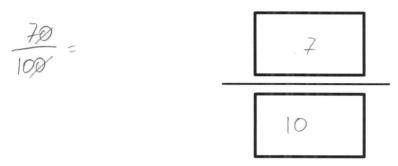

$$\frac{70}{100} =$$

$$\frac{.7}{10}$$

Quantitative Comparison Problem

Compare Quantity A and Quantity B, using the information below.

Quantity A	Quantity B
0.13, 13%	**13%**

Select one of the following answers.

a) Quantity A is greater.
b) Quantity B is greater.
c) The two quantities are equal.
d) The relationship cannot be determined from the information given.

Key Descriptors

Converting decimals to percents, converting fractions to percents, converting percents to fractions, converting percents to decimals, percent, percentage

DID YOU KNOW THAT?

An integer is evenly divisible by 9 if the sum of all of its digits is evenly divisible by 9.

CORE CONCEPT 18
Ratio and Proportion

Introduction

A **ratio** is a numerical comparison of two numbers. You may have heard expressions like "the ratio of wins to losses is 3 to 2." This can be written mathematically as a fraction, $\frac{3}{2}$, or using a colon, 3:2.

A **proportion** is an equation which shows the equivalence of two ratios.

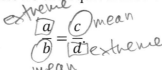

In this proportion, b and c are called the **means** and a and d are called the **extremes**. In any proportion, the product of the means is equal to the product of the extremes. You may have referred to this as "**cross multiplying**" when setting up an equation.

Example 1

Find the value of x in the following proportion.

$$\frac{17}{5} = \frac{x}{45}.$$

Solution 1

In this proportion, 5 and x are the means and 17 and 45 are the extremes. You can set up an equation by cross multiplying.

$$5x = 17 \cdot 45$$

$$5x = 765$$

$$x = 153.$$

Example 2

The three angles of a triangle are in the ratio 2:3:5. How many degrees are in the largest angle?

Solution 2

$2x + 3x + 5x = 180°$
$10x = 180$
$x = 18$

When three quantities are in the ratio 2:3:5, they can be represented by $2x$, $3x$, and $5x$, where $2x$ represents the smallest angle, $3x$ represents the middle angle, and $5x$ represents the largest angle. Since the sum of the interior angles of a triangle is 180 degrees, you can set up an equation.

$$2x + 3x + 5x = 180.$$

$$10x = 180$$

$$x = 18$$

Since $x = 18$, the largest angle, $5x$, is found by substituting 18 in for x. The largest angle is 90 degrees.

Fill in the Blanks

Ratios can be expressed as fractions. If two _ratios_ are set equal to each other, a _proportion_ is formed. In the proportion $\frac{r}{s} = \frac{t}{u}$, s and t are the _means_ and r and u are the _extremes_. In any proportion, the _products_ of the means is equal to the _product_ of the extremes, and this is often informally called _cross multiplying_.

Basic Problem

Find the value of y in the following proportion.

$5y = 420$
$y = 84$

$$\frac{60}{y} = \frac{5}{7}$$

a) 100   b) 84   c) 12   d) 420

Intermediate Problem

The ratio of cars to motorcycles at the Cruise Night parking lot is 9:2. If there are 132 vehicles in all, how many motorcycles are there?

a) 11   b) 12   c) 108   d) 24

[handwritten: C M]

$$9x + 2x = 132$$
$$11x = 132$$
$$x = 12$$
$$2 \cdot (12) = 24$$

Challenging Problem

There are 150 rookies (first-year players) at the Florence Baseball Academy and 180 non-rookies. What is the ratio of rookies to total players expressed as a fraction in simplest form?

a) $\frac{5}{11}$ b) $\frac{5}{6}$ c) $\frac{15}{18}$ d) $\frac{6}{11}$

$$\frac{150}{330} = \frac{15}{33} = \frac{5}{11}$$

Numeric Entry Problem

What is the value of *p* in the following proportion?

$$\frac{7.5}{6} = \frac{5}{p}$$

$$7.5p = 30 \qquad 1 \cdot 7.5$$
$$p = 4$$

4

Multiple Choice with Multiple Answers Problem

Which of the following proportions has the solution *p* = 4?

[a] $\frac{5}{20} = \frac{p}{16}$ [b] $\frac{p}{40} = \frac{3}{10}$ [c] $\frac{6}{p} = \frac{5}{20}$ [d] $\frac{7}{28} = \frac{1}{p}$

$$20p = 80$$
$$p = 4$$

$$10p = 120$$
$$p = 12$$

$$5p = 120$$
$$p = 24$$

$$7p = 28$$
$$p = 4$$

Key Descriptors

cross multiplying, product of the means and the extremes, proportion, ratio

CORE CONCEPT 19
Computations with Percent

Introduction

Recall that percent means "out of 100," so it involves a part of a whole. Percent is used often in daily life. Most financial issues involve percent, and computations with percent can be done using equations or the **percent proportion**. The percent proportion requires you to substitute known quantities and solve for an unknown quantity using a variable.

$$\frac{\text{part}}{\text{whole}} = \frac{\%}{100}.$$

This is sometimes informally remembered using the proportion in this form:

$$\frac{\text{"is"}}{\text{"of"}} = \frac{\%}{100}$$

You will see in the following three examples how the words 'is' and 'of' occur in different percent applications and how the proportion helps you solve them.

Example 1

Six percent of the students at Smithtown High School drive cars to school. There are 750 students. How many students drive cars to school?

Solution 1

Let's use the percent proportion and substitute.

$$\frac{\text{"is"}}{\text{"of"}} = \frac{\%}{100}$$

.06   6%

There are 750 students, so the phrase '*of* the students' means that 750 is the denominator of the first fraction. The percent is given as 6%, so 6 is the numerator of the second fraction. Notice that the second fraction, $\frac{6}{100}$, is another way of representing 6%. We want to know what *is* 6% of 750. The numerator of the first fraction can be represented as x. Substitute, cross multiply, and solve.

$$\frac{x}{750} = \frac{6}{100}$$

$$4{,}500 = 100x$$

$$x = 45$$

$$\frac{\text{"is"}}{\text{"of"}} = \frac{\%}{100}$$

Since 6% of 750 is 45, there are 45 students who drive to school.

Example 2

What percent of 150 is 22.5?

Solution 2

Use the percent proportion and substitute. The 'of 150' and 'is 22.5' make the substitutions clear. The words 'what percent' tells you where to place the variable x.

$$\frac{22.5}{150} = \frac{x}{100}$$

Cross multiply and solve the equation.

$$2{,}250 = 150x$$

$$x = 15$$

The answer is 15%.

Example 3

$$\frac{12}{x} = \frac{40}{100}$$

Twelve is 40% of what number?

Solution 3

Use the percent proportion and substitute. The '40%' and '12 is' make the substitutions clear. The phrase 'of what number' tells you where to place the variable x.

$$\frac{12}{x} = \frac{40}{100}$$

Cross multiply and solve the equation.

$$1{,}200 = 40x$$

$$x = 30$$

Twelve is 40% of 30.

Fill in the Blanks

The _percent_ _proportion_ is useful in solving many percent problems. In this proportion, the ratio $\frac{\text{part}}{\text{whole}}$ is set equal to the ratio $\frac{\%}{100}$ which represents the percent written as a _fraction_ with denominator _100_.

Basic Problem

Chloe buys a new car for $28,400. She is also charged 6% sales tax. How much sales tax must she pay?

a) $1,680   b) $1,704   c) $30,104   d) $26,696

$$\frac{x}{28{,}400} = \frac{6}{100}$$

$$100x = 28{,}400 \cdot 6$$
$$100x = 170{,}400$$
$$x = 1704$$

Intermediate Problem

Sixteen is what percent of 128?

a) 12.5%   b) 10%   c) 15%   d) 0.125%

$$\frac{16}{128} = \frac{x}{100}$$

$$128x = 1600$$
$$x = 12.5$$

Challenging Problem

Michelle sells audio equipment and is paid a commission for each month's sales. She receives 11% on her first $5,000 of sales and 5% on the rest of her sales. Last month she sold $6,300 worth of audio equipment. What was her commission?

a) $615   b) $550   c) $1,008   d) $65

$$\frac{x}{5000} = \frac{11}{100}$$

$$100x = 55{,}000$$
$$x = 550$$

$$\$550 + \$65 = \$615$$

$$\frac{x}{1300} = \frac{5}{100}$$

$$100x = 6500$$
$$x = 65$$

Numeric Entry Problem

Ten is 62% of what number? Round your answer to the nearest tenth.

$$\frac{10}{x} = \frac{62}{100}$$

$$62x = 1000$$
$$x = 16.129$$

> 16.1

Quantitative Comparison Problem

Compare Quantity A and Quantity B, using the information below.

Quantity A	Quantity B
Fifteen percent of forty.	**Forty percent of fifteen.**

Quantity A:
$$\frac{x}{40} = \frac{15}{100}$$
$$100x = 600$$
$$x = 6$$

Quantity B:
$$\frac{x}{15} = \frac{40}{100}$$
$$100x = 600$$
$$x = 6$$

Select one of the following answers.

a) Quantity A is greater.
b) Quantity B is greater.
c) The two quantities are equal.
d) The relationship cannot be determined from the information given.

Key Descriptors

finding a percent of a number, percent proportion

DID YOU KNOW THAT?

A number is **orthonymic** if the number of line segments it takes to write out the letters of the number is equal to the number. The only orthonymic number is 29. Count the number of line segments:

TWENTY NINE

CORE CONCEPT 20
Percent Change

Introduction

Ratio, proportions, and percent help us to compare. For example, if you found out that 40 people caught the flu at Marra Business School, you have no idea, from this raw number, if there is a flu problem or not. If the school has 110 students, there is a flu problem. If the school has 93,000 students, there is not a flu problem. A percent tells you this information immediately. "Eighty-two percent of students at Marra Business School" tells you immediately there is a severe problem. "Two percent of the students at Marra Business School" gives you a completely different picture.

Example 1

Dobby Ski Rental rented 150 pair of skis per day last winter. They estimate that this will increase 16% next winter. How many pairs of skis will they rent per day next winter?

$$150 \times 116\%$$
$$150 \times 1.16 = 174$$

Solution 1

We can compute the increase using the percent proportion and then add it on to the original amount. This requires two steps.

$$\frac{x}{150} = \frac{16}{100}$$

The increase is 24, and this must be added to the original rental number of 150, for a total of 174 pairs of skis rented per day next winter.

We can simplify these types of computations to one step. Next year's rental number is 100% of last year's, plus 16%, so next winter's rentals will be 116% of last year's rentals. Change 116% to a decimal and multiply.

$$150 \times 1.16$$

$$150(1.16) = 174.$$

Notice how this method gave us the answer in one step.

Example 2

Jordan wants to purchase new headphones. The regular price is $90 but they are on sale for 15% off. What is the sale price?

$$90 \times (1.00 - 0.15) = 90 \times (0.85) =$$

Solution 2

The discount rate represents a percent decrease. If Jordan is getting 15% off, view this as a 15% decrease.

$$90(1.00-0.15) = 90(0.85) = 76.5.$$

The sale price is $76.50.

Example 3

Tomika got a new job with a starting salary of $45,000. Her salary increases 2% each year. What will her salary be in five years?

$$45,000 \times (1.02) \times (1.02) \times (1.02) \times (1.02) =$$
$$\underset{1}{} \quad \underset{2}{} \quad \underset{3}{} \quad \underset{4}{} \quad \underset{5}{}$$

$$45,000 \times (1.02^4) =$$

Solution 3

Tomika's salary is 102% of each previous year's salary.

Her second-year salary is 45,000(1.02).

Her third-year salary is 102% of her second-year salary, which is shown in bold print:

$$\mathbf{45,000(1.02)}(1.02) = 45000(1.02)^2.$$

Using this pattern, her fourth-year salary is $45000(1.02)^3$ and her fifth-year salary is

$$45000(1.02)^4.$$

Using a calculator, we see that her fifth-year salary, rounded to the nearest cent, is

$$\$48,709.45$$

Example 4

Julianne bought a classic car in 2012 for $15,000. By 2022, it had increased in value to $21,000. What was the percent increase in value?

Solution 4

We need to use the percent change formula.

$$\text{percent change} = \frac{\text{new amount} - \text{original amount}}{\text{original amount}} \cdot 100$$

Substitute.

$$\text{percent change} = \frac{21{,}000 - 15{,}000}{15{,}000} \cdot 100$$

Simplify.

$$\text{percent change} = \frac{6{,}000}{15{,}000} \cdot 100 = 40$$

 The percent increase in value is 40%. Note that if the percent change is negative, there has been a *decrease*.

Fill in the Blanks

A positive percent change represents an __increase__ in quantity and a negative percent change represents a __decrease__ in quantity. When you multiply by a percent greater than 100% you __increase__ the original number and when you multiply by a percent less than 100% you __decrease__ the original number. If a quantity doubles, you can say it has *increased* __100__ %.

Basic Problem

The Smithville School District's budget was $5,444,000 this year. Next year it will increase 2%. What will the budget be next year?

102%

a) $108,880   b) $5,552,880   c) $6,532,800   d) $1,088,800

$5,444,000 × (1.02) = 5552880

Intermediate Problem

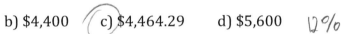

integer = whole # (not a fraction)

Camp Nittany has 550 campers this year. It is planning to expand, and increase the number of campers 8% each year for the next three years. How many campers will they have after those three years? Round to the nearest integer.

$550 \times (1.08)^3 =$

a) 584   b) 990   c) 594   (d) 693

Challenging Problem

Last year's orchestra budget was increased 12% to get this year's budget. This year's budget is $5,000. What was last year's budget? Round to the nearest cent.

a) $4,250   b) $4,400   (c) $4,464.29   d) $5,600

$5000 = 12\%$

12%

$12\% = 1.12$

$1.12x = 5000$

$x =$

Numeric Entry Problem

Express 101% as an equivalent decimal.

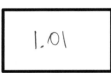

1.01

Multiple Choice with Multiple Answers Problem

Which of the following expressions represents a 17% change from 60?

(a) 60(1.00-0.17)   (b) 60(1.17)   (c) 60(1.00 + 0.17)   [d] 60(1.17-0.17)

Key Descriptors

percent change, percent decrease, percent discount, percent increase

CORE CONCEPT 21
English System Measurement Conversions

Introduction

In your career and in your daily life you deal with linear measurement (miles, feet, inches), volume (fluid ounces, quarts, gallons), and weight (pounds, ounces, tons). You might have trouble remembering some of the equivalences. Here are some you should know:

12 inches = 1 foot
3 feet = 1 yard
36 inches = 1 yard
5,280 feet = 1 mile
2 pints = 1 quart
4 quarts = 1 gallon
16 ounces = 1 pound
2000 pounds = 1 ton

You need to be careful to look for problems in which there are different units! You can use proportions to solve problems with English measurement conversions. When setting up a proportion to convert measurement units, keep the same unit in both numerators and keep the same unit in both denominators. For example,

$$\frac{\text{quarts}}{\text{gallons}} = \frac{\text{quarts}}{\text{gallons}} \quad \text{or} \quad \frac{\text{feet}}{\text{inches}} = \frac{\text{feet}}{\text{inches}}$$

Organizing your proportions like this will make your substitutions easier.

Example 1

Convert 81 inches to an equivalent measurement in yards.

Solution 1

Set up a proportion with inches in the numerators and yards in the denominators. The first fraction is the conversion ratio.

$$\frac{36 \text{ inches}}{1 \text{ yard}} = \frac{81 \text{ inches}}{x \text{ yards}}$$

$$\frac{36}{1} = \frac{81}{x}$$

Cross multiply and solve for x. The result is $x = 2.25$, so 81 inches is equivalent to 2.25 yards.

Example 2

Buddy's lawn mower holds 1.7 quarts of gasoline in its tank. He just filled his 2.5-gallon gas can at the station. How many times will he be able to fill his lawn mower tank from a full gas can?

Solution 2

First notice, when reading the problem, you should underline the units and note that the problem is worded using two different units. Since the oil changes are measured in quarts, let's convert to quarts first using a **conversion ratio** or **conversion factor**. A conversion ratio is equal to 1 since the numerator and denominator are equivalent.

$$\text{Since 4 quarts } = \text{ 1 gallon, } \frac{4 \text{ quarts}}{1 \text{ gallon}} = 1.$$

Let's set up the proportion to convert the gallons to quarts.

$$\frac{4}{1} = \frac{x}{2.5}$$

Cross multiply and you'll find that $x = 10$, so 2.5 gallons is equal to 10 quarts. Since the mower can hold 1.7 quarts, divide 10 by 1.7.

$$10 \div 1.7 \approx 5.9.$$

The result, 5.9, indicates that Buddy can fill up the mower 5 times. There is not enough gasoline to *fill it up* 6 times.

Fill in the Blanks

You can use a ___proportion___ to convert units in the English measurement system. When setting up this proportion, the first fraction should be the ___conversion ratio___, which is always equal to 1. Both numerators should have the same ___units___ and both denominators should have the same ___units___.

Basic Problem

A roll of duct tape contains 60 yards of tape. How many feet of tape does the roll contain?

a) 180   b) 20   c) 720   d) 2,160

$$\frac{3ft}{1yd} = \frac{xft}{60yd}$$

$$x = 180 \, ft$$

Intermediate Problem

A drum of oil contains 55 gallons. An oil change for a car requires 5 quarts. How many oil changes can the drum of oil cover?

a) 11   b) 44   c) 55   d) 22

$$\frac{4q}{1gal} \times \frac{x}{55gal}$$

$$x = 220$$

$\div 5$ quarts /per fill

$$= 44$$

Challenging Problem

Yoko is converting 2.1 miles into yards. Which of the following statements, I, II, III, are true?

$.1 \, mile \times \frac{5280ft}{1mile} \times \frac{1 \, yard}{3 \, ft} = 3696$ yards

I. The number of miles is more than the number of yards.
II. There are 1,760 yards in a mile.
III. The 2.1 miles equals more than 4,000 yards.

a) I only   b) II and III only   c) II only   d) I, II, and III

$$5,280 \, ft \div 3 \, ft =$$

$$1,760 \, y$$

Numeric Entry Problem

How many pounds are equivalent to 148 ounces?

$$\frac{16 \, oz}{1 lbs} = \frac{148 \, oz}{x}$$

$$16x = 148$$

$$x = 9.25$$

9.25

Quantitative Comparison Problem

Compare Quantity A and Quantity B, using the information below.

Quantity A   Quantity B

16.5 gallons   **65 quarts**

$$\frac{4q}{1\,gal} = \frac{x}{16.5\,gal}$$

$$x = 66\,q$$

Select one of the following answers.

a) Quantity A is greater.
b) Quantity B is greater.
c) The two quantities are equal.
d) The relationship cannot be determined from the information given.

Key Descriptors

conversion factor, conversion ratio, measurement conversion, units conversion

DID YOU KNOW THAT?

Cousin primes are prime numbers that are 4 apart from each other, such as

$\{3, 7\}, \{7, 11\}, \{13, 17\}, \{19, 23\}, \{37, 41\}$, etc.

It is not known if there are infinitely many cousin prime pairs.

This is another unsolved problem in mathematics that can be explained to a fourth grader!

Metric System Measurement Conversions

Introduction

The metric system of measurement is more widespread throughout the world than the English system. In your career and in your daily life you will often deal with the metric system, so it is advantageous to understand how it works.

The metric system uses meters (m) as the basic unit of length, liters (L) as the basic unit of liquid volume, and grams (g) as the basic unit of weight. A meter is about as long as a yard. A liter is approximately one quart. A gram is about as heavy as a paper clip. Prefixes are added to each of these units to form larger and smaller units. Conversions within the metric system are much easier because it uses powers of 10, like 10, 100, and 1,000.

The metric system uses prefixes in front of the unit names to form new units. Here are the basic prefixes:

Prefix	Multiple
kilo	1,000
hecto	100
deca	10
deci	0.1
centi	0.01
milli	0.001

d c m
.1 .01 .001

For example, a **kilo**meter (km) is **1000** meters, a **centi**liter (cL) is **0.01** (one hundredth) of a liter, and a **hecto**gram (hg) is **100** grams. The prefixes allow you to do conversion within the metric system without using proportions. To convert from metric to English or English to metric, you will have to use proportions.

K H D U d c m

Example 1

12.71 km = 127100 cm

Convert 12.71 km to an equivalent length in cm.

Solution 1

Write out the first letter of each prefix as shown here:

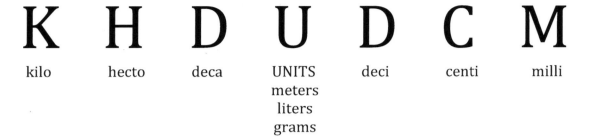

K	H	D	U	D	C	M
kilo	hecto	deca	UNITS meters liters grams	deci	centi	milli

Write 12.71 under the K. We want to convert to centimeters, so count the number of decimal places you need to move to get to the C.

Since you needed to move five places to the right, move the decimal point five places to the right to get the answer. You might have to add zeroes as placeholders. Add commas where necessary *after* moving the decimal point. Sometimes you might have to move the decimal point to the left.

12.71km = 1,271,000 cm.

You can use a mnemonic to help you remember the order of the letters. For example,

Kids **H**ave **D**eveloped **U**nderstanding **D**oing **C**oncentrated **M**ath

Example 2

An inch is equivalent to approximately 2.54 centimeters. How many inches are equivalent to 14.3 centimeters? Round to the nearest hundredth.

Solution 2

$$\frac{2.54 \text{ cm}}{1 \text{ in}} = \frac{14.3 \text{ cm}}{x}$$

Set up a proportion with centimeters in the numerators and inches in the denominators. The first fraction is the conversion ratio.

$$\frac{2.54 \text{ cm}}{1 \text{ inch}} = \frac{14.3 \text{ cm}}{x \text{ inches}}$$

$$\frac{2.54}{1} = \frac{14.3}{x}$$

Cross multiply and solve for x. The result is $x \approx 5.63$, so 14.3 cm is approximately 5.63 inches.

Fill in the Blanks

The basic unit of weight in the metric system is the __gram__. A kilogram is __1000__ grams. The basic unit of length in the metric system is the __meter__, and there are 100 meters in a __hectometer__. The basic unit of liquid volume in the metric system is the __L__, and a __milliliter__ is equivalent to $\frac{1}{1000}$ of a liter.

Basic Problem

k H D U d c m

How many meters are equivalent to 2,345 km?   2.345m   2,345000

a) 0.002345 m   b) 23.45 m   c) 2.345 m   (d) 2,345,000 m

Intermediate Problem

A liter is approximately 61.02 cubic inches. If a car engine is 427 cubic inches, how many liters is it? Round to the nearest tenth.   1L = 61.02 in³

(a) 7 L   b) 42.7 L   c) 0.7 L   d) 2,988 L $\frac{61.02 \, in^3}{1L} = \frac{427 in^3}{x}$

61.02x = 427

x = 6.997 L

Challenging Problem

The NextGen wireless router can cover a radius of 45.7m. The Big Boy wireless router can cover a radius of 23.1 m. The routers are located 100 meters from each other. A yard is approximately 0.9144m. 68.8 m

Which of the following statements, I, II, III, are true?

I. There is no location covered by both routers.
II. The routers are approximately 60 yards apart.
III. The NextGen router covers a radius of 457 cm.

a) I only   b) I and III only   c) II only   d) I, II, and III

Numeric Entry Problem

A kilogram is approximately 2.2 pounds. How many kilograms are equivalent to 135 pounds? Round to the nearest tenth.

61.4

$$\frac{2.2\,lbs}{1\,kg} = \frac{135\,lbs}{x}$$

$$2.2x = 135$$

$$x = 61.3636$$

$$135\,lbs \cdot \frac{1\,kg's}{2.2\,lbs} =$$

Multiple Choice with Multiple Answers Problem

K H D U d c m

Which of the following quantities are equivalent to 61,511 meters?

.061511 km

[a] 61.511 km   [b] 6,151,100 cm   [c] 0.61511 mm   [d] 6,151.1hm

Key Descriptors

metric system, metric system prefixes, metric system conversions, metric to English conversions

DID YOU KNOW THAT?

There is a rule that defines the order of the ten digits in the pattern below, which ends at 0. Think outside of the box! Can you figure out the rule?

8, 5, 4, 9, 1, 7, 6, 3, 2, 0.

These are the digits 0 - 9 in alphabetical order!

Functions

Introduction

A **function** is a rule, or a **mapping**, that assigns each **element** (member) of a set (the **domain**) to a unique member of another set, often called the **range**. The members of the domain can be referred to as **input variables**, and the members of the range can be considered **output variables**. For example, the height function would assign a numerical height to each person. The car color function could assign a color to each car. The triple function would assign a number's triple to each number inputted.

There are several different ways a function can be represented. You have probably already seen the notation $f(x)$, in which x is the input variable. This notation is very helpful. If you write that $f(3) = 17$, we know that the input value is 3 and the output value is 17. Had you just written $y = 17$, we would not have known what the input value was. Keep in mind that, in a function, for any input value, the output is unique.

Example 1

The function $\blacklozenge$ is defined as $x \blacklozenge y = 3x - 2y$. Find the value of $7 \blacklozenge 8$.

Solution 1

Substitute 7 for x and 8 for y in the rule for the function.

$$x \blacklozenge y = 3x - 2y$$

$$7 \blacklozenge 8 = 3(7) - 2(8)$$

$$7 \blacklozenge 8 = 21 - 16$$

$$7 \blacklozenge 8 = 5.$$

Example 2

The function $f(x)$ is defined as $f(x) = (3x - 16)^2 - 2x$. Find the value of $f(3)$.

Solution 2

Substitute 3 for x in the rule for the function.

$$f(x) = (3x - 16)^2 - 2x$$

$$f(3) = (3(3) - 16)^2 - 2(3)$$

$$f(3) = (9 - 16)^2 - 6$$

$$f(3) = (-7)^2 - 6$$

$$f(3) = 49 - 6$$

$$f(3) = 43.$$

Fill in the Blanks

A function is a mapping, or a __rule__, that assigns elements from the __domain__ to elements of the __range__. If the notation $f(x)$ is used, x can be called the __input__ variable, and a value of x is __substituted__ into the function rule so $f(x)$ can be computed. For each value of x, the value of $f(x)$ is __unique__.

Basic Problem

The function ♥ is defined as $a \heartsuit b = a^2 - 3b$. Find the value of $5 \heartsuit 2$.

a) 4   (b) 19   c) 20   d) -11

$5 \heartsuit 2 = 5^2 - 3(2)$
$5 \heartsuit 2 = 25 - 6$
$5 \heartsuit 2 = 19$

Intermediate Problem

Find the additive inverse of $f(7)$ if $f(x) = (x + 7)^2$.

(a) -196   b) 196   c) 28   d) -28

$f(7) = (7 + 7)^2$
$f(7) = 14^2$
$f(7) = 196$

Challenging Problem

If $f(x) = |x^2 - 2x - 16|$, what is the closest prime number to $f(4)$?

a) 9 b) 7 c) 8 d) 11

$f(4) = |4^2 - 2(4) - 16|$
$f(4) = |16 - 8 - 16|$
$f(4) = |-8|$ $f(4) = 8$

Numeric Entry Problem

The function ♣ is defined as x ♣ $y = (2x - y)^2$. Find the value of 1.1 ♣ 1.

1.44

$1.1 ♣ 1 = (2(1.1) - 1)^2$
$1.1 ♣ 1 = (2.2 - 1)^2$
$= (1.2)^2$
$= 1.44$

Quantitative Comparison Problem

Compare Quantity A and Quantity B, using the information below.

Quantity A	Quantity B
$f(7)$, if $f(x) = 3x$	$g(7)$, if $g(x) = f(x) + 5$

$f(7) = 3 \cdot 7$ $f(7) = 21$

$g(7) = 21 + 5 = 26$

Select one of the following answers.

a) Quantity A is greater.
b) Quantity B is greater.
c) The two quantities are equal.
d) The relationship cannot be determined from the information given.

Key Descriptors

domain of a function, functions, input variable, mapping, output variable, range of a function

Combining Like Terms

Introduction

An **equation** has an equal sign, so $5x + 7y = 13$ is an equation. An **expression** does not have an equal sign. Examples of expressions are shown below:

$$2x + 3y - 7$$

$$x^2 + 7x - 12xy + 4$$

quotient - result of division $6 \div 2 = \dfrac{3}{\text{quotient}}$

An expression that is written as a product or quotient of numbers or variables is called a **term**. Four examples of terms are shown below:

$$17x \qquad 4y^5 \qquad \frac{4}{5}xp^2 \qquad \frac{2x}{y}$$

An algebraic expression with only one term is called a **monomial**. An algebraic expression with more than one term is called a **polynomial**. A polynomial with two terms is a **binomial**. A polynomial with three terms is a **trinomial**. If a term is just a number, that number is often called a **constant**.

If the variable parts of two monomials are exactly the same, they are called **like terms**. Look at the following:

$$3x^2 \text{ and } 4x^2 \text{ and } -8x^2 \text{ are all like terms}$$

$$4xy \text{ and } 6xy \text{ are like terms}$$

$$5a^2 \text{ and } 5b^2 \text{ are not like terms}$$

The number in front of the variable part is called a **coefficient**. Like terms can be added or subtracted by combining their coefficients and keeping the variable part the same. This is called **combining like terms**.

Example 1

Simplify the expression $5xy + 6 - 7x^3y^2 + 1 + 4xy - 12x^3y^2$ by combining like terms.

Solution 1

Focus on terms with the same variable part by highlighting them, circling them, underlining them, etc., using the same highlighting for each set of like terms.

$$\underline{5xy} + \underline{6} \left(\!-7x^3y^2\!\right) + \underline{1} + \underline{4xy} \left(\!-12x^3y^2\!\right)$$

Then add or subtract the coefficients as indicated.

$$5xy + 4xy = 9xy$$

$$6 + 1 = 7$$

$$-7x^3y^2 - 12x^3y^2 = -19x^3y^2$$

The expression simplifies to $9xy + 7 - 19x^3y^2$.

This is often written using descending order of exponents as $-19x^3y^2 + 9xy + 7$.

Remember when there is "no" coefficient, as in x^3y^2z, the coefficient is 1.

Fill in the Blanks

An algebraic expression with one term is called a _monomial_ and an algebraic expression with more than one term is called a _polynomial_. You can simplify a polynomial by highlighting the _like_ terms and using the _coofficients_ of the like terms to combine them.

Basic Problem

If the expression $\widehat{3xp^2} + 6x - \widehat{7xp^2} - 4x^2p$ has its like terms combined, what is the simplified expression? $-4xp^2 + 6x - 4x^2p$

a) $-x^2p + 6x$ b) $-4x^3p^3 + 6x$ c) $-8xp^2 + 6x$ (d) $-4xp^2 - 4x^2p + 6x$

$-2x^2y - x^2y$
$-3x^2y$

$11xy^2 - 12xy^2$
$-1xy^2$

$-7x^2y^2 + 3x^2y^2$
$-4x^2y^2$

Intermediate Problem

$-4x^2y^2 - 3x^2y - 1xy^2$

Simplify the expression $-2x^2y + 11xy^2 - 7x^2y^2 - x^2y + 3x^2y^2 - 12xy^2$ by combining like terms.

a) $13x^2y - xy^2 - 4x^2y^2$
c) $-3x^2y - xy^2 - 10x^2y^2$

b) $-3x^2y + 23xy^2 - 4x^2y^2$
d) $-3x^2y - xy^2 - 4x^2y^2$

Challenging Problem

"flipped number" $\frac{2}{3} \div \frac{7}{9} = \frac{2}{3} \cdot \frac{9}{7}$ ↑ reciprocal

Two like terms are being combined. The variable part is k^2mp^5. The two coefficients are the largest prime number less than 30 and the reciprocal of the smallest prime number. What is the simplest form after these two like terms are combined?

a) $29.5\ k^2mp^5$
k^2mp^5

b) $27.5\ k^2mp^5$

c) $31.5\ k^2mp^5$
$29 + \frac{1}{2}$

d) $31\ k^2mp^5$

Numeric Entry Problem

If the polynomial $9abc + 6ab - 7ab^2 - abc + 4ab - 12a^3b^2$ is simplified by combining like terms, what is the coefficient of the abc term?

8

Multiple Choice with Multiple Answers Problem

Which of the following expressions are equivalent to $19x^3$?

[a] $10x^3 + 9x^3$
$19x^3$

[b] $20x^3 - x^3$

[c] $-x^3 + 18x^3$

[d] $11x^3 + 10x^3 - x^3$

Key Descriptors

binomial, coefficient, combining like terms, constant term, like monomials, like terms, monomial, polynomial, trinomial

CORE CONCEPT 25
Sums and Differences of Polynomials

Introduction

Adding and subtracting polynomials is much like combining like terms. You highlight each set of like terms. In a subtraction problem, the first number is called the **minuend** and the number being subtracted is called the **subtrahend**. So, in the example 5 - 2 = 3, 5 is the minuend and 3 is the subtrahend. When subtracting polynomials, you will need to use the **distributive property**. This will be illustrated in Example 2.

Example 1

Find the sum of $5x^2 - 7x + 12$ and $7x^2 + 11x - 16$.

Solution 1

Write the sum as one long polynomial and combine like terms.

$$5x^2 - 7x + 12 + 7x^2 + 11x - 16$$

$$12x^2 + 4x - 4.$$

Example 2

Subtract $4x^2y^2 - 9xy + 10$ from $7x^2y^2 + 13xy + 5$.

Solution 2

Put parentheses around each polynomial to group them. The word 'from' tells you which number goes in "front." Write the difference as one long polynomial.

minuend   subtrahend
$$(7x^2y^2 + 13xy + 5) - (4x^2y^2 - 9xy + 10)$$

Insert a 1 in front of the second set of parentheses.

$$(7x^2y^2 + 13xy + 5) - 1(4x^2y^2 - 9xy + 10)$$

distributive property

Remove the first set of parentheses. Distribute the -1 over the second polynomial as you remove the parentheses. Notice how the signs change after each coefficient is multiplied by -1.

$$7x^2y^2 + 13xy + 5 - 4x^2y^2 + 9xy - 10$$

Combine like terms as usual.

$$3x^2y^2 + 22xy - 5.$$

Fill in the Blanks

Adding and subtracting polynomials requires the same skills as <u>combining</u> <u>like</u> <u>terms</u>. When subtracting, it is important to put parentheses around the <u>subtrahend</u> and place a 1 in front of the parentheses, so you remember to use the <u>distributive</u> property before combining like terms.

Basic Problem

Subtract $-2x^2 - 8x + 19$ from $3x^2 + 10x - 7$.

$$\left(3x^2 + 10x - 7\right) - 1\left(-2x^2 - 8x + 19\right)$$
$$3x^2 + 10x - 7 + 2x^2 + 8x - 19$$
$$5x^2 + 18x - 26$$

a) $x^2 + 2x + 12$

c) $5x^2 + 18x - 26$

b) $-5x^2 + 2x + 26$

d) $-5x^2 + 2x + 12$

Intermediate Problem

product of subtracting

If -4kp is subtracted from 10kp, what is the <u>difference?</u>

a) 14kp b) 6kp c) -4kp d) -14kp

$$10kp - 1(-4kp)$$
$$10kp + 4kp \qquad 14kp$$

Challenging Problem

If $14x^ay^3$ and $9x^5y^b$ are like terms, what is the <u>value</u> of ab?

$$5 \cdot 3 = 15$$

a) 9   b) 15   c) 25   d) 8

Numeric Entry Problem

If the following three binomials are combined, what is the <u>coefficient</u> of the x^5y^4 term?

$$(14x^5y^4 - 11) - (8x^5y^4 - 1) + (2.5x^5y^4 + 6.2)$$

8.5

[handwritten: $14x^5y^4 - 11 - 8x^5y^4 + 1$
$6x^5y^4 - 10 + 2.5x^5y^4 + 6.2$
$8.5x^5y^4 -$]

Quantitative Comparison Problem

Compare Quantity A and Quantity B, using the information below.

<u>Quantity A</u>	<u>Quantity B</u>
3x + 7x - 2y	**8x + 9x - y**
10x - 2y	*17x - y*

Select one of the following answers.

a) Quantity A is greater.
b) Quantity B is greater.
c) The two quantities are equal.
d) The relationship cannot be determined from the information given.

Key Descriptors

adding polynomials, combining polynomials, difference between two polynomials, distributive property, subtracting polynomials

DID YOU KNOW THAT?

If you have a **gross** of bubblegum balls, you have a dozen dozens, which is 144 bubblegum balls.

Literal Equations

Introduction

You already know several of the processes used in solving different types of equations. You want to isolate a variable by "undoing" some of the operations in the equation's expressions. You are used to solving equations with numbers like

$$2x - 17 = 23.$$

Think of the processes you use to solve this. First, you add 17 to both sides of the equation.

$$2x = 40$$

Then you divide both sides by 2.

$$x = 20.$$

Literal equations consist mostly of letters. Many formulas you are familiar with are literal equations, for example,

$$a^2 + b^2 = c^2$$

$$A = \pi r^2$$

$$A = \frac{1}{2}(b_1 + b_2)$$

$$x = \frac{-b \pm \sqrt{b^2 - 4ac}}{2a}.$$

Look at this literal equation:

$$ax - b = k$$

Notice how it looks much like $2x - 17 = 23$, with letters replacing the numbers. If you wanted to solve $ax - b = k$ for x, you can use steps analogous to the steps used in solving $2x - 17 = 23$. First, you add b to both sides of the equation.

$$ax = k + b$$

Then you divide both sides by a.

$$x = \frac{k + b}{a}.$$

You could also solve $ax - b = k$ for a, b, or k.

Example 1

Solve the equation $ax - b = k$ for b.

Solution 1

Subtract ax from both sides of the equation.

$$-b = k - ax$$

Divide both sides by -1.

$$b = \frac{k - ax}{-1} = ax - k.$$

Example 2

Solve the equation $x = \frac{2d - m}{pk}$ for d.

Solution 2

Write x as a fraction to make this easier.

$$\frac{x}{1} = \frac{2d - m}{pk}$$

Cross multiply to eliminate the fraction.

$$xpk = 2d - m$$

Add m to both sides.

$$xpk + m = 2d$$

Divide both sides by 2 to isolate d.

$$d = \frac{xpk + m}{2}.$$

Fill in the Blanks

Equations that are made up primarily of letters are called *literal* *equations*. Many *formulas* you already know, like the Pythagorean theorem, or area and perimeter formulas, or the quadratic formula, are literal equations. Since a *literal* *equation* has several letters, it is possible to isolate, or solve for, any of the letters.

Basic Problem

Solve the equation $7a + 3b = \frac{5x}{4}$ for b.

$$7a + 3b = \frac{5x}{4}$$
$$5x = 28a + 12b \quad |-28a$$
$$12b = 5x - 28a \quad |\div 12$$
$$b = \frac{5x - 28a}{12}$$

a) $b = \frac{5x-7a}{12}$ b) $b = \frac{5x-28a}{12}$ c) $b = \frac{5x-28a}{3}$ d) $b = \frac{5x-28a}{3}$

Intermediate Problem

Solve the equation $x^2 - \frac{p^2}{4} = 5$ for p.

$$x^2 - \frac{p^2}{4} = 5 \quad \left(+\frac{p^2}{4}\right)$$
$$x^2 = 5 + \frac{p^2}{4} \quad |-5$$
$$x^2 - 5 = \frac{p^2}{4} \quad |\cdot 4$$
$$4x^2 - 20 = p^2$$

a) $p = \pm\sqrt{4x^2 - 20}$ b) $p = \pm\sqrt{4x^2 - 5}$

c) $p = \pm\sqrt{4x^2 + 20}$ d) $p = 2x^2 - 10$

Challenging Problem

If $5cx - 20x = 13r$ is solved for x, for what value of c is x undefined?

a) 5   b) 13   c) 4   d) 20

$$5cx - 20x = 13r \quad |-5cx$$
$$-20x = 13r - 5cx \quad |\div(-20)$$
$$x = -\frac{13r - 5cx}{20}$$

Numeric Entry Problem

If the equation $5x + 41y = 3z$ is solved for y, what is the denominator?

$5x + 41y = 3z$ | $-5x$

$41y = 3z - 5x$ | $\div 41$

$y = \dfrac{3z - 5x}{41}$

$$\boxed{41}$$

Multiple Choice with Multiple Answers Problem

When solved for y, which of the following expressions is equivalent to $a + b$?

[a] $a + y - b = 0$ $\quad$ [b] $b + a - y = 0$ $\quad$ [c] $\frac{a}{y} = b$ $\quad$ [d] $\frac{1}{a+b} = \frac{1}{y}$

$y = b - a$ $\qquad$ $y = b + a$ $\qquad$ $y = \frac{a}{b}$ $\qquad$ $y = a + b$

?

Key Descriptors

formulas, isolating variables, literal equations, solving for variables

DID YOU KNOW THAT?

A **score** of years is equal to 20 years. A score of footballs is equal to 20 footballs.

Systems of Linear Equations

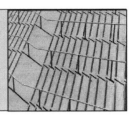

Introduction

Equations with two variables, each with exponent 1, are called **linear equations** because their graph forms a straight line. The solutions to a linear equation like $2x + 3y = 12$ are ordered pairs of numbers (x, y). There are infinitely many solutions to this linear equation. Here are some of them:

$$3 \cdot \frac{2}{3} = \frac{6}{3} = 2$$

$$(0, 4) \qquad (6, 0) \qquad (1.5, 3) \qquad \left(5, \frac{2}{3}\right)$$

If you have more than one equation with the same variables, you have a **system of equations**. When you look for a solution to a system of equations, you are looking for solutions that satisfy *all* of the equations in the system.

 We will first look at two equations in two unknowns. These systems can have zero solutions, one solution, or infinitely many solutions. Those are the only possibilities. We will examine two methods of solving these equations. One is called the **elimination** method and the other is called the **substitution** method.

Example 1

Solve the following system of equations using the elimination method:

$$5x + 3y = 14$$
$$2x + \ y = 6$$

Solution 1

The idea is to eliminate one variable, solve for the remaining variable, and then use that solution to solve for the second variable. Get one of the variables to have coefficients that are additive inverses. In this example, we multiply the second equation by -3. The system becomes:

add the equations after using an additive inverse in the variable

$$5x + 3y = 14$$
$$-6x - 3y = -18$$

$$-x = -4$$

Add the equations. Notice how the addition of the additive inverse coefficients of the *y* terms *eliminated* the *y* terms.

$$-x = -4$$

Multiply both sides by -1.

$$x = 4$$

Substitute 4 for *x* into either original equation.

$$2x + y = 6$$

$$2(4) + y = 6$$

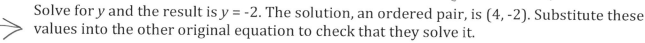

$$8 + y = 6 \quad | -8$$
$$y = 6 - 8 \quad y = -2$$

Solve for *y* and the result is *y* = -2. The solution, an ordered pair, is (4, -2). Substitute these values into the other original equation to check that they solve it.

Example 2

Solve the following system using the substitution method.

$$c = d + 4$$

$$2c - 5d = 8$$

Solution 2

Notice that, in the first equation, the variable *c* is expressed in terms of *d* already. Replace the *c* in the second equation with its equivalent, *d* + 4.

$$2(d + 4) - 5d = 8$$

Distribute.

$$2d + 8 - 5d = 8$$

Subtract 8 from both sides and combine like terms.

$$-3d = 0$$

Divide both sides by -3 to get *d* = 0. Substitute *d* = 0 into the second equation to get *c* = 4. The solution expressed as an ordered pair (*c*, *d*) is (4, 0).

Fill in the Blanks

We reviewed two methods of solving a system of two linear equations in two unknowns.
One method is the _elimination_ method and the other is the _substitution_ method.
In the elimination method, one variable is eliminated because its coefficients were
engineered to become _additive_ _inverses_. In the _substitution_
method, one variable is isolated and the expression it is equal to is substituted into the
second equation.

Basic Problem

Solve the following system of equations and express the solution as an ordered pair (x, y).

$$2x - 3y = 1$$
$$4x + 3y = 29$$

$6x = 30$
$x = 5$

a) (5, 3)   b) (5, -3)   c) (3, 5)   d) (-3, 5)

Intermediate Problem

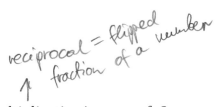

reciprocal = flipped number
↑ fraction of a number

If the following system of equations is solved, what is the <u>multiplicative inverse of s</u>?

$$r + 3s = 17$$
$$3r + 2s = 23$$

$r + 3s = 17$ $| -3s$
$r = 17 - 3s$
$3(17 - 3s) + 2s = 23$
$51 - 9s + 2s = 23$
$51 - 7s = 23$
$-7s = 23 - 51$
$-7s = -28$ $s = 4$ $\frac{1}{4}$

a) 0.25   b) 4   c) -4   d) -0.25

Challenging Problem

The sum of two numbers, x and y, is 17. The difference $x - y$ is 7. What is the <u>product</u> of the
<u>numbers</u>?

$x + y = 17$
$x - y = 7$ } add the equations
$2x = 24$
$x = 12$

a) 119   b) 7   c) 60   d) 17

product = multiplication

$12 + y = 17$ $| -12$
$y = 17 - 12$
$y = 5$

$12 \times 5 = 60$

Numeric Entry Problem

If the following system is solved, what is the value of k, expressed as a decimal?

$$2k - 5m = -4$$

$$8k + 5m = 9$$

$10k = 5$ $|:10$

$k = \dfrac{5}{10}$

$k = \dfrac{1}{2}$

$$\boxed{0.5}$$

Quantitative Comparison Problem

Compare Quantity A and Quantity B, using the information below.

<u>Quantity A</u>   <u>Quantity B</u>

The value of x in the solution to the system   **The value of y in the solution to the system**

$x + y = -2$ $2x = 6$ $x + y = -2$ $3 + y = -2$

           $x = 3$

$x - y = 8$ $x - y = 8$ $y = -2 - 3$

                                            $y = -5$

Select one of the following answers.

a) Quantity A is greater. *(circled)*
b) Quantity B is greater.
c) The two quantities are equal.
d) The relationship cannot be determined from the information given.

Key Descriptors

ordered pairs, systems of linear equations, solving systems by elimination, solving systems by substitution, two equations in two unknowns

CORE CONCEPT 28
Inequalities

Introduction

Inequality signs are used to compare quantities. In Core Concept 1 you compared numerical inequalities. You can also compare algebraic expressions. One property is the **transitive property of inequalities**, which is somewhat intuitive.

- If $x < y$ and $y < z$, then $x < z$.
- If $a > b$ and $b > c$, then $a > c$.
- If $2x + 5 < 7$ and $7 < p + 1$, then $2x + 5 < p + 1$.

Algebraic inequalities can be solved using techniques similar to solving equations. Inequalities can have infinitely many solutions, so the solutions can't be listed. They are often graphed on a number line.

Let's compare an equation to some analogous inequalities.

$$2x + 4 = 14$$

Subtract 4 from both sides: $\qquad\qquad 2x = 10$

Divide both sides by 2: $\qquad\qquad\quad x = 5$

Look how the same steps can be applied to the following four inequalities. The solution sets are also graphed on the number line for each. The open circles are used for "strict" inequalities like < and >, and the closed circles are used for ≤ and ≥.

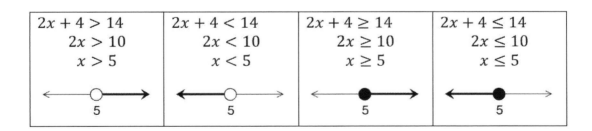

$2x + 4 > 14$	$2x + 4 < 14$	$2x + 4 \geq 14$	$2x + 4 \leq 14$
$2x > 10$	$2x < 10$	$2x \geq 10$	$2x \leq 10$
$x > 5$	$x < 5$	$x \geq 5$	$x \leq 5$

Notice how the inequality sign does not change direction in the four problems shown. Now take a look at this inequality.

$$-2x > 26$$

One solution to this inequality is -14, since -2(-14) = 28, which is greater than 26. Recall that -14 is less than -13 since it is to the left on the number line. All numbers *less than* -13 satisfy the inequality.

$$x < -13$$

When you multiply or divide both sides of an inequality by a negative number, the inequality sign must be reversed.

Example 1

Solve the following system of inequalities and graph the solution set.

$$2x - 5 < 11$$

$$3x + 7 \geq 16$$

Solution 1

Since this is a system of inequalities, the solutions have to work for one inequality *and* the other. Solve each separately and find the interval on the number line which has solutions to both inequalities.

$2x - 5 < 11$	$3x + 7 \geq 16$
$2x < 16$	$3x \geq 9$
$x < 8$	$x \geq 3$

The solutions are numbers that are greater than or equal to 3 and less than 8. This can be shown on the number line.

This can be written as the **compound inequality** $3 \leq x < 8$.

Example 2

If $-3x + 1 > 16$ or $5x + 3 \leq -7$, find the solution set.

Solution 2

Notice that this is an 'or' situation. The solution does not have to satisfy both inequalities, just at least one of them. Solve them individually,

$$3x + 1 > 16 \qquad\qquad 5x + 3 \leq -7$$

$$3x > 15 \qquad\qquad 5x \leq -10$$

$$x > 5 \qquad\qquad x \leq -2$$

This can be written using set notation as $\{ x > 5 \text{ or } x \leq -2\}$. When graphed on the number line, it becomes clear that there is not any number that satisfies both inequalities.

Fill in the Blanks

The _transitive_ property states that if $a > d$ ___ $d > m$, then _$a > m$_. Algebraic inequalities can be solved much like equations can be solved, but since there could be infinitely many solutions, the solution set is shown using set notation or by graphing on the _number_ _line_. Remember that when multiplying or dividing both sides of an inequality by a _negative_ number, you must remember to reverse the direction of the inequality sign.

Basic Problem

Find the solution set of the inequality $2x + 15 < 49$.

a) $\{x < 32\}$ b) $\{x < 17\}$ c) $\{x > 17\}$ d) $\{x < 12\}$

(handwritten)
$2x + 15 < 49$
$2x < 49 - 15$
$2x < 34$
$x < 17$

Intermediate Problem

Which is not a solution to the following system of inequalities?

$$3x - 1 \geq 20$$

$$-5x + 2 \geq -43$$

a) 6.9　　　b) 9　　　c) 7　　　d) 8.5

Handwritten work:

$3x - 1 \geq 20$
$3x \geq 20 + 1$
$x \geq 7$

$-5x + 2 \geq -43$
$-5x \geq -43 - 2$
$5x \leq 45$
$x \leq 9$

Challenging Problem

If the literal inequality $-4x - b \geq k + 7$ is solved for x, what is the solution?

a) $x \geq \frac{b+k+7}{-4}$　　　b) $x \leq \frac{k-b+7}{-4}$　　　c) $x \leq \frac{b+k+7}{4}$　　　d) $x \leq \frac{b+k+7}{-4}$

Handwritten work:

$-4x - b \geq k + 7$
$-4x \geq k + 7 + b$
$x \leq \frac{k+7+b}{-4}$

Numeric Entry Problem

What is the only solution to the following system of inequalities?

$$2x \geq 10 \quad x \geq 5$$

$$x + 1 \leq 6 \quad x \leq 5$$

$$\boxed{5}$$

Handwritten: $x = 5$

Multiple Choice with Multiple Answers Problem

Which of the following inequalities has 5 in its solution set?

[a] $x + 1 \leq 6$　　　[b] $-2x + 1 < 12$　　　[c] $3x + 1 > 15$　　　[d] $5x < -25$

Handwritten work:

[a] $x \leq 5$

[b] $-2x < 11$
　　$x > -5.5$

[c] $3x > 14$
　　$x > 4.6$

[d] $x < -30$

Key Descriptors

compound inequalities, inequalities on the number line, linear inequalities, transitive property of inequalities

Laws of Exponents

Introduction

You have used exponents to express repeated multiplication. For example,

$$3 \cdot 3 \cdot 3 \cdot 3 \cdot 3 = 3^5.$$

In the expression 3^5, 3 is called the **base**, 5 is the **exponent**, and 3^5 is the **power**, which is 243. Expressions like $2x^3$ and $5x^8$ are called **powers of the same base**, and there is a shorthand way to simplify their product.

$$2x^3 \cdot 5x^8 = 2xxx \cdot 5xxxxxxxx = 10xxxxxxxxxxx = 10x^{11}.$$

When multiplying powers of the same base, you keep the same base, and add their exponents to find the product.

$$x^a \cdot x^b = x^{a+b}$$

Let's look at dividing powers of the same base. Remember that the denominator cannot equal 0, and if x is not 0, $\frac{x}{x} = 1$.

$$\frac{8x^7}{2x^3} = \frac{8xxxxxxx}{2xxx} = 4x^4.$$

When dividing powers of the same base, you keep the same base and subtract their exponents to find the quotient.

$$\frac{x^a}{x^b} = x^{a-b}$$

Let's look at raising a monomial to a power.

$$(x^3)^4 = x^3 \cdot x^3 \cdot x^3 \cdot x^3 = x^{12}.$$

Notice how you can multiply the exponents when a monomial is raised to a power.

$$(x^a)^b = x^{ab}$$

Example 1

Use the laws of exponents to express the product $2^5 \cdot 2^6$ in exponential form.

Solution 1

Since these are powers of the same base, the product is found by keeping the base and adding the exponents. The solution is

$$2^{11}.$$

If you were "tempted" to write 4^{11}, be careful! That is a common error. Remember to keep the same base, as you would have if the problem was $x^5 \cdot x^6 = x^{11}$. Notice how the same base, x, was kept in the product.

Example 2

Simplify $\frac{4y^3 \cdot 9y^7}{(2y^2)^3}$ using the laws of exponents.

Solution 2

Simplify the numerator and denominator separately first.

$$\frac{4y^3 \cdot 9y^7}{(2y^2)^3} = \frac{36y^{10}}{8y^6}$$

Simplify the coefficients and subtract the exponents.

$$\frac{36y^{10}}{8y^6} = \frac{9}{2}y^4$$

Fill in the Blanks

In the expression $7x^{12}$, 7 is the ___coefficient___, x is the ___base___ and 12 is the ___exponent___. When multiplying powers of the same ___base___, you keep the same base, and add their ___exponents___ to find the product. When dividing powers of the same base, you keep the same base and ___subtract___ their exponents to find the ___quotient___. If a monomial is raised to a power, you can ___multiply___ the exponents to simplify. Be sure to remember that a monomial like x has an "invisible" exponent on the x that is equal to ___1___.

Basic Problem

Which of the following expressions is equivalent to $4x^3 \cdot 5x^2$?

$$20x^5$$

(a) $20x^5$ b) $20x^6$ c) $9x^5$ d) $9x^6$

Intermediate Problem

Which monomial is equivalent to the expression $3x^5 + 2x^5 + 2x^2 \cdot 3x^3$ in simplified form?

a) $10x^6$ (b) $11x^5$ c) $11x^6$ d) $10x^5$

$$3x^5 + 2x^5 + 6x^5$$
$$11x^5$$

Challenging Problem

Simplify $\dfrac{5x^{11}y^3 \cdot 8x^2 y^7}{(2x^3 y^2)^3}$ using the laws of exponents.

a) $5x^6 y^5$ b) $\frac{20}{3}x^4 y^4$ c) $5xy^4$ (d) $5x^4 y^4$

$$\frac{5x^{11}y^3 \cdot 8x^2 y^7}{(2x^3 y^2)^3} = \frac{5x^{11} \cdot 8x^2 \cdot y^3 \cdot y^7}{8x^9 \cdot 27y^6} = \frac{40x^{13} \cdot y^{10}}{8x^9 \cdot y^8} = \frac{5x^{13} \cdot y^{10}}{x^9 \cdot y^6} =$$

$$5x^4 \cdot y^4$$

Numeric Entry Problem

If the expression $(5m^5)^2$ is simplified using the laws of exponents, what is the product of the coefficient and the exponent?

$(5m^5)^2$

$25m^{10}$

$25 \times 10 = 250$

250

Quantitative Comparison Problem

Compare Quantity A and Quantity B, using the information below.

<u>Quantity A</u>   <u>Quantity B</u>

$3x^4 + 11$ $7x^5 + 25$

Select one of the following answers.

a) Quantity A is greater.
b) Quantity B is greater.
c) The two quantities are equal.
d) The relationship cannot be determined from the information given.

Key Descriptors

base, exponent, laws of exponents, multiplying powers of the same base, powers

DID YOU KNOW THAT?

FORTY is the only number that has all of its letters in alphabetical order.

40

CORE CONCEPT 30
Dividing a Polynomial by a Monomial

Introduction

Consider the following fraction.

$$\frac{35}{5}$$

Previously we reviewed how to divide the numerator and denominator by the greatest common factor, 5, to simplify the fraction to 7. Now look at this fraction:

$$\frac{25 + 10}{5}$$

The numerator is 35, so the fraction still simplifies to 7. Also note that this fraction could have been separated into two fractions. Recall when we reviewed adding fractions.

$$\frac{25 + 10}{5} = \frac{25}{5} + \frac{10}{5} = 5 + 2 = 7.$$

greatest common factor

The two fractions can *each* be simplified using the GCF. You don't have to physically separate the fractions as long as you remember to divide the 25 *and* the 10 by 5 when simplifying.

Let's look at an algebraic analogy. The numerator is a polynomial and the denominator is a monomial. You can call this a fraction or a **rational expression**.

$$\frac{6x^7 + 8x^5 - 12x^3}{2x^2}$$

Imagine treating this, in your head, as three separate fractions. Then you can simplify each separately by remembering to divide *each* monomial of the numerator by the denominator, and using the laws of exponents. The result is

$$3x^5 + 4x^3 - 6x.$$

When dividing a polynomial by a monomial, it is a common error to "cancel" the denominator with only the first monomial in the numerator. Be sure to avoid this!

Keep in mind that, as long as x is not 0,

$$\frac{x^7}{x^7} = 1.$$

By the laws of exponents,

$$\frac{x^7}{x^7} = x^0.$$

So, we can define x^0 to be equal to 1 as long as $x \neq 0$. It's not intuitive, but you can see why it makes sense.

$$\text{If } x \neq 0, \frac{x^n}{x^n} = x^0 = 1.$$

Example

Simplify the following fraction:

$$\frac{6x^7y^4 - 10x^5y^8 + 15x^4y^5}{5x^3y^2}$$

Solution

Treat this in your head as three separate fractions. Divide the coefficients and then use the laws of exponents to simplify.

$$\frac{6x^7y^4 - 10x^5y^8 + 15x^4y^5}{5x^3y^2} = \frac{6}{5}x^4y^2 - 2x^2y^6 + 3xy^3.$$

In this simplification, notice that one of the coefficients became a fraction and the exponent 1 on the last x does not need to be written.

Fill in the Blanks

When dividing a polynomial by a monomial, you must remember to divide each _monomial_ in the numerator by the denominator. You can break the original fraction into _separate_ fractions and simplify each fraction, either physically, or in your head. These fractions can also be called _rational_ _expression_. Remember to follow the _laws of_ _exponents_ when simplifying.

Basic Problem

Simplify the following rational expression: $\frac{5w^4+7w^6-11w^8-w^{12}}{w^2}$.

$5w^2 + 7w^4 - 11w^6 - w^{10}$

a) $5w^2 + 7w^4 - 11w^6 - w^{10}$ (circled)

b) $5w^2 + 7w^3 - 11w^4 - w^6$

c) $5w^2 + 7w^4 - 11w^6 - 10$

d) $5w^2 + 7w^4 - 11w^6 - 6$

Intermediate Problem

Simplify the rational expression $\frac{25x^{10}y^5-50x^5y^{15}+250x^{20}y^{10}}{5(xy)^5}$.

$\frac{25x^{10}y^5 - 50x^5y^{15} + 250x^{20}y^{10}}{5(xy)^5} \quad \frac{5x^5y^5}{}$

$5x^5 - 10y^{10} + 50x^{15}y^5$

a) $5x^2 - 10xy^3 + 50x^4y^2$

b) $x^2 - 2xy^3 + 10x^4y^2$

c) $x^5 - 2y^{10} + 10x^{15}y^5$

d) $5x^5 - 10y^{10} + 50x^{15}y^5$ (circled)

Challenging Problem

If $x \neq 0$, for what value of m does the rational expression $\frac{x^{5m+7}}{x^{4m+10}}$ equal x?

a) 4

b) -16   (circled)

c) -4

d) -2

$5m + 7 - 4m + 10 = 1$

$m =$

Numeric Entry Problem

If the rational expression $\frac{12x^6+16x^5+8x^3}{4x^2}$ is simplified, what is the <u>sum of the coefficients</u>?

9

$$\frac{12x^6+16x^5+8x^3}{4x^2}=$$

$$3x^4+4x^3+2x$$

Multiple Choice with Multiple Answers Problem

Which of the following fractions simplifies to $\underline{5x^2}$?

[a] $\frac{60x^6}{12x^2}$ [b] $\frac{20x^6}{4x^3}$ [c] $\frac{20x^3}{4x}$ [d] $\frac{-20x^4}{-4x^2}$

$5x^4$ $5x^3$ $5x^2$ $-5x^2 = 5x^2$

Key Descriptors

dividing a polynomial by a monomial, simplifying rational expressions, simplifying algebraic fractions

DID YOU KNOW THAT?

This is a Math Limerick:

$$\frac{12 + 144 + 20 + 3\sqrt{4}}{7} + (5 \cdot 11) = 9^2 + 0$$

A dozen, a gross, and a score,
Plus three times the square root of four
Divided by seven
Plus five times eleven
Is nine squared and not a bit more.

Negative Exponents

Introduction

When you first learned about exponents they made so much sense-a shorthand way to express repeated multiplication.

$$x^5 = x \cdot x \cdot x \cdot x \cdot x$$

Then it got a little weird with the laws of exponents, when it was necessary to define x^0.

$$\text{If } x \neq 0, \text{ then } x^0 = 1.$$

Certainly the "flavor" of what exponents are became more abstract with x^0.

Let's recall dividing powers of the same base. Remember that the denominator cannot equal 0, and if x is not $0, \frac{x}{x} = 1$.

$$\frac{8x^7}{2x^3} = \frac{8xxxxxxx}{2xxx} = 4x^4.$$

When dividing powers of the same base, you keep the same base and subtract their exponents to find the quotient. Look at the following example in which, after cancelling, there are four factors of x left in the denominator.:

$$\frac{8x^3}{2x^7} = \frac{8xxx}{2xxxxxxx} = \frac{4}{x^4}.$$

By the laws of exponents,

$$\frac{8x^3}{2x^7} = \frac{8xxx}{2xxxxxxx} = 4x^{-4}.$$

From these two equations it is apparent that $\frac{4}{x^4} = 4x^{-4}$. We can now see why negative exponents are defined this way. Look at the following carefully.

$$5x^{-3} = \frac{5}{x^3} \text{ and } \frac{7}{x^{-2}} = 7x^2.$$

Again, note that the "flavor" of what an exponent originally meant is now more abstract, but it fits beautifully with the laws of exponents. Negative exponents are an abstract extension of the original concept of exponents.

If you are learning a new language in school, you probably don't "think" in that language. If you wanted to blurt out "I dropped my spoon" in that new language, you'd probably have to translate it, almost word-for-word first, and then say it. Similarly, it's often difficult to "think" in negative exponents since we don't run across them that often.

Example

Evaluate $\frac{2x^4y^{-2}}{z^{-3}}$ if $x = 1, y = 3,$ and $z = 2.$

Solution

Let's rewrite the expression with positive exponents first. If a negative exponent expression is a factor of the numerator, place it as a factor in the denominator with a positive exponent. If a negative exponent expression is a factor in the denominator, place it as a factor in the numerator with a positive exponent.

$$\frac{2x^4z^3}{y^2}.$$

Substitute.

$$\frac{2(1)^4(2)^3}{(3)^2} = \frac{2 \cdot 1 \cdot 8}{9} = \frac{16}{9} = 1\frac{7}{9}.$$

Fill in the Blanks

Negative exponents are a somewhat _____ extension of the original notion of exponents. If a negative exponent is a factor of the _____, you can place it in the denominator with a positive exponent. If a negative exponent expression is a factor in the denominator, place it as a factor in the _____ with a positive exponent.

Basic Problem

Which of the following is equivalent to 2^{-3} ?

a) -8   b) $\frac{1}{8}$ c) $-\frac{1}{8}$ d) $\frac{1}{6}$

Intermediate Problem

Express $\frac{5}{8}a^{-2}b^5c^{-3}$ as a rational expression using only positive exponents.

a) $\frac{5b^5}{8a^2c^3}$
b) $\frac{5}{8a^2b^5c^3}$
c) $\frac{5b^5c^3}{8a^2}$
d) $\frac{5a^2c^3}{8b^5}$

Challenging Problem

Which of the following is equivalent to $(2x^2)^{-3}$?

a) $2x^{-6}$
b) $-\frac{1}{8x^6}$
c) $\frac{1}{8x^6}$
d) $\frac{8}{x^6}$

Numeric Entry Problem

Find the value of $4x^{-2}$ when $x = -5$.

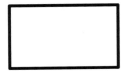

Quantitative Comparison Problem

Compare Quantity A and Quantity B, using the information below.

Quantity A	Quantity B
$4x^{-3}$ when $x = 2$	$2x^{-2}$ when $x = -3$

Select one of the following answers.

a) Quantity A is greater.
b) Quantity B is greater.
c) The two quantities are equal.
d) The relationship cannot be determined from the information given.

Key Descriptors

computations with negative exponents, examples of negative exponents, interpreting negative exponents, negative exponents, reciprocals and negative exponents, multiplicative inverses and negative exponents

Fractional Exponents

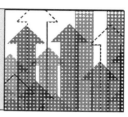

Introduction

We just reviewed how negative exponents are an abstract extension of the original concept of exponents. Without a little background, it is hard to bridge the gap from

$$x^5 = x \cdot x \cdot x \cdot x \cdot x,$$ which makes sense, to an expression like $x^{\frac{1}{2}}$.

How can we interpret fractional exponents? The abstract extension of positive integer exponents to fractional exponents will depend on roots, radicals, and the laws of exponents.

Recall the **radical sign** and square roots. The **square root** of 23 is a number, such that when it is multiplied by itself, equals 23.

$$\sqrt{23} \cdot \sqrt{23} = 23$$

You know that $2 \cdot 2 \cdot 2 = 8$. The **cube root** of 8 can be written as $\sqrt[3]{8}$, and

$$\sqrt[3]{8} = 2 \text{ since } 2^3 = 8.$$

Let's analyze $\sqrt[3]{x}$ using the laws of exponents. First let's write them as radicals.

$$\sqrt[3]{x} \cdot \sqrt[3]{x} \cdot \sqrt[3]{x} = x$$

Next let's write them using exponents.

$$x^n \cdot x^n \cdot x^n = x$$

Remember $x = x^1$.

$$x^n \cdot x^n \cdot x^n = x^1$$

What value of n will satisfy the laws of exponents?

$$n + n + n = 1$$

$$3n = 1$$

$$n = \frac{1}{3}.$$

So, we define

$$\sqrt[3]{x} = x^{\frac{1}{3}}.$$

If you raised the cube root to the second power, you'd write

$$\sqrt[3]{x}^{2} = \left(x^{\frac{1}{3}}\right)^{2}.$$

By the laws of exponents,

$$\left(x^{\frac{1}{3}}\right)^{2} = x^{\frac{2}{3}}.$$

From these examples you can see that fractional exponents are a natural, even if a little strange, extension of the original notion of exponents. You can express radical expressions using fractional exponents, and vice-versa. The number inside the radical sign is called a **radicand**.

$$\sqrt[r]{x}^{p} = x^{\frac{p}{r}}$$

You usually won't "think" in fractional exponents, you'll probably change them to radical expressions to interpret them.

$$\underset{\text{root}}{\overset{\text{power}}{\sqrt[r]{x}^{p}}} = x^{\frac{p}{r}}$$

There is a way to remember how to interpret fractional exponents. Think "flower power." The numerator is the exponent, or **power** (rhymes with flower) and the denominator, the "bottom" is the **root**, and roots are at the bottom of the flowers.

Example

Evaluate $125^{-\frac{2}{3}}$.

Solution

First address the negative exponent. That tells us to put $125^{\frac{2}{3}}$ in the denominator.

$$125^{-\frac{2}{3}} = \frac{1}{125^{\frac{2}{3}}}$$

Express the denominator $125^{\frac{2}{3}}$ as a radical.

$$\frac{1}{\sqrt[3]{125}^2}$$

The cube root of 125 is 5.

Squaring 5 gives 25.

The solution is $\frac{1}{25}$.

Fill in the Blanks

The original idea of using exponents to be a shorthand for repeated multiplication extends to a 0 exponent, a negative exponent, and a fractional exponent. In the expression $\sqrt[a]{x}^b$, a is the _____ and b is the _____, or power. When expressed using fractional coefficients, a becomes the _____ of the fractional exponent and b becomes the _____.

Basic Problem

Express $\sqrt[5]{6}^3$ using fractional exponents.

a) $5^{\frac{3}{6}}$ b) $6^{\frac{3}{5}}$ c) 6^3 d) $6^{\frac{3}{5}}$

Intermediate Problem

Find the sum of $16^{-\frac{1}{4}} + 16^{\frac{3}{2}}$.

a) -64.5   b) 64.5   c) 66   d) $32^{\frac{5}{4}}$

Challenging Problem

Find the sum of $4^{3.5}$ and $9^{2.5}$.

a) 36.5   b) 36^6 c) 371   d) 31,104

Numeric Entry Problem

If $\sqrt[4]{36}^5$ is expressed using fractional exponents, what is the reciprocal of the exponent?

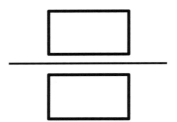

Multiple Choice with Multiple Answers Problem

Which of the following expressions simplifies to 8?

[a] $2 \cdot \sqrt[3]{64}$ [b] $64^{\frac{2}{3}}$ [c] $16^{\frac{3}{2}}$ [d] $\frac{\sqrt[3]{64}^2}{2}$

Key Descriptors

converting radicals to fractional exponents, evaluating expression with fractional exponents, fractional exponents, power, radicand, rational exponents, root

CORE CONCEPT 33
Scientific Notation

Introduction

You have often seen how mathematics can create shorthand notations that express thoughts more concisely. Look at these examples:

- The **expanded form** of a number looks like

$$(7 \times 1000) + (4 \times 100) + (6 \times 10) + 2.$$

  Place values are used to express this number as 7,462. This is the number in **standard notation**, a form of shorthand.

- Multiplication is repeated addition.

  Rather than writing 2 + 2 + 2 + 2 + 2 + 2 + 2 you can write 7 × 2.

- Exponents are also a "shorthand" notation.

  Rather than writing $2 \times 2 \times 2 \times 2 \times 2 \times 2 \times 2$ you can write 2^7.

- Well-defined abbreviations also provide a shorthand.

  Rather than writing "the probability of event A occuring is 0.4" you can write $P(A) = 0.4$.

- Symbols can also provide a shorthand.

  Rather than writing "angle ABC" you can write $\angle ABC$.

Scientific notation is a shorthand notation that allows you to express very large and very small numbers, that might contain many digits, as an efficient, convenient decimal expression. When a number is expressed in scientific notation, it is written as the product of a terminating decimal between 1 and 10, and an integer power of 10.

The power of 10 often means there will be several placeholders of 0. These are sometimes called **trailing zeros** and **leading zeroes**. The numbers that are not leading or trailing zeroes are called **significant digits**. The trailing and leading zeroes occur between the first or last significant digit and the decimal point. If a zero occurs between two non-zero digits, it is considered a significant digit. Look at these examples:

23,600,000 has five trailing zeroes and significant digits 236

0.0000000329 has seven leading zeroes and significant digits 329

3,207,000 has three trailing zeros and significant digits 3207

0.00002401 has four leading zeros and significant digits 2401

Notice that the left-most 0 in 0.00002401 is not considered a leading 0.

Let's look at how numbers are converted to scientific notation from standard notation and vice-versa.

Example 1

Express 5,402,000 in scientific notation.

Solution 1

First, move the decimal point, which is to the right of the last trailing 0, to the right of 5, to create a number between 1 and 10. In this case the decimal point was moved 6 places to the left. Write the significant digits, creating a number between 1 and 10.

$$5.402$$

Multiply by 10^6 to "restore" the 5.402 back to the original number. The number 5,402,000 can be expressed in scientific notation as

$$5.402 \times 10^6.$$

Keep in mind that in some cases the decimal is moved to the right. For an example, let's convert the number 0.00341 into scientific notation.

First, move the decimal point, which is to the left of the first leading 0, to the right of 3, to create a number between 1 and 10. In this case the decimal point was moved 3 places to the right. Write the significant digits, creating a number between 1 and 10.

$$3.41$$

Multiply by 10^{-3} to "restore" the 3.41 back to the original number. The number 0.00341 can be expressed in scientific notation as 3.41×10^{-3}.

Example 2

Express 4.17×10^4 in standard notation.

Solution 2

The multiplication by 10^4 is equivalent to moving the decimal point 4 places to the right. The result is

$$41,700.$$

How would you know when to move the decimal point to the left? Look for the negative exponent. Converting 2.83×10^{-3} to standard notation would require you to move the decimal point 3 places to the left. The result would be

$$0.00283.$$

Remember that the 0 to the left of the decimal point in a decimal less than 1 is not part of conversions involving scientific notation.

Example 3

Find the product of (5.3×10^3) and (1.41×10^5) and express your answer in scientific notation.

Solution 3

You are multiplying four numbers, and by the **commutative property of multiplication**, they can be multiplied in any order. Use parentheses to group the numbers together two at a time. This is called the **associative property of multiplication**. Multiply the significant-digit numbers by each other, and then multiply the powers of 10 by each other.

$$5.3 \times 10^3 \times 1.41 \times 10^5 = (5.3 \times 1.41) \times (10^3 \times 10^5)$$

Multiply 5.3 by 1.41.

$$5.3 \times 1.41 = 7.473.$$

Multiply 10^3 by 10^5 using the laws of exponents.

$$10^3 \times 10^5 = 10^8$$

The product, expressed in scientific notation, is 7.473×10^8.

Example 4

Express the quotient $\frac{5.2 \times 10^9}{1.3 \times 10^3}$ in scientific notation.

Solution 4

Based on what you know about multiplying fractions, you can split the given fraction.

$$\frac{5.2}{1.3} \times \frac{10^9}{10^3}$$

Notice that these two fractions, if multiplied, would give us the original fraction.

The first fraction simplifies to 4.0 and the second simplifies to 10^6. The quotient, expressed in scientific notation, is 4.0×10^6.

Fill in the Blanks

When expressing a number in scientific notation, you need to create _____ numbers that multiply to equal your original number. The first number is a decimal between _____ and _____, and the digits of this number are called _____ _____. The second number is written with an exponent as a power of _____.

Basic Problem

Express the number 34,709,000,000 in scientific notation.

a) 3.4709×10^6 b) 0.34709×10^6 c) 0.34709×10^{11} d) 3.4709×10^{10}

Intermediate Problem

Express the following quotient in scientific notation.

$$\frac{5.85 \times 10^8}{1.3 \times 10^4}$$

a) 4.55×10^4 b) 4.5×10^4 c) 4.5×10^2 d) 4.55×10^5

Challenging Problem

Find the product of (6.2×10^9) and (4.43×10^5) and express your answer in scientific notation.

a) 27.466×10^{14} b) 2.7466×10^{15} c) 2.7466×10^{14} d) 2.7466×10^{45}

Numeric Entry Problem

Express 3.41×10^{-3} as a decimal in standard notation.

Quantitative Comparison Problem

Compare Quantity A and Quantity B, using the information below.

<u>Quantity A</u>   <u>Quantity B</u>

$$9.113 \times 10^3$$ $$\sqrt[3]{1000}^4$$

Select one of the following answers.

a) Quantity A is greater.
b) Quantity B is greater.
c) The two quantities are equal.
d) The relationship cannot be determined from the information given.

Key Descriptors

associative property of multiplication, commutative property of multiplication, expanded notation, leading zeroes, scientific notation, significant digits, standard notation, trailing zeroes

Simplifying Radical Expressions

Introduction

When you first learned about square roots, you worked with **perfect squares**. That made it easiest to understand the square root concept when it was new to you.

$$\text{Since } 5^2 = 25, \sqrt{25} = 5.$$

$$\text{Since } 9^2 = 81, \sqrt{81} = 9.$$

Square roots of non-perfect squares are irrational numbers, which are decimals that do not terminate and do not repeat.

You can have a coefficient in front of a radical, like $3\sqrt{15}$ or $12\sqrt{10}$. **Like radicals** have the same radicand. Recall that the radicand is the number inside the radical sign.

There are several different ways to simplify expressions with radicals. You can **combine like radicals**, **simplify a radical**, and **rationalize a denominator**. Let's reacquaint you with these three procedures.

Example 1

Simplify the expression $6\sqrt{5} + 7\sqrt{11} - 2\sqrt{5} + \sqrt{11}$ by combining like radicals.

Solution 1

This is very analogous to combing like *terms*. Recall that

$$6x + 7y - 2x + y = 4x + 8y.$$

Similarly,

$$6\sqrt{5} + 7\sqrt{11} - 2\sqrt{5} + \sqrt{11} = 4\sqrt{5} + 8\sqrt{11}.$$

Note that the coefficient of $\sqrt{11}$ is 1.

Example 2

Express $5\sqrt{72}$ in **simplest radical form**.

Solution 2

You can break up $\sqrt{72}$ into a product of two radicals, one of which is the largest perfect square factor of the radicand. (If you do not choose the *largest* perfect square factor, you will have to repeat the process to get *simplest* radical form). It is helpful to write the perfect square radicand first.

$$5\sqrt{72} = 5 \cdot \sqrt{36} \cdot \sqrt{2}$$

Since $\sqrt{36} = 6$, simplify.

$$5\sqrt{72} = 5 \cdot 6 \cdot \sqrt{2}$$

Multiply.

$$5\sqrt{72} = 30\sqrt{2}.$$

If the radicand does not have a perfect square factor, it can't be simplified.

Example 3

Express $\frac{48}{\sqrt{3}}$ as a decimal, rounded to the nearest thousandth.

Solution 3

Imagine converting $\frac{48}{\sqrt{3}}$ to a decimal. You'd be dividing by an irrational number, $\sqrt{3}$, which is a non-terminating, non-repeating decimal. There is a way to make this division easier. The process is called **rationalizing a denominator**.

Multiply $\frac{48}{\sqrt{3}}$ by 1, writing 1 in the form $\frac{\sqrt{3}}{\sqrt{3}}$.

$$\frac{48}{\sqrt{3}} \cdot \frac{\sqrt{3}}{\sqrt{3}} = \frac{48\sqrt{3}}{3}$$

This simplifies to $16\sqrt{3}$.

Fill in the Blanks

The square root of a non-perfect square is an _____ number, which means it is a non-terminating, non-repeating decimal. If the denominator of a fraction is a radical, you can _____ the denominator by multiplying the fraction by 1 in a certain form. Combining _____ radicals is much like combining like _____, and simplifying a radical requires that one of the radicand's factors be a _____

_____.

Basic Problem

Simplify $\sqrt{24}$ into simplest radical form.

a) $2\sqrt{6}$ b) $6\sqrt{2}$ c) $4\sqrt{6}$ d) $2\sqrt{12}$

Intermediate Problem

Express $9\sqrt{48} - 2\sqrt{12}$ in simplest radical form.

a) $20\sqrt{12}$ b) $16\sqrt{12}$ c) $32\sqrt{3}$ d) $40\sqrt{3}$

Challenging Problem

Express $\dfrac{5+\sqrt{19}^2}{\sqrt{8}}$ in simplest form.

a) $6\sqrt{2}$ b) $\dfrac{24\sqrt{8}}{8}$ c) $3\sqrt{8}$ d) $6\sqrt{2}$

Numeric Entry Problem

What is the value of $\frac{2}{5}\sqrt{\frac{16}{9}}$ in simplest form?

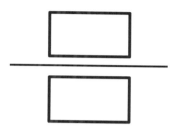

Multiple Choice with Multiple Answers Problem

Which of the following expressions simplifies to 3?

[a] $\frac{\sqrt{24}}{\sqrt{8}}$ [b] $\frac{\sqrt{27}}{\sqrt{9}}$ [c] $\frac{\sqrt{81}}{3}$ [d] $\frac{\sqrt{18}}{\sqrt{2}}$

Key Descriptors

combining like radicals, perfect squares, rationalizing a denominator, simplest radical form, simplifying square roots, square roots

DID YOU KNOW THAT?

A man walks into a convenience store and purchases four different items with different prices. The counterman multiplies the four prices and says, "That'll be $7.70."

The customer says, "You were supposed to *add* the four prices, not multiply them!"

The counterman says, "OK, you are right. That'll be...ugh...$7.70."

What were the prices of the four items?

{$1, $1.25, $1.60, $3.85}

CORE CONCEPT 35
Factoring Quadratic Trinomials

Introduction

You might remember multiplying two binomials, for example,

$$(x + 5)(x - 3).$$

There are several techniques for doing this, one of the most popular is the FOIL (Firsts, Outers, Inners, Lasts) technique.

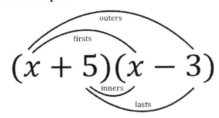

The solution is the **trinomial** $x^2 + 2x - 15$. This is sometimes called a **quadratic trinomial**, and you have probably seen dozens (hundreds?!) of them in your high school career. The general form of a quadratic trinomial is

$$ax^2 + bx + c.$$

In this form, a, b, and c are the coefficients, and c is also called the **constant**.

The reverse procedure requires you to **factor** a given quadratic trinomial into its two binomial factors. There are many procedures for doing this, and your teachers probably had their favorites. You can look online for videos explaining the different procedures.

Example 1

Factor the quadratic trinomial $x^2 - 9x + 20$.

Solution 1

We can set up the binomial factors, and insert the first term of each, which is x.

$$(x \quad)(x \quad)$$

Next, we look at the constant, 20. The last terms must have a product of 20, which is positive. That means the signs in each binomial are the same, either both positive or both negative. Since $a = 1$, we can look at the sign of the b coefficient to help us. Also, since $a = 1$, the sum of the last terms must add to b, which is -9. Since b is negative, our signs are negative.

$$(x - \quad)(x - \quad)$$

The last terms -4 and -5 add to -9 and have a product of 20.

$$(x - 4)(x - 5)$$

This is the correct factorization of $x^2 - 9x + 20$.

Example 2

Factor the quadratic trinomial $2x^2 - 8x - 42$.

Solution 2

It is important to notice that there is a greatest common factor, 2, that can be factored out first.

$$2x^2 - 8x - 42 = 2(x^2 - 4x - 21).$$

Factor the remaining trinomial. Don't forget that 2 is one of the factors of $2x^2 - 8x - 42$.

$$2(x^2 - 4x - 21) = 2(x - 7)(x + 3).$$

When there are multiple steps to a factoring problem, sometimes the directions are to **factor completely**.

Example 3

Factor the quadratic trinomial $2x^2 - 7x - 15$.

Solution 3

Notice that there is no GCF in this problem. Again, there are several procedures for doing this. The first terms are shown here:

$$(2x \quad)(x \quad)$$

The last terms multiply to -15. No matter what procedure you use, you'll find the last terms to be +3 and -5. These terms must be placed correctly in the binomials. Be sure to use the FOIL technique to check your factorization when it is done.

$$(2x + 3)(x - 5)$$

These two binomials do multiply out to $2x^2 - 7x - 15$.

Fill in the Blanks

When you multiply two binomials, you are finding their _____. In certain cases, their product is a quadratic _____, which has _____ terms. When you _____ a quadratic trinomial, you reverse the multiplication, and you should look first to see if you can factor out a _____ _____ _____. Whenever you factor a quadratic trinomial, check your result by multiplying the two binomials you came up with.

Basic Problem

Which is the correct factorization of $x^2 - x - 6$?

a) $(x + 3)(x - 2)$

b) $(x - 3)(x + 2)$

c) $(x - 3)(x - 2)$

d) $(x - 6)(x + 1)$

Intermediate Problem

Which is the correct complete factorization of $3y^2 + 18y - 48$?

a) $3(y - 3)(y + 16)$

b) $3(y - 2)(y + 8)$

c) $(3y - 2)(y + 8)$

d) $(y - 2)(3y + 8)$

Challenging Problem

Which is the correct complete factorization of $4m^2 - 18m - 10$?

a) $2(2m - 5)(m + 1)$

b) $2(2m + 1)(m - 5)$

c) $(4m + 2)(m - 5)$

d) $(4m - 5)(m + 2)$

Numeric Entry Problem

If $x^2 + 7x + 10$ is factored into the two binomial factors $(x + 2)$ and $(x + k)$, what is the value of k?

Quantitative Comparison Problem

Compare Quantity A and Quantity B, using the information below.

<u>Quantity A</u>   <u>Quantity B</u>

$$(x + 2)(x + 5)$$ $$x^2 + 7x + 11$$

Select one of the following answers.

a) Quantity A is greater.
b) Quantity B is greater.
c) The two quantities are equal.
d) The relationship cannot be determined from the information given.

Key Descriptors

factoring quadratic trinomials, factoring trinomials, multiplying binomials, quadratic expressions

DID YOU KNOW THAT?

A quadratic equation with three consecutive-integer coefficients, such as

$$7x^2 + 8x + 9 \quad \text{or} \quad 23x^2 + 24x + 25$$

will *never* be factorable!

CORE CONCEPT 36
Solving Quadratic Equations

Introduction

Recall that *expressions* don't have equal signs, but *equations* do. So $5x^2 - 18x - 9$ is a quadratic expression, and $5x^2 - 18x - 9 = 0$ is a **quadratic equation**. A quadratic equation can have 0, 1, or 2 solutions. You have learned several ways to solve quadratic equations. Three of them are **factoring**, the **quadratic formula**, and **completing the square**. Read and work through the following three examples to see how much of each procedure you remember. In addition to this review, there are excellent videos online that will help you if you forgot some of the procedures.

Example 1

Solve the quadratic equation $2x^2 - 8x + 7 = 1$ by factoring.

Solution 1

To solve a quadratic equation by factoring you must first set it equal to 0. Subtract 1 from both sides to get

$$2x^2 - 8x + 6 = 0.$$

When you solve an equation that is set equal to 0, the solutions are also called the **roots** of the equation. We are finding the roots of $2x^2 - 8x + 6 = 0$. Factor out the GCF, which is 2.

$$2(x^2 - 4x + 3) = 0$$

Factor the remaining trinomial.

$$2(x - 1)(x - 3) = 0.$$

If the product of several factors is equal to 0, at least one of the factors must be 0. Set each of the variable factors equal to 0. Note that 2 is not a variable factor, it is a constant.

$$(x - 1) = 0 \qquad (x - 3) = 0$$

$$x = 1 \qquad x = 3$$

The solutions are 1 and 3. This is sometimes written in set notation as {1, 3}. You can verify that these satisfy the original equation by substituting each solution into the original equation.

Example 2

Solve the quadratic equation $x^2 + 5x - 7 = 2x$.

Solution 2

First get the quadratic equal to 0. Subtract $2x$ from both sides.

$$x^2 + 3x - 7 = 0$$

The quadratic does not factor, so we will use the quadratic formula.

If $a \neq 0$ and $ax^2 + bx + c = 0$, you can find the roots of the quadratic equation by substituting a, b, and c into the quadratic formula, shown here:

$$x = \frac{-b \pm \sqrt{b^2 - 4ac}}{2a}$$

Let's substitute $a = 1$, $b = 3$, and $c = -7$.

$$x = \frac{-3 \pm \sqrt{3^2 - 4(1)(-7)}}{2(1)} = \frac{-3 \pm \sqrt{9 + 28}}{2} = \frac{-3 \pm \sqrt{37}}{2}.$$

The two solutions are $\frac{-3+\sqrt{37}}{2}$ and $\frac{-3-\sqrt{37}}{2}$. With a calculator, you could evaluate these irrational solutions to any desired number of decimal places.

The quadratic formula *always* works--even if the quadratic was factorable! You should memorize the quadratic formula. The radicand of the quadratic formula, $b^2 - 4ac$, is called the **discriminant**. If the discriminant is a perfect square, that means that the quadratic is factorable. You can use it anytime you want to know before trying to factor if the quadratic is factorable.

Example 3

Solve the quadratic equation $x^2 + 6x + 7 = -1$ by completing the square.

Solution 3

When you complete the square, you do not set the equation equal to 0. You will bring the constant over to the other side. Subtract 7 from both sides. Leave some blank space where the constant was because you will be completing the square.

$$x^2 + 6x \qquad = -8$$

Take half of the b coefficient. Half of 6 is 3. Square 3 to get 9. Add 9 to both sides.

$$x^2 + 6x + 9 = 1$$

Factor the left side of the equation. It will always factor into the square of a binomial.

$$(x + 3)^2 = 1$$

Take the square root of both sides. Note that we need to take the positive and negative square roots on the right side.

$$(x + 3) = \pm 1$$

Form and solve two equations.

$$(x + 3) = 1 \text{ and } (x + 3) = -1$$

Subtract 3 from both sides to get the two solutions, $x = -2$ and $x = -4$.

Fill in the Blanks

If you have to solve a quadratic equation, there are three common methods. If the quadratic equation _____, you can solve it by _____. You can use the

_____ _____ to solve *any* quadratic equation, so it is a good idea to memorize it. Both of these methods require getting the equation into a form that is equal to

_____. A third method, _____ _____ _____, does not require that the equation be set equal to 0.

Basic Problem

Using factoring, find the solution set for the quadratic equation $x^2 + 3x - 30 = -2$.

a) {-7, 4}   b) {7, -4}   c) {-7, -4}   d) {-3, 4}

Intermediate Problem

Find the roots of the equation $x^2 - 3x - 4 = 1$ to the nearest tenth.

a) {4, -1}   b) {4.2, -1.2}   c) {4.2, -4.2}   d) {4.1, -1.1}

Challenging Problem

If the discriminant of the quadratic equation $x^2 + 8x + k = 0$ is 4, find the value of k.

a) 15   b) 60   c) 16   d) 1

Numeric Entry Problem

If the quadratic equation $x^2 - 10x = 11$ is solved by completing the square, what number must be added to both sides of the equation?

Multiple Choice with Multiple Answers Problem

Which of the following are roots of the quadratic equation $x^2 - 6x + 10 = 2$?

[a] 2   [b] 4   [c] 6   [d] 8

Key Descriptors

completing the square, discriminant, quadratic formula, roots of a quadratic equation, solving quadratic equations by factoring, solving quadratic equations using the quadratic formula, solving quadratic equations by completing the square

The Difference of Two Perfect Squares

Introduction

As we have seen previously, the product of two binomials is often, but not always, a trinomial. Let's take a look at the product of these two binomials.

$$(x + 9)(x - 9).$$

Notice that the first terms are identical and the last terms are additive inverses. This special form is called the **sum and difference of two numbers**. Watch what happens when we "FOIL" the binomials:

$$(x + 9)(x - 9) = x^2 + 9x - 9x - 81 = x^2 - 81.$$

Pay close attention to the fact that the middle terms, 9x and -9x, are additive inverses and cancel each other out when like terms are combined. Also notice that both remaining terms are perfect squares. As a result, it is usually easy to multiply the sum and difference of two quantities, and see that they yield the **difference of two perfect squares**. Notice how this difference is another binomial.

Now imagine factoring a difference of two perfect squares, for example,

$$y^2 - 100.$$

This factors into the sum and difference of two numbers, the square roots of y^2 and 100.

$$y^2 - 100 = (y - 10)(y + 10).$$

Similarly, $9x^2 - 49y^2$ is also a difference of two perfect squares.

$$9x^2 - 49y^2 = (3x - 7y)(3x + 7y).$$

If the difference of two perfect squares is in a quadratic equation, you can solve it by factoring. If you used the quadratic formula or completing the square, you'd have to remember that the b coefficient is 0.

Example 1

Find the product of $(x + 6)(x - 6)$.

Solution 1

Once you identify this as the sum and difference of two quantities, you can find the product mentally.

$$(x + 6)(x - 6) = x^2 - 36.$$

Example 2

Factor $25m^2 - 64p^2$.

Solution 2

Once you recognize this as the difference between two perfect squares, you can factor it mentally as the sum and difference of two quantities.

$$25m^2 - 64p^2 = (5m + 8p)(5m - 8p).$$

Example 3

Solve the quadratic equation $3k^2 - 47 = 1$.

Solution 3

Subtract 1 from both sides to get

$$3k^2 - 48 = 0.$$

Factor out the GCF, which is 3.

$$3(k^2 - 16) = 0$$

Factor the difference of two squares.

$$3(k + 4)(k - 4) = 0$$

The solution set is {4, -4}. Notice that the solutions are additive inverses.

Fill in the Blanks

When the binomials $(x + 7)$ and $(x - 6)$ are multiplied, the product, since it has three terms, is called a _____, and when the binomials $(x + 5)(x - 5)$ are multiplied, the answer is a binomial. The difference of two perfect squares factors into the _____ and _____ of two numbers, which are the square roots of the original squares. You can multiply the sum and difference between two numbers mentally, since the product of the outer terms and the product of the inner terms are _____ _____, and cancel out to 0.

Basic Problem

Find the product of $(2x - 5)$ and $(2x + 5)$.

a) $4x^2 - 25$ b) $2x^2 - 25$ c) $4x^2 - 10x - 25$ d) $4x^2 + 25$

Intermediate Problem

Factor $81k^2 - 16m^2$.

a) $(9k + 8m)(9k - 8m)$ b) $(9k + 4m)(9k - 4m)$

c)) $(3k + 4m)(3k - 4m)$ d)) $(9k - 4m)(9k - 4m)$

Challenging Problem

Find the solution set for the quadratic equation $3x^2 - 120 = 27$.

a) {4, -4}   b) {21, -21}   c) {7, -7}   d) {49, -49}

Numeric Entry Problem

If $x^2 - 4k$ factors into $(x + 10)(x - 10)$, find the value of k.

Quantitative Comparison Problem

Compare Quantity A and Quantity B, using the information below.

<u>Quantity A</u>   <u>Quantity B</u>

$$(3x + 7)(3x - 7) \qquad\qquad 9x^2 - 49$$

Select one of the following answers.

a) Quantity A is greater.
b) Quantity B is greater.
c) The two quantities are equal.
d) The relationship cannot be determined from the information given.

Key Descriptors

difference of two perfect squares (D.O.T.S.), sum and difference of two numbers

DID YOU KNOW THAT?

The quadratic formula has been transformed into lyrics! People have written songs that help students memorize the quadratic formula. Do an Internet search and listen for yourself!

Linear Absolute Value Equations and Inequalities

Introduction

You reviewed absolute value in Core Concept 2. You reviewed solving inequalities in Core Concept 28. Now we are going to look at absolute value equations and inequalities. Here are three examples of the type of linear absolute value equations we will be looking at:

$$|5x + 3| = 17 \qquad |3 - 4x| + 2 = 5 \qquad |6x + 11| - 7 = 9$$

Let's take a look at $|5x + 3| = 17$. If an x value makes the expression inside the absolute value bars, $5x + 3$, equal to 17, that x is a solution. However, also notice that if an x value makes the expression inside the absolute value bars, $5x + 3$, equal to -17, that x is also a solution. This is because, if the expression inside the absolute value bars equals -17, the absolute value bars would make the left side of the equation equal to 17. So, when solving an absolute value equation, we need to create two new equations. Example 1 will show you this in detail.

Here are three examples of the type of linear absolute value inequalities we will be looking at:

$$|5x + 3| \leq 17 \qquad |3 - 4x| + 2 > 5 \qquad |6x + 11| - 7 < 9$$

Similarly, we will create two inequalities without absolute value bars and solve them individually. Example 2 will show you this in detail.

Example 1

Find the solution set for the equation $|2x + 1| + 11 = 42$.

Solution 1

First isolate the absolute value expression on one side of the equation. Subtract 11 from both sides.

$$|2x + 1| = 31$$

Remove the bars and create two equations. First, set the expression inside the bars equal to the other side of the equation. Then, set the expression inside the bars equal to the additive inverse of the other side of the equation. In other words, multiply that other side by -1. Here are the two equations:

$$2x + 1 = 31 \qquad\qquad\qquad 2x + 1 = -31$$

$$2x = 30 \qquad\qquad\qquad 2x = -32$$

$$x = 15 \qquad\qquad\qquad x = -16$$

The solution set is {15, -16}. Substitute to verify that they make the original equation true.

Example 2

Find the solution set for the inequality $|2x - 13| + 5 > 12$.

Solution 2

Isolate the absolute value expression on one side of the equation. Subtract 5 from both sides.

$$|2x - 13| > 7$$

Remove the bars and create two inequalities. First, rewrite the inequality and delete the absolute value bars. Then solve, as you did in Core Concept 28.

$$2x - 13 > 7$$

$$2x > 20$$

$$x > 10$$

Then, rewrite the inequality, delete the absolute value bars, reverse the inequality sign, and negate the side of the equation that did not contain the absolute value expression. In other words, multiply that side by -1.

$$2x - 13 < -7$$

$$2x < 6$$

$$x < 3$$

Remember that an inequality can have infinitely many solutions, so you can't list them--the list would never end! So, we can use set notation or the number line. The solution set is
$$\{x < 3 \text{ or } x > 10\}.$$

This can be represented on the number line.

Notice the use of the word 'or' in the solution set. One single number cannot be less than 3 *and* greater than 10. Pick some numbers from the solution set to verify they solve the inequality. Then, pick some numbers *not* in the solution set, and verify that they *don't* solve the inequality.

Fill in the Blanks

When solving an absolute value equation, first _____ the absolute value expression on one side of the equation. Then create _____ equations and solve each of them. When solving an absolute value inequality, isolate the absolute value expression on one side of the inequality. Then create two new _____ and solve each of them.

Basic Problem

What is the solution set for the equation $|4x + 1| = 61$?

a) {15, -15.5}   b) {15.5, -15}   c) {15, -30}   d) {-15, 30}

Intermediate Problem

What is the solution set for the inequality $|2x + 3| + 4 < 27$?

a) $\{-13 < x < 10\}$ b) $\{-10 < x < 13\}$

c) $\{x < -13 \text{ or } x > 10\}$ d) $\{x < -10 \text{ or } x > 13\}$

Challenging Problem

What is the solution set for the inequality $|5 - 2x| - 7 \geq 20$?

a) $\{-9 \leq x \leq 11\}$ b) $\{-11 \leq x \leq 9\}$

c) $\{x \leq -9 \text{ or } x \geq 11\}$ d) $\{x \leq -11 \text{ or } x \geq 16\}$

Numeric Entry Problem

What is the sum of the solutions to $|x - 5| = 15$?

Multiple Choice with Multiple Answers Problem

Which of the following are solutions for the equation $|5x + 21| = 71$?

[a] -10   [b] 10   [c] -18.4   [d] -14.5

Key Descriptors

absolute value equations, absolute value inequalities, compound inequalities, solving absolute value equations, solving absolute value inequalities

DID YOU KNOW THAT?

A trucker carrying a truckload of cheese between Los Angeles and Sacramento discovered a procedure for approximating square roots of numbers without using a calculator!

Arithmetic Sequences

Introduction

A **recursive** sequence is a sequence of numbers in which each term is created by a rule involving a previous term or terms. You may be familiar with the Fibonacci sequence, a recursive sequence in which each term is the sum of the two previous terms.

$$1, 1, 2, 3, 5, 8, 13, 21, 34, \ldots$$

An **arithmetic sequence** is a recursive sequence of numbers with a given first term usually called a_1. In sequences, the little numbers to the side are called **subscripts**, and they tell you what number term you are referring to. In an arithmetic sequence, after a_1, each term increases by adding a real number constant, called the **common difference** d, to the previous term. The common difference can be positive or negative.

For example, look at this sequence:

$$4, 11, 18, 25, 32, 39, 46, \ldots$$

The three dots at the end are called an **ellipsis**, and they indicate that the sequence continues. This is an example of an **infinite arithmetic sequence**. If we looked at only the first twenty terms of this sequence we would have a **finite arithmetic sequence**.

The first term, a_1, is 4. The common difference d is 7, found by subtracting any number in the sequence from the number after it. The next term after 46 is 53, found by adding 7.

The common difference can be any real number--a decimal, fraction, radical, etc.

Example 1

Find the 12th term of the following arithmetic sequence:

$$3, 7, 11, 15, 19, \ldots$$

Solution 1

Think about this. The first term is 3. The common difference, found by subtracting any two consecutive terms, is 4. If you are looking for the 12th term, you would need to add 4 to the first term eleven times.

$$4 \cdot 11 = 44$$

Add 44 to the first term.

$$3 + 44 = 47$$

The 12th term is 47.

Based on this line of logic, let's create a general formula to find the nth term of an arithmetic sequence, a_n, with first term a_1 and common difference d.

We need to add d to a_1 exactly $(n - 1)$ times to get the nth term a_n. The formula for the nth term of an arithmetic sequence is

$$a_n = a_1 + (n - 1)d.$$

Example 2

Find the sum of the first 19 terms of the following arithmetic sequence:

$$1, 4, 7, 10, 13, 16, \dots$$

Solution 2

It would be cumbersome and much too time-consuming to write out all 19 terms and add them. There is a formula to find the sum, S_n, of the first n terms of an arithmetic sequence with first term a_1, common difference d, and nth term a_n.

$$S_n = \frac{n(a_1 + a_n)}{2}.$$

Notice that you need to compute the nth term a_n, as you did in Example 1, to use this formula.

In our example, $a_1 = 1$ and $d = 3$, so the 19th term is $1 + 18 \cdot 3 = 55$. Now we can substitute into the S_n formula.

$$S_n = \frac{n(a_1 + a_n)}{2} = \frac{19(1 + 55)}{2} = \frac{19 \cdot 56}{2} = 532.$$

The sum of the first 19 terms is 532.

Fill in the Blanks

The first term of an arithmetic sequence is usually denoted _____. Successive terms are found by adding the _____ _____ to the previous term. You can find any term in the sequence as long as you have the previous term and the _____ _____. There is a formula to find S_n, which is the _____ of the first _____ terms of an arithmetic sequence.

Basic Problem

Find the 22nd term of the arithmetic sequence whose 20th term is 70 and 21st term is 78.

a) 94   b) 84   c) 88   d) 86

Intermediate Problem

An arithmetic sequence has first term 4 and common difference 5. Find the sum of the first 21 terms.

a) 1,134   b) 104   c) 2,268   d) 108

Challenging Problem

In an arithmetic sequence, the first term is 2 and the 11th term is 72. What is the common difference?

a) 6   b) 7.2   c) 7   d) 6.2

Numeric Entry Problem

The tenth term of an arithmetic sequence with common difference 3 is 46. What is the first term?

Quantitative Comparison Problem

Compare Quantity A and Quantity B, using the information below.

<table>
<tr><td align="center">Quantity A</td><td align="center">Quantity B</td></tr>
<tr><td align="center">The tenth term of the arithmetic sequence

1, 4, 7, 10...</td><td align="center">The sixth term of the arithmetic sequence with first term 2 and common difference 5.</td></tr>
</table>

Select one of the following answers.

a) Quantity A is greater.
b) Quantity B is greater.
c) The two quantities are equal.
d) The relationship cannot be determined from the information given.

Key Descriptors

arithmetic progression, arithmetic sequences, finite arithmetic sequence, infinite arithmetic sequence, recursive sequence, sum of an arithmetic sequence

DID YOU KNOW THAT?

Look at the following pattern. Where would **30** go? What is the reason numbers are placed in the rows as they are?

Answer: The top row's numbers are all made with straight lines, the bottom row's numbers are made with only curved lines, and the middle row is a combination of straight and curved lines. The number 30 would go in the bottom row.

Geometric Sequences

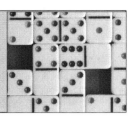

Introduction

A **geometric sequence** is a recursive sequence of numbers with a given first term usually denoted a_1. Each successive term is a constant multiple of the previous term. This constant multiple is called the **common ratio** r. The common ratio can be any positive or negative real number.

For example, look at this sequence:

$$4, 12, 36, 108, 324, ...$$

The three dots indicate that the sequence continues. This is an example of an **infinite geometric sequence**. If we looked at only the first twenty terms of this sequence we would have a **finite geometric sequence**.

The first term, a_1, is 4. The common ratio r is 3, found by dividing any number in the sequence by the previous number. The next term after 324 is 972, found by multiplying 324 by 3.

Analogously to an arithmetic sequence, there is a formula to find the nth term of a geometric sequence, and a formula to find the sum of a geometric sequence.

Example 1

Find the 8th term of the following geometric sequence:

$$1, 4, 16, 64, ...$$

Solution 1

The first term is 1. The common ratio, found by dividing one term by the previous term, is 4. If you are looking for the 8th term, you would need to multiply the first term, 1, by 4 seven times. Use exponents to indicate the repeated multiplication.

$$1 \cdot 4^7 = 16{,}384$$

The 8th term is 16,384.

Based on this line of logic, let's create a general formula to find the nth term of a geometric sequence, a_n, with first term a_1 and common ratio r.

We need to multiply a_1 by r exactly $(n - 1)$ times to get the nth term a_n. The formula for the nth term of a geometric sequence is

$$a_n = a_1 r^{n-1}.$$

Example 2

Find the sum of the first 12 terms of the following geometric sequence:

$$7, 14, 28, 56, \ldots$$

Solution 2

There is a formula to find the sum of the first n terms of a geometric sequence, S_n, with first term a_1, common ratio r.

$$S_n = \frac{n(1 - r^n)}{1 - r}.$$

Notice that you do not need to compute the nth term a_n, as you did when finding the sum of an arithmetic sequence, to use this formula. You just need n and r.

In our example, $n = 12$ and $r = 2$. Substitute into the S_n formula.

$$S_n = \frac{12(1 - 2^{12})}{1 - 2} = \frac{12(-4095)}{-1} = 49{,}140.$$

The sum of the first 12 terms is 49,140.

Notice that the terms in a geometric sequence can decrease if r is a positive number less than 1, and the terms of the geometric sequence can actually alternate being positive and negative if r is negative. For example, using the first term 5 and the common ratio -3, we can create the sequence

$$5, -15, 45, -135, 405, -1215, \ldots$$

The signs alternate due to the multiplication by a negative number.

Fill in the Blanks

Successive terms of a geometric sequence are found by multiplying the previous term by the _____ _____. If you are given a geometric sequence, you can find the common ratio by _____ any given term by the previous term. There is a formula to find a_n, which is the _____ term of the geometric sequence, and S_n, which is the _____ of the first _____ terms of a geometric sequence.

Basic Problem

Find the 4th term of a geometric sequence whose 6th term is 486 and whose 7th term is 1,458.

a) 728   b) 54   c) 162   d) 18

Intermediate Problem

Find the sum of the first seven terms of the following geometric sequence:

$$1, 5, 25, \ldots$$

a) 136,717   b) 15,625   c) 78,124   d) 27,342

Challenging Problem

Which could be the missing term in the following geometric sequence?

$$3, \underline{\quad}, 48, 192, \ldots$$

a) 16   b) 12   c) $\sqrt{48}$ d) 24

Numeric Entry Problem

Find the 7th term of the following geometric sequence: 4000, 2000, 1000, 500, ...

Multiple Choice with Multiple Answers Problem

Which of the following are geometric sequences with common ratio 3?

[a] 2, 5, 8, ...   [b] 4, 12, 36, 108, ...   [c] 1, 3, 9, 27, ...   [d] 3, 6, 9, 27, ...

Key Descriptors

geometric progression, geometric sequences, finite geometric sequence, infinite geometric sequence, recursive sequence, sum of a geometric sequence

DID YOU KNOW THAT?

In this 3 by 3 grid, the numbers are carefully arranged so that the sum of the integers across any row, column, or diagonal is 15. It is called a **Magic Square**.

4	9	2
3	5	7
8	1	6

Appreciation and Depreciation

Introduction

Think about a new car that loses value each year. The **depreciation** is the amount it loses. Now think about a classic car that gains in value--the **appreciation** is the amount it increases in value. There are different ways to compute different types of appreciation and depreciation. For example, an item could gain or lose a constant $800 per year in value each year. That is called **straight line depreciation**. It could gain or lose at a constant percent rate each year, say 10% of its value each year. In that case, the actual dollar amount it changes in value would differ each year. In this Core Concept we will look at quantities that appreciate (grow) or depreciate (decay) by a given percent each period. These problems are sometimes called **exponential growth** or **exponential decay** problems, and they can be modeled by using **exponential functions**.

If a car kept 100% of its value x in the next year, it did not appreciate or depreciate. If it gained 9% in the year, its value would be 100% + 9%, or 109%, of the original value. This exponential growth function can be expressed as

$$(1 + .09)x = (1.09)x$$

If that value, $(1.09)x$, gained another 9% in the second year, we'd have to multiply the previous year's value by 1.09 again, to get

$$x(1.09)(1.09) = x(1.09)^2$$

Notice how the exponent tells you how many times the percent increase occurred. If a vintage motorcycle sold for y and it appreciated 9% for each of the next five years, its value after the five years would be

$$y(1.09)^5.$$

The value after appreciating 9% each year for the n years would be $y(1.09)^n$.

If a collectible item currently valued at p lost 9% in the year, its value would be 91%, or 100% - 9%, of the original value. This exponential decay function can be expressed as

$$(1 - .09)p = (0.91)p$$

If a new motorcycle sold for $m and it depreciated 9% for each of the next three years, its value after the three years would be

$$m(0.91)^3.$$

The value after depreciating 9% each year for the n years would be $m(0.91)^n$.

Notice the pattern in the exponents. Notice that expressions like these have an initial value and a repeated multiplication by a constant, so they are actually terms of a geometric sequence. Also, recall how to change a percent to an equivalent decimal.

Example 1

Mario's Pizza currently sells 12,000 pizza pies per year. They estimate that the number of pies sold will grow at a rate of 6% per year. How many pizza pies will they sell four years from now if their estimate holds true? Round to the nearest integer.

Solution 1

The current sales amount is 12,000. This increases 6% per year for the next four years. Use the formula:

$$12,000(1.06)^4 \approx 15,150, \text{when rounded to the nearest integer.}$$

Mario's should project sales of 15,150 pizza pies four years from now, if the predicted percent of growth continues.

Example 2

Due to declining interest and market value, Michael's baseball yearbook collection is predicted to lose 13% of its current value for each of the next three years. The collection is currently worth $5,400. What will it be worth in three years? Round to the nearest dollar.

Solution 2

The current value is $5,400. This decreases 13% per year for the next three years. Use the formula:

$$5,400(0.87)^3 \approx, 3,556 \text{ when rounded to the nearest dollar.}$$

Michael's yearbook collection will be worth approximately $3,556 in three years, if the predicted depreciation rate holds.

Fill in the Blanks

If something gains value as time passes, we say it _____, and if something loses value as time passes, we say it _____. If an item appreciates at a constant percent rate per year, we can model it using an _____ growth function. If it depreciates at a constant percent rate each year, we can model it using an exponential _____ function.

Basic Problem

A record collection is currently valued at $1,000 and it increases annually. The following expression shows its value after 4 years.

$$1,000(1.045)^4$$

At what percent does the collection increase each year?

a) 1.45%   b) 4.5%   c) .45%   d) 45%

Intermediate Problem

Apollo, age 66, is currently eligible to get $30,500 in Social Security each year. If she waits four years to take the benefits, until age 70, the benefits will increase 8% each year after age 66. What will her annual Social Security benefit be if she waits until age 70 to take it? Round to the nearest dollar.

a) $38,421   b) $35,575   c) $32,940   d) $41,495

Challenging Problem

Imagine a $2,000,000 property investment that is projected to grow at a rate of 8.5% annually. In how many years will it double in value at this rate?

a) between 6 and 7 years   b) between 8 and 9 years
c) between 9 and 10 years   d) between 7 and 8 years

Numeric Entry Problem

Noah has a vintage baseball card that was worth $90 eight years ago, but it depreciated at the rate of 2% per year since then. What is its current value? Round to the nearest dollar.

Quantitative Comparison Problem

Compare Quantity A and Quantity B, using the information below.

Quantity A	Quantity B
The value of a $1000 collectible that will increase 4% each year, in three years.	The value of a $1500 collectible that will decrease 5% each year, in six years.

Select one of the following answers.

a) Quantity A is greater.
b) Quantity B is greater.
c) The two quantities are equal.
d) The relationship cannot be determined from the information given.

Key Descriptors

appreciation problems, depreciation problems, exponential decay, exponential functions, exponential growth, exponential models, straight line depreciation

DID YOU KNOW THAT?

The repeating decimal $0.\overline{9}$ is an infinite string of 9's, and it is *exactly* equal to 1.

$$0.9999999999... = 1$$

Simple and Compound Interest Formulas

Introduction

Money paid for the use of money is often called **interest**. Banks pay their customers interest because they used the customers' money to provide loans to other customers. People who borrow money from a bank pay interest at a higher rate than the bank pays its depositors. That allows the bank to make a profit.

Interest is based on the annual rate of interest, the **principal**, which is the balance in the account, and the length of time the money is in the account. Interest rates are usually reported as annual rates. **Simple interest** is based only on the original principal deposited into the account. **Compound interest** is based on the principal amount and the interest that accumulates on it in every interest period. Interest periods can be semiannual (twice each year), quarterly (four times each year), monthly (twelve times each year), or daily (365 times per year). The **balance** is the amount in the account after the interest is added.

Example 1

How much simple interest does a $6,000 account earn at an annual rate of 2.5% after three years?

Solution 1

The simple interest formula uses these variables:

principal (p)
interest (I),
annual interest rate expressed as a decimal (r)
time in years (t)

Interest is the product of principal, rate, and time, as shown by the formula

$$I = prt.$$

Substitute.

$$I = 6,000 \cdot 0.025 \cdot 3$$

$$I = 450.$$

The account earns $450 interest in the three years.

Example 2

If interest is compounded monthly at an annual rate of 2%, how much interest does $6,000 earn after three years? Round to the nearest cent.

Solution 2

The compound interest formula uses these variables:

> balance (B)
> principal (P)
> interest (i),
> annual interest rate expressed as a decimal (r)
> the number of times interest is compounded per year (n)
> time in years (t)

This is the compound interest formula:

$$B = P\left(1 + \frac{r}{n}\right)^{nt}$$

Notice that the compound interest formula gives the *balance*, not the interest.

Substitute.

$$B = 6,000\left(1 + \frac{0.02}{12}\right)^{12(3)}$$

You'll need a calculator to do most compound interest problems.

$$B = 6,000\left(1 + \frac{0.02}{12}\right)^{12(3)} \approx 6,370.70 \text{ to the nearest cent.}$$

Remember that the interest is the amount earned on the principal, but the formula gives you the balance. The principal was $6,000. Subtract to find the interest.

$$6,370.70 - 6,000 = 370.70.$$

The interest is $370.70.

Fill in the Blanks

When you put your money in a bank, the bank pays _____ for the use of that money. The amount you deposit is called the _____. Simple interest is based only on the original principal deposited into the account, while _____ _____ is based on the principal amount and the interest that has already been added to the account.

Basic Problem

How much simple interest does $8,000 earn at an annual rate of 1% after three years?

a) $240   b) $80   c) $8,240   d) $720

Intermediate Problem

What is the balance after six years if $10,000 is deposited in an account that compounds interest semiannually at an annual rate of 3%? Round to the nearest dollar.

a) $1,800   b) $11,800   c) $1,956   d) $11,956

Challenging Problem

A college's endowment fund has $100 million dollars in it. How much less would it earn in one year at 3.5% simple interest compared to 3.5% interest compounded daily? Round to the nearest dollar.

a) $3,500,000   b) $3,561,797   c) $61,797   d) $3,561

Numeric Entry Problem

A simple interest savings account that paid 4% annual interest earned $300 after three years. What was the principal, in dollars?

Multiple Choice with Multiple Answers Problem

Which of the following equations represents the balance B on an account that compounds interest at an annual rate of 5.2%?

[a] $B = 6{,}000\left(1 + \frac{5.2}{365}\right)^{365(10)}$

[b] $B = 6{,}000\left(1 + \frac{0.052}{12}\right)^{12(3)}$

[c] $B = 6{,}000\left(1 + \frac{12}{0.052}\right)^{12(7)}$

[d] $B = 6{,}000\left(1 + \frac{0.052}{4}\right)^{4(8)}$

Key Descriptors

compound interest, compound interest formula, principal, simple interest, simple interest formula

DID YOU KNOW THAT?

If you walked into a store that had a 25%-off sale, and they gave you additional 10%-off if it was your birthday, it would not matter in which order the percent discounts were taken--you'd pay the same amount either way if it was your birthday!

CORE CONCEPT 43
Direct and Inverse Variation

Introduction

Take a look at the following table and see if you notice a pattern.

x	y
2	8
3	12
4	16
6	24
10	40

Notice, by inspection, that every y value is 4 times the corresponding x value. You can verify this by dividing each y by its corresponding x. We say y **varies directly** with x if y is a constant multiple of x. In other words, y varies directly with x if, for some real number k,

$$y = kx.$$

We can also say that y is **directly proportional** to x. Keep in mind that since k is any real number, it could be a fraction or a negative number.

Now take a look at the table below. Do you notice any pattern?

x	y
2	18
3	12
4	9
6	6
9	4

First notice that as x increases, y decreases. Notice, by inspection, that the product of each x and its corresponding y is 36. We say y **varies indirectly** with x if their product is a constant k. In other words, y varies inversely with x if, for some real number k,

$$xy = k.$$

We can also say that y is **inversely proportional** to x. This can also be written as

$$y = \frac{k}{x}.$$

Keep in mind that since k is any real number, it could be a fraction or a negative number.

Example 1

If y is directly proportional to x and $y = 35$ when $x = 7$, find y when $x = 12$.

Solution 1

In a direct proportion y is a multiple of x.

$$y = kx$$

Substitute and solve to find k.

$$35 = k \cdot 7$$

$$k = 5.$$

Substitute $k = 5$ and $x = 12$ to find y.

$$y = 5 \cdot 12 = 60.$$

When $x = 12$, $y = 60$.

Example 2

If y is inversely proportional to x and $y = 10$ when $x = 3$, find x when $y = 8$.

Solution 2

In an inverse proportion xy is a constant k.

$$xy = k$$

Substitute and solve to find k.

$$3 \cdot 10 = k$$

$$k = 30.$$

Substitute $k = 30$ and $x = 8$ to find y.

$$8y = 30$$

$$y = 3.75.$$

When $y = 8$, $x = 3.75$.

Fill in the Blanks

If x varies directly with y, y is a constant _____ of x. If $y = kx$ and $k > 1$, as x increases, y _____. We can say that y is _____ _____ to x. If y varies inversely with x, the product xy is a _____, and we can say that y is _____ _____ to x. Since the equation $xy = k$ models an inverse proportion, if x and its corresponding y were negative, k would be _____.

Basic Problem

If y is inversely proportional to x and $y = 16$ when $x = 3$, find x when $y = 24$.

a) 48   b) 24   c) 1   d) 2

Intermediate Problem

Variables y and x vary inversely as depicted in the following table.

x	y
2	12
3	8
4	6
6	4
8	3

What is the value of x when $y = 2.4$?

a) 2.4   b) 9.6   c) 10   d) 1.2

Challenging Problem

If y is directly proportional to x^2, and $y = 12$ when $x = 2$, find y when $x = 5$.

a) 30   b) 75   c) 60   d) 10

Numeric Entry Problem

If y is directly proportional to x and $y = 20$ when $x = 4$, find x when $y = 22$.

Quantitative Comparison Problem

Compare Quantity A and Quantity B, using the information below.

<u>Quantity A</u>   <u>Quantity B</u>

The value of x when   **The value of y when**
$y = 1.2$ if x and y are   **$x = 11$ if x and y are**
inversely proportional   **directly proportional**
and $x = 4$ when $y = 12$.   **and $x = 15$ when $y = 60$.**

Select one of the following answers.

a) Quantity A is greater.
b) Quantity B is greater.
c) The two quantities are equal.
d) The relationship cannot be determined from the information given.

Key Descriptors

direct variation, directly proportional, inverse variation, inversely proportional

CORE CONCEPT 44
Simplifying Algebraic Fractions

Introduction

In Core Concept 11 you reviewed how to simplify numeric fractions.

$$\frac{2}{4} = \frac{1}{2} \text{ and } \frac{6}{8} = \frac{3}{4}$$

In Core Concept 29 you reviewed how to simplify fractions using the laws of exponents.

$$\frac{36y^{10}}{8y^6} = \frac{9}{2}y^4$$

In Core Concept 30 you reviewed how to simplify fractions with a polynomial as the numerator and a monomial as the denominator.

$$\frac{60x^7y^4 - 10x^5y^8 + 15x^4y^5}{5x^3y^2} = 12x^4y^2 - 2x^2y^6 + 3xy^3$$

All of these examples involved dividing the numerator and denominator by a **common factor**. We will continue that procedure as we review more intricate algebraic fractions.

Example 1

Express $\frac{3x+12}{5x+20}$ in simplest form.

Solution 1

Factor the numerator and the denominator.

$$\frac{3x + 12}{5x + 20} = \frac{3(x + 4)}{5(x + 4)}$$

Divide the numerator and the denominator by the common factor $(x + 4)$. The answer is $\frac{3}{5}$.

Note that the original fraction is undefined when $x = -4$, since the denominator would be 0. Therefore, the simplified version is only applicable for values of x not equal to -4.

Example 2

Express $\dfrac{x^2-9x+20}{4x^2-100}$ in simplest form.

Solution 2

Factor the numerator and the denominator.

$$\frac{x^2-9x+20}{4x^2-100} = \frac{(x-4)(x-5)}{4(x^2-25)} = \frac{(x-4)(x-5)}{4(x-5)(x+5)}$$

Divide the numerator and the denominator by the common factor $(x - 5)$. The answer is $\dfrac{(x-4)}{4(x+5)}$.

Keep in mind that the original fraction is undefined when $x = 5$ or -5, since the denominator would be 0. Therefore, the simplified version is only applicable for values of x not equal to 5 or -5.

Fill in the Blanks

If the denominator of a fraction is equal to 0, we say the fraction is _____. For all values for which the fraction is defined, you can simplify by dividing the _____ and the _____ by a _____ _____.

Basic Problem

Express $\dfrac{x^2-49}{5x+35}$ in simplest form.

a) $\dfrac{x-7}{5}$　　　　b) $\dfrac{x+7}{5}$　　　　c) $\dfrac{(x-7)(x+7)}{5}$　　　　d) $\dfrac{x-7}{5x+35}$

Intermediate Problem

Express $\frac{7y-21x}{14x+7k}$ in simplest form.

a) $\frac{y-3x}{2x}$

b) $\frac{y-3x}{2x+k}$

c) $\frac{y-3x}{2x+7k}$

d) $\frac{y-21x}{2x+k}$

Challenging Problem

Express $\frac{2x^2-10x-12}{x^2+11x+10}$ in simplest form.

a) $\frac{2x-6}{(x+10)}$

b) $\frac{2(x+6)}{(x+10)}$

c) $\frac{2x+6}{(x+1)}$

d) $\frac{2(x-6)}{(x+10)}$

Numeric Entry Problem

The following fraction is undefined for two values of y. What is the product of those two values?

$$\frac{y^2 - 8y + 20}{y^2 - 11y + 10}$$

Multiple Choice with Multiple Answers Problem

Which of the following simplify to $\frac{x-1}{x+2}$?

[a] $\frac{x^2+6x-7}{x^2+9x+14}$

[b] $\frac{7x-1}{7x+14}$

[c] $\frac{x^2+2x-3}{x^2+5x+6}$

[d] $\frac{x^2-4}{x^2+4x+4}$

Key Descriptors

common factor, simplfying algebraic fractions

Multiplying and Dividing Algebraic Fractions

Introduction

Recall how to multiply numerical fractions. Read over Core Concept 12: Multiplying Numerical Fractions to get yourself reacquainted with multiplying numerical fractions. Do one of the problems. The procedure we will use here is a perfect analogy.

Look at the following multiplication of algebraic fractions problem.

$$\frac{20x^2}{x^2 - 9} \cdot \frac{x^2 - 7x + 12}{15x^3} =$$

We can simplify each individual fraction first if that is possible, but it isn't here. We will then do the analogous cancelling of common factors diagonally across from each other. Let's factor:

$$\frac{20x^2}{(x - 3)(x + 3)} \cdot \frac{(x - 3)(x - 4)}{15x^3} =$$

Notice that $(x - 3)(x + 3)$ and $(x - 3)(x - 4)$ have common factor $(x - 3)$. Notice that $20x^2$ and $15x^3$ have common factor $5x^2$. Now you can simplify by cancelling common factors.

$$\frac{\overset{4}{\cancel{20x^2}}}{\cancel{(x-3)}(x+3)} \cdot \frac{\cancel{(x-3)}(x-4)}{\underset{3x}{\cancel{15x^3}}} =$$

The multiplication problem simplifies to

$$\frac{4}{(x + 3)} \cdot \frac{(x - 4)}{3x} = \frac{4(x - 4)}{3x(x + 3)}.$$

The correct product is $\dfrac{4(x-4)}{3x(x+3)}$.

Next, look at the following division of algebraic fractions problem.

$$\frac{8y^5}{x^2 + 8x + 15} \div \frac{16y^2 - 4y}{x^2 + 2x - 3} =$$

Read over Core Concept 13: Dividing Numerical Fractions to refresh your memory on dividing fractions. Try one of those problems. Also review Core Concept 6: Undefined Fractions so you remember for what values of x the fractions in this lesson are undefined. Recall that every division of fractions problem can be transformed into a multiplication of fractions problem using "keep-change-flip." This problem becomes

$$\frac{8y^5}{x^2 + 8x + 15} \cdot \frac{x^2 + 2x - 3}{16y^2 - 4y} =.$$

Now it is treated as a multiplication of algebraic fractions problem! It will be solved in Example 2.

Example 1

Find the product of $\frac{x^2+9x+20}{8x^3}$ and $\frac{12x^6}{2x^2-50}$.

Solution 1

Factor.

$$\frac{(x + 4)(x + 5)}{8x^3} \cdot \frac{12x^6}{2(x - 5)(x + 5)} =$$

Cancel out common factors to simplify. Note that $8x^3$ and $12x^6$ have common factor $4x^3$.

$$\frac{(x + 4)\cancel{(x+5)}}{\underset{2}{\cancel{8x^3}}} \cdot \frac{\overset{3x^3}{\cancel{12x^6}}}{2(x - 5)\underset{1}{\cancel{(x+5)}}} =$$

Multiply.

$$\frac{(x + 4)}{2} \cdot \frac{3x^3}{2(x - 5)} = \frac{3x^3(x + 4)}{4x - 20}.$$

The correct product is $\frac{3x^3(x+4)}{4x-20}$, or, equivalently, $\frac{3x^3(x+4)}{4(x-5)}$.

Example 2

Perform the indicated division and express the quotient in simplest form.

$$\frac{8y^5}{x^2 + 8x + 15} \div \frac{16y^2 - 4y}{x^2 + 2x - 3} =$$

Solution 2

Change the division to a multiplication and flip the second fraction.

$$\frac{8y^5}{x^2 + 8x + 15} \cdot \frac{x^2 + 2x - 3}{16y^2 - 4y} =$$

Factor.

$$\frac{8y^5}{(x + 3)(x + 5)} \cdot \frac{(x + 3)(x - 1)}{4y(4y - 1)} =$$

Simplify by cancelling out common factors.

$$\frac{\overset{2y^4}{\cancel{8y^5}}}{\underset{1}{\cancel{(x+3)}(x + 5)}} \cdot \frac{\underset{1}{\cancel{(x+3)}(x - 1)}}{\underset{1}{\cancel{4y}(4y - 1)}} =$$

The division problem simplifies to

$$\frac{2y^4}{(x + 5)} \cdot \frac{(x - 1)}{(4y - 1)} = \frac{2y^4(x - 1)}{(x + 5)(4y - 1)}.$$

Fill in the Blanks

Multiplying algebraic fractions is much like _____ numeric fractions. The gist is to _____ each numerator and denominator, cancel out the _____ factors to simplify, then multiply the _____ and multiply the denominators. Division problems can be changed to _____ problems using "keep-change-flip" and the multiplication steps.

Basic Problem

Find the product of $\frac{x^2 - 49}{x^2 + 2x + 1}$ and $\frac{x^2 - 1}{2x - 14}$.

a) $\frac{x^2 + 6x - 7}{2x + 2}$ b) $\frac{x^2 + 6x - 7}{2x + 1}$ c) $\frac{x^2 + 6x - 7}{x - 1}$ d) $\frac{x^2 - 6x - 7}{2}$

Intermediate Problem

What is the quotient when $\frac{8x^4y^3}{5x^2-15x}$ is divided by $\frac{6x^2y^4}{x^2-9}$?

a) $\frac{4x^3+12x^2}{3y}$

b) $\frac{4x^3+3}{15xy}$

c) $\frac{4x^3+12x^2}{15y}$

d) $\frac{4x^3+12x^2}{15xy}$

Challenging Problem

Find the product of $\frac{14x^5+7x}{x^2-49}$ and $\frac{(x+7)^2}{14x^2}$.

a) $\frac{(2x^3+1)(x+7)}{2x(x-7)}$

b) $\frac{(2x^4+1)}{-2x}$

c) $\frac{(2x^4+1)(x+7)}{2x(x-7)}$

d) $\frac{(2x^4+1)}{2x(x-7)}$

Numeric Entry Problem

For what value of x does the product $\frac{5x}{7y} \cdot \frac{21y}{x^2}$ equal 3?

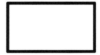

Quantitative Comparison Problem

Compare Quantity A and Quantity B, using the information below.

Quantity A	Quantity B
The reciprocal of $\frac{5x}{y}$ when $x = 4$ when $y = 12$.	The quotient $\frac{x}{3y} \div \frac{21x}{y}$.

Select one of the following answers.

a) Quantity A is greater.
b) Quantity B is greater.
c) The two quantities are equal.
d) The relationship cannot be determined from the information given.

Key Descriptors

dividing algebraic fractions, multiplying algebraic fractions

Adding and Subtracting Algebraic Fractions

Introduction

It would be a smart idea to review Core Concept 14: Adding and Subtracting Numerical Fractions before proceeding with this lesson. Reviewing the procedures for numerical fractions will allow you to handle the algebraic fractions more efficiently.

Adding and subtracting algebraic fractions with the same denominator ("like" denominators) is pretty intuitive; the answer uses the same denominator, and the numerators are added or subtracted, as indicated by the sign.

$$\frac{11x+8}{x^2-16} + \frac{6x+3}{x^2-16} = \frac{17x+11}{x^2-16} \text{ and } \frac{8m}{9y^3} - \frac{3m}{9y^3} = \frac{5m}{9y^3}.$$

When the denominators are different, you need to use the **least common denominator (LCD)** to do the problem. Recall that each of the original denominators is a factor of the LCD.

Also review Core Concept 6: Undefined Fractions so you remember for what values of x the fractions in this lesson are undefined.

Example 1

Find the sum of $\frac{2x}{x-3}$ and $\frac{5}{4x^2}$.

Solution 1

Notice the two different denominators. We need to find the lowest common denominator, which is an expression that is the least common multiple of $(x - 3)$ and $4x^2$. The LCD is the product $4x^2(x - 3)$.

We need to change each fraction to an equivalent fraction with denominator $4x^2(x - 3)$. We accomplish this by multiplying by 1 in a fractional form convenient to get the desired denominator. First, we multiply $\frac{2x}{x-3}$ by 1 in the form $\frac{4x^2}{4x^2}$ to give us an equivalent fraction with denominator $4x^2(x - 3)$.

$$\frac{2x}{x-3} \cdot \frac{4x^2}{4x^2} = \frac{8x^3}{4x^2(x-3)}.$$

Next, we multiply $\frac{5}{4x^2}$ by 1 in the form $\frac{x-3}{x-3}$ to give us an equivalent fraction with denominator $4x^2(x-3)$.

$$\frac{5}{4x^2} \cdot \frac{x-3}{x-3} = \frac{5x-15}{4x^2(x-3)}.$$

Now we've created like denominators, so we add the numerators and keep the denominator.

$$\frac{8x^3}{4x^2(x-3)} + \frac{5x-15}{4x^2(x-3)} = \frac{8x^3 + 5x - 15}{4x^2(x-3)}$$

The correct sum is $\frac{8x^3+5x-15}{4x^2(x-3)}$. This fraction is not defined if $x = 0$ or $x = 3$, since those values would make the denominator equal to 0.

Example 2

Subtract $\frac{x-6}{x^2+5x+6}$ from $\frac{7}{x^2-4}$.

Solution 2

Set up the subtraction and factor the denominators so we can use the factors to create the LCD.

$$\frac{7}{(x-2)(x+2)} - \frac{x-6}{(x+3)(x+2)} =$$

The LCD is $(x-2)(x+2)(x+3)$. By looking at the factors you can see that both of the original denominators are factors of this LCD. We need to change each fraction to an equivalent fraction with denominator $(x-2)(x+2)(x+3)$.

First we multiply $\frac{7}{(x-2)(x+2)}$ by 1 in the form $\frac{(x+3)}{(x+3)}$ to give us an equivalent fraction with denominator $(x-2)(x+2)(x+3)$. Then we multiply $\frac{x-6}{(x+3)(x+2)}$ by 1 in the form $\frac{(x-2)}{(x-2)}$ to give us an equivalent fraction with denominator $(x-2)(x+2)(x+3)$. The fractions are now rewritten with like denominators and subtracted.

$$\frac{7(x+3)}{(x-2)(x+2)(x+3)} - \frac{(x-6)(x-2)}{(x-2)(x+2)(x+3)} = \frac{7(x+3) - (x-6)(x-2)}{(x-2)(x+2)(x+3)}$$

The difference is simplified. Carefully notice how the negative sign gets distributed in the second fraction.

$$\frac{7(x+3)-(x-6)(x-2)}{(x-2)(x+2)(x+3)} = \frac{7(x+3)-(x^2-8x+12)}{(x-2)(x+2)(x+3)} = \frac{7(x+3)-x^2+8x-12}{(x-2)(x+2)(x+3)}$$

Distribute the 7 and combine like terms in the numerator.

$$\frac{7x+21-x^2+8x-12}{(x-2)(x+2)(x+3)} = \frac{-x^2+15x+9}{(x-2)(x+2)(x+3)}.$$

The correct difference is $\frac{-x^2+15x+9}{(x-2)(x+2)(x+3)}$.

Notice that this fraction is undefined if $x=2, x=-2,$ or $x=-3$.

Fill in the Blanks

The answer to an addition problem is called the _____ and the answer to a subtraction problem is called the _____. To add or subtract fractions with unlike denominators, you need to find the _____ _____ _____ before you can add or subtract. To find the LCD, you need to multiply each fraction by ___ in a form that will create equivalent fractions that have the same _____.

Basic Problem

Find the sum of $\frac{13}{12y^5}$ and $\frac{7-y}{4y^2}$.

a) $\frac{-3y^4+21y^3+13}{12y^5}$

b) $\frac{3y^4+21y^3+13}{12y^5}$

c) $\frac{-3y^3+21y^3+13}{12y^5}$

d) $\frac{20-y}{12y^5}$

Intermediate Problem

Subtract $\frac{x-1}{2x+10}$ from $\frac{6}{x^2-25}$.

a) $\frac{x^2+6x+7}{2x^2-25}$

b) $\frac{-x^2+6x+7}{x^2-50}$

c) $\frac{-x^2+6x+7}{2x^2-50}$

d) $\frac{-x^2+6x+7}{2x^2-25}$

Challenging Problem

What is the product of the solutions to the equation $\frac{5}{p} - \frac{6}{p^2} = 1$?

a) 6   b) -6   c) 30   d) -30

Numeric Entry Problem

What is the coefficient of c in the lowest common denominator used to subtract $\frac{5}{36c}$ from $\frac{y^2}{24c}$?

Multiple Choice with Multiple Answers Problem

Which of the following fraction problems have a least common denominator of

$$2(x-2)(x-3)?$$

[a] $\frac{x^2}{x-2} + \frac{55}{x-3} =$

[b] $\frac{8x}{2x-4} - \frac{9}{2x-6} =$

[c] $\frac{5x-1}{x-3} - \frac{17}{2x^2-10x+12} =$

[d] $\frac{19x^2}{2} + \frac{55}{x^2-5x+6} =$

Key Descriptors

adding algebraic fractions, finding common denominators for algebraic fractions, subtracting algebraic fractions

Distance Problems

Introduction

If you traveled at a **rate** of 60 miles per hour (mph) on cruise control, for a **time** of 7 hours, you would travel a **distance** of 420 miles. Distance (D), rate (R), and time (T) are related by the formula

$$R \cdot T = D.$$

Algebraically these can be transformed into two other helpful equations.

$$R = \frac{D}{T} \text{ or } T = \frac{D}{R}$$

Distance problems require you to read carefully and set up a diagram that depicts the travel scenario. If two cars travel towards each other from points A and B which are 10 miles apart, and you want to know when they meet, the diagram might look like this:

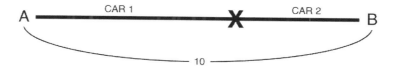

If two cars start from the same point A and head in opposite directions, the diagram might look like this:

In addition to a diagram, it is helpful to set up a table to solve distance problems. You can put the units in the table. When reading a problem, look at the units carefully. The speed may be given in miles per *hour*, but the question could ask something about *minutes*.

Since $R \cdot T = D$, if you have two of the variables, you can represent the third using multiplication or division, using the formulas given above. You use these expressions to create an equation based on the problem.

	Rate (mph)	Time (hours)	Distance (miles)
Car	45	$x + 4$	?
Jogger	?	3	k
Bicyclist	y	?	120

- Using the formula $R \cdot T = D$, we can express the car's distance as $45(x + 4)$.
- Using the formula $R = \frac{D}{T}$, we can express the jogger's rate as $\frac{k}{3}$.
- Using the formula $T = \frac{D}{R}$, we can express the bicyclist's time as $\frac{120}{y}$.

If you traditionally have had difficulty with word problems, note how the diagram and the table are a systematic way to help you navigate distance problems.

Example 1

Two trains 600 miles apart leave at the same time and travel towards each other on parallel tracks, one at an average of 65 mph and the other at an average of 83 mph. In how many hours will they first meet?

Solution 1

We can use a diagram like the first diagram presented in the Introduction. Since they started at the same time, they have traveled the same amount of time when they meet. Let's set up the table.

	Rate (mph)	Time (hours)	Distance (miles)
Slow train	65	x	$65x$
Fast train	83	x	$83x$

We can set up an equation, since both distances must sum to 600.

$$65x + 83x = 600$$

$$148x = 600$$

$$x \approx 4.05 \text{ hours}$$

The trains will meet in a little over 4 hours.

Example 2

A car travels to a convention at an average rate of 40 mph. It returns over the same roads at an average speed of 50 mph. How far was the convention if the total round trip took 9 hours?

Solution 2

We can use a diagram like the second diagram presented in the Introduction. The distance to the convention is the same as the distance from the convention. Let's set up the table.

	Rate (mph)	Time (hours)	Distance (miles)
Going There	40	$\dfrac{x}{40}$	x
Coming Back	50	$\dfrac{x}{50}$	x

We can set up an equation, since both times must sum to 9 hours.

$$\frac{x}{40} + \frac{x}{50} = 9$$

The LCD is 200.

$$\frac{5x}{200} + \frac{4x}{200} = 9$$

Add the fractions.

$$\frac{9x}{200} = 9$$

Cross multiply and solve for x to find that $x = 200$ miles and the convention was 200 miles away.

Example 3

A car uses 28 gallons of gas to travel 876 miles. How many miles per gallon (*MPG*) does the car get?

Solution 3

Use the formula $D = MPG \cdot G$ where D is the distance in miles and G is the number of gallons used. You can set up a table like you did for the other distance formula, or just substitute. Round to the nearest tenth.

$$D = MPG \cdot G$$

In this problem $D = 876$ and $G = 28$. Let x represent MPG and then substitute and solve.

$$876 = 28x$$

$$x \approx 31.3$$

The car got approximately 31.3 miles per gallon on the trip.

Fill in the Blanks

The distance formula relates distance, rate, and _____ to each other using the equation _____. Distance divided by rate equals _____ and distance divided by time equals _____. There is another distance formula that relates distance, miles per gallon, and _____. With either distance formula, if you have expressions for two of the variables, you can create an expression for the third variable using _____.

Basic Problem

Two trains at stations 440 miles apart leave at the same time and travel towards each other on parallel tracks. The faster train traveled an average of 20 mph faster than the slower train. They met each other after 4 hours. What was the speed of the faster train?

a) 50   b) 55   c) 65   d) 45

Intermediate Problem

Jordan left his home and walked on a hike and bike path to Sunken Meadow Park, at an average rate of 4 mph. Two hours later Cameron left to bike to the park on the same path, at a speed of 9 mph. How much time did it take for Cameron to overtake Jordan?

a) 72 minutes   b) 96 minutes   c) 48 minutes   d) 120 minutes

Challenging Problem

Two planes left from the same airport. They flew in opposite directions. One left an hour later than the other, but flew 50 mph faster than the first plane. Four hours after the second plane left, they were 2900 miles apart. Find the speed of the faster plane.

a) 344 mph   b) 300 mph   c) 350 mph   d) 317 mph

Numeric Entry Problem

A jogger jogs at the rate of 1 mile every 12 minutes. After 5 miles she changes pace to 1 mile every 15 minutes. How many miles does she cover in an hour and a half?

Quantitative Comparison Problem

Compare Quantity A and Quantity B, using the information below.

Quantity A	Quantity B
The number of miles a car going 45 mph goes in 6 hours.	The number of miles a car going 42 mph goes in 6 hours and 10 minutes.

Select one of the following answers.

a) Quantity A is greater.
b) Quantity B is greater.
c) The two quantities are equal.
d) The relationship cannot be determined from the information given.

Key Descriptors

distance problems, distance/rate/time problems, miles per gallon problems, motion problems

Number Problems

Introduction

Word problems often intimidate people. If you read them slowly and carefully, don't skim, and *use* the words, you might meet with more success. The ability and confidence you obtain from solving word problems of any type help you solve problems in all walks of life.

You just reviewed strategies to solve distance problems. Let's now look at **number problems**. We'll start by examining algebraic expressions that mimic situations found in number problems.

"Twice a number x"	$2x$
"Three less than twice a number n"	$2n - 3$
"Five more than a number y"	$y + 5$
"Eight decreased by a number b"	$8 - b$

Let's look at some verbal passages that are translated into equations.

"The sum of a number r and its triple is three more than its double."

$$r + 3r = 2r + 3$$

"Five less than twice a number x exceeds its triple by 2."

$$2x - 5 = 3x + 2$$

"Four less than twice the square of a number b is 14."

$$2b^2 - 4 = 14$$

Keep in mind that 'number' does not necessarily mean 'integer.' Carefully note that if the sum of two numbers is 16, one can be represented by x and the other by $16 - x$. Either expression can represent the smaller of the two numbers.

"The sum of two numbers is 16. Twice the larger decreased by the smaller is 11."

$$2(16 - x) - x = 11$$

As you solve these problems, first create algebraic expressions that follow the relationships mentioned in the problem, and then create an equation that relates the expressions you created.

Example

The sum of two integers is 10. Twelve times the smaller integer, decreased by twice the larger, is one more than three times the larger. Find the integers.

Solution

Let x = the smaller integer.
Let $10 - x$ = the larger integer.

$$12x - 2(10 - x) = 1 + 3(10 - x)$$

Notice how the equations follows the words in the problem!

Distribute and combine like terms on each side of the equation.

$$12x - 20 + 2x = 31 - 3x$$

$$14x - 20 = 31 - 3x$$

$$17x = 51 \text{ so } x = 3.$$

The smaller number is 3, and since the sum of the two original numbers is 10, the larger number is 7. Look how these numbers satisfy the problem.

Twelve times the smaller integer	36
...decreased by twice the larger	$36 - 2 \cdot 7 = \mathbf{22}$
...is one more than three times the larger	$1 + 3 \cdot 7 = \mathbf{22}$

An Internet search for number problems will give you plenty of examples to practice with.

Fill in the Blanks

If two numbers have a sum of 51 and one number is represented by p, the other number can be algebraically represented by _____. If m represents the smaller of two numbers, and the larger is five less than the triple of m, the larger can be algebraically represented as _____. The expression "nine less than y" can be represented algebraically as _____.

Basic Problem

One integer is 12 less than another. Their sum is 52. What is the smaller of the integers?

a) 5.5   b) 40   c) 32   d) 20

Intermediate Problem

The larger of two numbers is 15 more than the smaller. If the smaller is tripled, the result is the same as if the larger is increased by 11. What is the larger number?

a) 39   b) 13   c) 28   d) 26

Challenging Problem

Three numbers have a sum of 50. The second is 6 more than the first, and the third is 5 more than the second. What is the largest number?

a) 49   b) 22   c) 17   d) 33

Numeric Entry Problem

One number is three more than twice another number. The sum of the numbers is 45. What is the smaller number?

Multiple Choice with Multiple Answers Problem

Which of the following represents "seven more than twice a number"?

[a] $7 + 2x$ [b] $7 - 2x$ [c] $2x - 7$ [d] $2x + 7$

Key Descriptors

number problems, number problems in one variable, solving algebraic number problems

Consecutive Integer Problems

Introduction

Consecutive integer problems have always fascinated mathematicians. For example, there are several sets of consecutive integers that add to 15, such as

$$4 + 5 + 6 = 15 \quad \text{and} \quad 1 + 2 + 3 + 4 + 5 = 15 \quad \text{and} \quad 7 + 8 = 15.$$

There are no sets of consecutive integers that add to 8, or 16. Try it!

Consecutive integers can be represented algebraically. Typically, x can represent the first integer of the set of consecutive integers. Since each consecutive integer is 1 more than the integer before it, the next integer is represented by $x + 1$. The integer after that is $x + 2$, etc.

Consecutive even integers can be represented algebraically. The first integer of the set of consecutive even integers is x. Since each consecutive even integer is 2 more than the even integer before it, the next consecutive even integer is represented by $x + 2$. The even integer after that is $x + 4$, then $x + 6$, etc.

Consecutive odd integers follow the same pattern. The first integer of the set of consecutive odd integers is x. Since each consecutive odd integer is 2 more than the odd integer before it, the next consecutive odd integer is represented by $x + 2$. The odd integers after that are $x + 4$, then $x + 6$, etc.

These algebraic representations can be used in formulating equations that translate the relationships described in the problems. Consecutive integer problems are much like the number problems you have already reviewed.

Example 1

The sum of four consecutive integers is 38. Find the numbers.

Solution 1

The four integers can be represented as $x, x + 1, x + 2,$ and $x + 3$. Their sum is 38, so set up an equation.

$$x + x + 1 + x + 2 + x + 3 = 38$$

Combine like terms.

$$4x + 6 = 38$$

$$x = 8.$$

The four consecutive integers are 8, 9, 10, and 11. Their sum is 38.

Example 2

In a set of three consecutive odd integers, twice the sum of the first two is 3 more than the triple of the third. Find the numbers.

Solution 2

The three consecutive odd integers can be represented as $x, x + 2,$ and $x + 4$. "Twice the sum of the first two is 3 more than the triple of the third" can be translated into this equation:

$$2(x + x + 2) = 3(x + 4) + 3$$

Distribute and combine like terms to find that $x = 11$. The three consecutive odd integers are 11, 13, and 15. Notice that the sum of the first two is 24, and twice that sum is 48, which is three more than the triple of 15.

Fill in the Blanks

If the first integer of a set of consecutive even integers is n, the next consecutive even

integer is represented by _____. If $y + k$ represents an integer, the next consecutive

integer can be represented as _____. Since each consecutive odd integer is 2 more

than the odd integer before it, the next consecutive odd integer after an odd integer p is

represented as _____.

Basic Problem

The sum of three consecutive odd integers is 69. What is the largest of these three integers?

a) 27   b) 23   c) 21   d) 25

Intermediate Problem

The sum of four consecutive integers is 54. Find the sum of the two even integers in this set of four consecutive integers.

a) 26   b) 27   c) 28   d) 12

Challenging Problem

In a set of three consecutive even integers, three times the first decreased by twice the second is equal to 14. What is the largest of the three integers?

a) 22   b) 20   c) 18   d) 40

Numeric Entry Problem

The sum of two consecutive even integers is 18. What is the product of those two integers?

Quantitative Comparison Problem

Compare Quantity A and Quantity B, using the information below.

Quantity A	Quantity B
The product of two consecutive integers whose sum is 9.	**The average of two consecutive even integers whose sum is 22.**

Select one of the following answers.

a) Quantity A is greater.
b) Quantity B is greater.
c) The two quantities are equal.
d) The relationship cannot be determined from the information given.

Key Descriptors

consecutive integer problems, consecutive number problems

CORE CONCEPT 50
Work Problems

Introduction

Work can be done by people or machines. Work problems require you to analyze what fraction of a job is completed in a given number of hours.

- The **Work Rate** is the part of a job completed in one unit of time. Think about this. If you take 2 hours to mow your lawn, in 1 hour you get $\frac{1}{2}$ of the job done. If a machine completes 1 whole job in 55 minutes, it completes $\frac{1}{55}$ of the job in 1 minute. Work rates are per unit of time.
- The **Work Time** is the amount of time the work went on.
- The **Fraction of Job Completed** is the part of the job finished in the given time. The number 1 plays a significant role since the object is to see how long it takes to complete 1 whole job.

These three quantities are related.

(Work Rate) × (Work Time) = Fraction of Job Completed

You will need to use a "Let" statement to tell what your variable represents. Then you can use a table. You will also be using your recently reviewed skills with algebraic and numeric fractions.

Example 1

Janice can paint a garage floor in 2 hours. Her daughter Lisa can paint the same floor in 6 hours. How long will it take them to paint the floor if they work together?

Solution 1

Let x = the number of hours they work together.

Since Janice can do the whole job alone in 2 hours, her rate per hour is $\frac{1}{2}$. She gets half the job done in an hour. Since Lisa can do the whole job alone in 6 hours, her rate per hour is $\frac{1}{6}$.

Lisa can get $\frac{1}{6}$ of the job done in an hour. But they work more than one hour. Use the formula

$$\textbf{(Work Rate)} \times \textbf{(Work Time)} = \textbf{Fraction of Job Completed.}$$

Substitute into the table.

	Work Rate	Work Time	Fraction of Job Completed
Janice	$\frac{1}{2}$	x	$\frac{x}{2}$
Lisa	$\frac{1}{6}$	x	$\frac{x}{6}$

The object is to get 1 whole job done. The two 'fraction of job completed' expressions from the table must add to 1, so set up the equation

$$\frac{x}{2} + \frac{x}{6} = 1.$$

Use the common denominator 12 to solve.

$$\frac{6x}{12} + \frac{2x}{12} = 1$$

$$\frac{8x}{12} = 1$$

$$x = 1.5 \text{ hours.}$$

If they work together, the job will get done in 1.5 hours.

Example 2

Zoe and Zack, working together, take 3 hours to rake all the leaves around their home. Zoe can do the whole job, working alone, in 4 hours. How long would it take Zack, working alone, to rake all of the leaves?

Solution 2

Let x = the number of hours Zack would take to do the job alone.

Since Zoe can do the whole job alone in 4 hours, her rate per hour is $\frac{1}{4}$. She gets a quarter of the job done in an hour. Zack can do the job himself in x hours, so he gets $\frac{1}{x}$ of it done in an hour. They work three hours at those rates. Use the formula

(Work Rate) × (Work Time) = Fraction of Job Completed.

Substitute into the table.

	Work Rate	Work Time	Fraction of Job Completed
Zoe	$\frac{1}{4}$	3	$\frac{3}{4}$
Zack	$\frac{1}{x}$	3	$\frac{3}{x}$

The object is to get 1 whole job done, so set up the equation

$$\frac{3}{4}+\frac{3}{x}=1.$$

Use the common denominator $4x$ to solve.

$$\frac{3x}{4x}+\frac{12}{4x}=1$$

$$\frac{3x+12}{4x}=1$$

$$3x+12=4x$$

$$x=12.$$

Zack will take 12 hours to do the job himself.

Fill in the Blanks

If Paolo can complete a job in y hours, he can complete $\frac{3}{y}$ of the job in _____ hours. If Rashesh can complete a job in 5 hours, he can complete _____ of the job in 2 hours. If a machine can complete a job in m hours, it can complete $\frac{4}{m}$ of the job in _____ hours.

Basic Problem

Machine A can shred a palette of paper in 3 hours. Machine B can shred the same palette of paper in 6 hours. How long will the two machines take, working simultaneously, to shred a palette of paper?

a) 1 hour   b) 1.5 hours   c) 2 hours   d) 2.5 hours

Intermediate Problem

Arsh can paint a garage door in 2 hours. His friend Nikki can paint it in 5 hours. Arsh painted alone for 1 hour and then quit. How many hours will it take Nikki to finish the painting job alone?

a) 1 hour   b) 1.5 hours   c) 2 hours   d) 2.5 hours

Challenging Problem

Raoul takes twice as long as his sister Penny to shovel snow off the driveway. They take 2 hours to do the job together. How long would it take Raoul to do it alone?

a) 1 hour   b) 2 hours   c) 2.5 hours   d) 3 hours

Numeric Entry Problem

If it takes a machine 30 hours to dig a well, what percent of the job can it complete in 6 hours?

%

Multiple Choice with Multiple Answers Problem

Which of the following are equivalent measures of time?

[a] 50 minutes   [b] $\frac{5}{6}$ hour   [c] 3,000 seconds   [d] 0.8 hours

Key Descriptors

work problems

Review/Renew

How many common prime factors do the numbers 24 and 45 have?

a) 1   b) 2   c) 3   d) 4

DID YOU KNOW THAT?

The numbers 1, 3, 6, 10, 15, 21, ... are called **triangular numbers.** Notice that each new row being added to the bottom of each array models the addition of the next consecutive counting number.

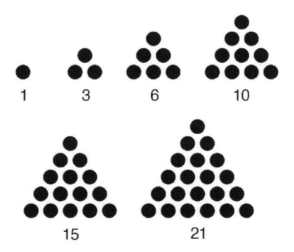

Perimeter

Introduction

A **polygon** is a **closed plane figure** with straight sides. It is a plane figure because it is two-dimensional. A **regular polygon** is a polygon with congruent sides and congruent interior angles. Figure I below is not a polygon because it has a curved "side." Figure II is not a polygon because it is not closed. Figure III is a regular hexagon (6 congruent sides and 6 congruent angles) and Figure IV is an irregular pentagon (5 sides with different lengths).

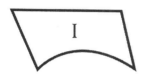 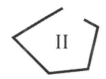 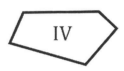

The **perimeter** of a polygon is the distance around the polygon—the sum of the lengths of its sides. The units of the perimeter are the same as the units for the sides. So, if the sides are in feet, the perimeter is in feet. If the sides are in centimeters, the perimeter can be expressed in centimeters, etc.

You are already familiar with equilateral triangles, isosceles triangles, scalene triangles, parallelograms, rhombuses, squares, rectangles, and trapezoids. You might want to review the properties of each. When solving perimeter problems, it is a good idea to draw a diagram if the polygon is simple enough.

Example 1

A rectangle has length that is five more than twice its width. Its perimeter is 130. What is its length?

Solution 1

Let x represent the width.
Let $2x + 5$ represent the length.
Draw a diagram. Notice that all four sides are labelled. This reminds you to add *four* sides to get the perimeter.

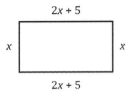

Set up an equation and solve for x.

$$2x + 2(2x + 5) = 130$$

Since $x = 20$, the width is 20 and the length is $2(20) + 5 = 45$.

Example 2

A regular octagon (8 sides) has sides with length k. When the side lengths are increased by 3, the perimeter is 80. What is the original side length?

Solution 2

The original regular octagon has eight sides of length k. The larger octagon's sides can be represented as $k + 3$. It is probably not necessary to draw a diagram. Set up an equation.

$$8(k + 3) = 80$$

Since $k = 7$, the original side length is 7.

Fill in the Blanks

A polygon is a closed _____ figure with _____ sides. The _____ of a polygon is the sum of the side lengths. If a polygon is a regular polygon, its sides are _____. A regular quadrilateral (4 sides) is commonly known as a _____. A square with perimeter 32 has side lengths of _____. The perimeter of an equilateral triangle with side lengths represented by $2x + 5$ can be represented as _____.

Basic Problem

A triangle has side lengths that are consecutive integers. The perimeter is 36. What is the length of the longest side?

a) 11   b) 12   c) 13   d) 14

Intermediate Problem

Which of the following, I, II, III, are true statements about an 8' by 20' rectangle?

        I.   The perimeter is 28'.
        II.   The length is four more than twice the width.
        III.   The perimeter is the same as the perimeter of a square whose side is 14'.

a) I only   b) II only   c) II and III only   d) I, II, and III

Challenging Problem

A rectangle has sides 5 and 8. If all sides are increased by the same amount, the new perimeter is 42. What is the width of the rectangle with the increased sides?

a) 4   b) 9   c) 12   d) 42

Numeric Entry Problem

The perimeter of a rectangle is 39. Its length is 15. What is its width?

Quantitative Comparison Problem

Compare Quantity A and Quantity B, using the information below.

Quantity A	Quantity B
The perimeter of a 12' by 20' rectangle.	**The side of a regular pentagon with perimeter 300'.**

Select one of the following answers.

a) Quantity A is greater.
b) Quantity B is greater.
c) The two quantities are equal.
d) The relationship cannot be determined from the information given.

Key Descriptors

closed plane figures, perimeter, polygon, regular polygon, irregular polygon

Review/Renew

What is the value of $100 - 6(1 + 3^2) \div 4$?

a) 85   b) 10   c) 2,350   d) 115

DID YOU KNOW THAT?

There are infinitely many real numbers, and there are as many real numbers between 0 and 1 as there are between 0 and 100. Pretty counterintuitive, huh?!

CORE CONCEPT 52
Circumference and Arc Length

Introduction

Recall the parts of a circle that you a familiar with. A line segment that connects the circle's center to any point on the circle is a **radius**. A line segment that goes through the center and connects two points on the circle is a **diameter**. The length of the diameter is twice the length of the radius. A region formed by two radii and the arc they intercept is called a **sector**. A slice cut from a circular pizza is in the shape of a sector.

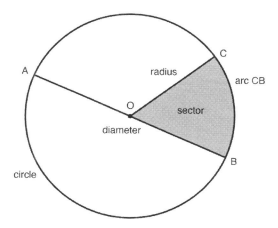

In circle O above, O is the center, $\overline{AB}$ is a diameter, $\overline{OA}, \overline{OB}$, and $\overline{OC}$ are radii, and arc CB is labelled. Sector COB is shaded.

A circle does not have "perimeter," but there is a measurable distance around a circle. Imagine placing a string around a circle and then measuring the string. That length is called the circle's **circumference**. You might recall the circumference formulas you first learned in middle school. They involved the Greek letter **pi**, which is written as π. This is the ratio of a circle's circumference to its diameter, and it is approximately 3.14.

The formulas for the circumference C of a circle, given either the diameter d or the radius r, are

$$C = 2\pi r \text{ and } C = \pi d.$$

Remember that the diameter's length is twice the length of the radius, so once you know one of these quantities, you automatically know the other and can use either formula. Sometimes you will need to substitute 3.14 for π, and sometimes problems will say "leave in terms of π" which means you can leave the π in your answer.

Example 1

A circle has radius 7.5. What is its circumference, to the nearest tenth?

Solution 1

Substitute into the circumference formula. Usually you multiply 2 by the radius first, and then multiply the result by 3.14.

$$C = 2\pi r$$

$$C = 2 \cdot 3.14 \cdot 7.5 = 2 \cdot 7.5 \cdot 3.14$$

$$C \approx 15 \cdot 3.14 = 47.1$$

The circumference is approximately 47.1.

Example 2

A circle is inscribed in a square whose perimeter is 40. What is the circumference of the circle, to the nearest tenth?

Solution 2

Since the circle is inscribed in the square, it is tangent to each side. A diagram would be very helpful here-it can actually help "suggest" a path to the solution!

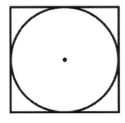

If you draw in a horizontal diameter, you notice that the diameter is the same length as a side of the square. Since the perimeter of the square is 40, a side is 10, so the diameter is 10. Substitute into the circumference formula.

$$C = \pi d$$

$$C = 3.14 \cdot 10$$

$$C \approx 31.4$$

The circumference is 31.4 to the nearest tenth.

Example 3

A sector of a circle with radius 12" has a central angle of 45°. What is the length of the arc of the sector, in terms of π?

Solution 3

A diagram will help suggest a solution.

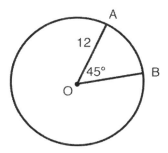

The arc length is a fraction of the circumference. The circumference of the circle is found using the formula

$$C = 2\pi r.$$

$$C = 2 \cdot \pi \cdot 12$$

$$C = 24\pi$$

The entire central angle of the circle contains 360°. The central angle of the sector is 45°. Create a fraction to see what part of the entire circle is represented by the sector's arc.

$$\frac{45}{360} = \frac{1}{8}.$$

The arc is $\frac{1}{8}$ of the circle, so find $\frac{1}{8}$ of 24π.

$$\frac{1}{8} \cdot \frac{24\pi}{1} = 3\pi$$

In terms of π, arc AB has a length of 3π.

Fill in the Blanks

The line segment that connects the center of a circle to the circle is called a _____. The length of a diameter is twice the length of a _____. The length of the circle itself is called its _____, and the formula to find this length uses the Greek letter _____ which is approximately equal to _____. If a circle's diameter is 40, its radius is _____.

Basic Problem

The circumference of a circle, in terms of π, is 17π. What is the radius of the circle?

a) 17   b) 8.5   c) 34   d) 26.7

Intermediate Problem

A circle with radius 9 is inscribed in a square. What is the perimeter of the square?

a) 36   b) 72   c) 18   d) 54

Challenging Problem

A string is placed around a semicircle with radius 10, along the diameter from A to B and then around the arc back to A.

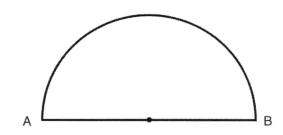

Find the length of the string (the distance all the way around the semicircle) to the nearest tenth of a foot. Use $\pi \approx 3.14$.

a) 62.8   b) 31.4   c) 51.4   d) 82.8

Numeric Entry Problem

What is the circumference of a circle whose radius is the product of the two smallest prime numbers? Use $\pi = 3.14$ and round to the nearest tenth.

Multiple Choice with Multiple Answers Problem

Which of the following have an arc length of 6π?

[a] A sector with a central angle of 90° in a circle with radius 12.

[b] A sector with a central angle of 60° in a circle with radius 18.

[c] A sector with a central angle of 30° in a circle with diameter 72.

[d] A sector with a central angle of 45° in a circle with diameter 48.

Key Descriptors

central angle of a sector of a circle, circumference of a circle, circumference formulas, pi, sector of a circle, arc length in circles

Review/Renew

Find the multiplicative inverse of the least common multiple of 4 and 14.

a) $\frac{1}{2}$ b) -28   c) $\frac{1}{28}$ d) $-\frac{1}{28}$

Areas of Polygons

Introduction

The **area** of a polygon is the amount of space inside it. Area is measured in **square units**. Look at a 3 by 4 rectangle.

1	2	3	4
5	6	7	8
9	10	11	12

There are twelve 1 by 1 squares that fill the interior, so the area of the rectangle is 12 square units.

You have already learned formulas for the areas of common polygons.

Polygon	Diagram	Area Formula
triangle		$A = \dfrac{1}{2}bh$
rectangle		$A = lw$
parallelogram		$A = bh$

Remember that a square is just a rectangle with four congruent sides, and a rhombus is a parallelogram with four congruent sides. The area of a trapezoid is $A = \frac{1}{2}(b_1 + b_2)$, where h is the height and b_1 and b_2 are the bases.

Example 1

A triangle has area 54. Its height is 9. Find the length of its base.

Solution 1

The area formula for a triangle is $A = \frac{1}{2}bh$. Substitute and solve for the base b.

$$A = \frac{1}{2}bh$$

$$54 = \frac{1}{2}b \cdot 9$$

$$54 = 4.5b$$

$$b = 12.$$

The base of the triangle is 12.

Example 2

A rectangle has length 10 more than its width. Its area is 39. Find the dimensions of the rectangle.

Solution 2

The area formula for a rectangle is $A = lw$. The width can be represented by x and the length by $x + 10$. Set up a quadratic equation.

$$A = lw$$

Substitute.

$$x(x + 10) = 39$$

Distribute.

$$x^2 + 10x = 39$$

Subtract 39 from both sides.

$$x^2 + 10x - 39 = 0$$

Factor, and then set each factor equal to 0.

$$(x + 13)(x - 3) = 0.$$

The equation has two solutions, $x = -13$ and $x = 3$, The negative solution is rejected since a rectangle cannot have a negative side length. The width is 3 and the length is 13, and a rectangle with those dimensions does have an area of 39. If you need to review solving quadratic equations, see Core Concept 36.

Example 3

A triangle has the same area as a square with perimeter 22. Its base is 10. Find the height of the triangle.

Solution 3

Since the perimeter of the square is 22, divide by 4 to find that a side is 5.5. The area of the square (and the area of the triangle) is

$$5.5^2 = 30.25.$$

The area formula for a triangle is $A = \frac{1}{2} bh$. Substitute and solve for the height h.

$$30.25 = \frac{1}{2} \cdot 10 \cdot h$$

$$30.25 = 5h$$

$$h = 6.05.$$

The height of the triangle is 6.05.

Fill in the Blanks

The amount of space inside a polygon is called its _____. Area is measured in _____ units. The area of a triangle with base k and height h is _____. The area of a parallelogram with base 10 and height 4 is _____ square units. A rectangle is a special type of parallelogram with angles that measure _____ degrees. The area of a rectangle with length l and width w is _____.

Basic Problem

A rectangle has width represented by the expression $2x^3$ and length represented as $5x^4$. What is the expression for its area?

a) $7x^7$ b) $10x^{12}$ c) $10x^7$ d) $7x^{12}$

Intermediate Problem

What is the perimeter of a square whose area is 196 square feet?

a) 14'   b) 88'   c) 28'   d) 56'

Challenging Problem

A regular heptagon (7 sides) has an inscribed circle with radius 5. Its perimeter is 33.6. What is its area?

a) 84   b) 280   c) 20   d) 40

Numeric Entry Problem

What is the length of a rectangle with area 50 square units and width 4?

Quantitative Comparison Problem

Compare Quantity A and Quantity B, using the information below.

Quantity A	Quantity B
A side of a square with area 169 square feet.	The diameter of a circle with circumference 13π feet.

Select one of the following answers.

a) Quantity A is greater.
b) Quantity B is greater.
c) The two quantities are equal.
d) The relationship cannot be determined from the information given.

Key Descriptors

area, area of a parallelogram, area of a polygon, area of a rectangle, area of a square, area of a triangle

Review/Renew

The ratio of bicyclists to joggers at a local charity event is 7:5. If there are 240 people in the event, how many joggers are there?

a) 20   b) 140   c) 100   d) 120

DID YOU KNOW THAT?

A **skewsquare** is quadrilateral with perpendicular, congruent diagonals. Figure ABCD is a skewsquare. If you connect the midpoints of the sides of any skewsquare, it will always form a square. Try it!

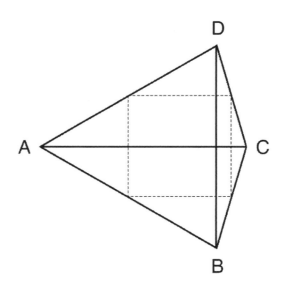

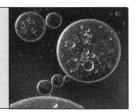

CORE CONCEPT 54
Areas of Circles and Sectors

Introduction

Think of a square with side r. Its area is r^2. Look at the shaded circle below in Figure I. It has area A. Let's compare this area A to the areas of several shaded polygons.

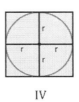

I   II   III   IV   V

- From Figure II we can see that the shaded square, with area r^2, has area less than A.

- From Figure III we can see that the two shaded squares, with area $2r^2$, has area less than A.

- From Figure IV we can see that the four shaded squares, with area $4r^2$, clearly has area greater than A.

- Look at Figure V. It seems reasonable that the parts of the three shaded squares that "stick out" beyond the circle could be cut up and reassembled to closely fit the unshaded quarter of the circle. The area of a circle is reasonably close to $3r^2$.

Recall that $\pi \approx 3.14$, which is very close to 3. You might remember the area of a circle formula from middle school. In a circle with radius r, the area, A, of a circle is

$$A = \pi r^2.$$

Remember that the diameter's length is twice the length of the radius, so if you know the diameter, you can divide by 2 and get the radius, and use the area formula. Sometimes you will need to substitute 3.14 for π, and sometimes problems will say "leave in terms of π" which means you can leave the π in your answer.

If you are given the circle's area in terms of π, you can find the radius by taking the square root of the coefficient of π. For example, if a circle has area 25π, its radius is $\sqrt{25}$, which is 5.

Example 1

A circle has diameter 16 feet. Find its area in terms of π.

Solution 1

The radius is 8' since it is half of the diameter. Use the area formula $A = \pi r^2$ and substitute.

$$A = \pi r^2$$

$$A = \pi \cdot 8^2$$

$$A = 64\pi$$

The area of the circle is 64π square feet.

Example 2

A circle has radius 12. Find, to the nearest tenth, the area of a sector of a circle with central angle 40°.

Solution 2

A diagram will help you visualize the scenario.

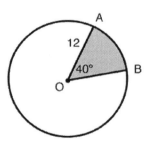

The sector's area is a fraction of the circle's area. The area of the circle is found using the formula

$$A = \pi r^2.$$

$$A = \pi \cdot 12^2$$

$$A = 144\pi \approx 144 \cdot 3.14 = 452.16.$$

The entire central angle of the circle contains 360°. The central angle of the sector is 40°. Create a fraction to see what part of the circle's area is represented by the sector's area. Simplify the fraction.

$$\frac{40}{360} = \frac{1}{9}.$$

The area of the sector is $\frac{1}{9}$ of the circle, so find $\frac{1}{9}$ of 452.16.

$$\frac{1}{9} \cdot \frac{452.16}{1} = 50.24$$

Rounded to the nearest tenth, sector AOB has an approximate area of 50.2 square units.

Fill in the Blanks

If a circle has radius k, the area of the circle is _____. Since the circle's area formula requires inputting the radius, if you are given the diameter, you can find the radius by

_____ _____ _____. If you are given the circle's area in terms of π, you can find the radius by taking the _____ _____ of the coefficient of π.

Basic Problem

A circle has diameter 40. Find its area in terms of π.

a) 20π b) 1600π c) 40π d) 400π

Intermediate Problem

A circle is inscribed in a square whose area is 100. Find the area of the circle to the nearest tenth.

a) 314   b) 78.5   c) 31.4   d) 157

Challenging Problem

A sector of a circle has a 60° central angle, and its area is 13.5π. What is the length of its diameter?

a) 18   b) 27   c) 81   d) 40.5

Numeric Entry Problem

A circle has area, in terms of π, of 49π. What is the diameter of the circle?

Multiple Choice with Multiple Answers Problem

Which of the following have equivalent areas?

[a] a circle with radius 4   [b] a circle with circumference 8π

[c] a circle with diameter 8   [d] a circle with circumference 4π

Key Descriptors

area of a circle, area of a sector of a circle, $A = \pi r^2$

Review/Renew

Convert $\frac{5}{8}$ to an equivalent percent.

a) 160%   b) 62.5%   c) 0.625%   d) 1.6%

DID YOU KNOW THAT?

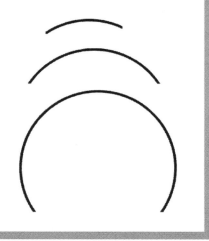

If the arcs on the right were completed to become full circles, which would have the greatest area?

They are all arcs from the same circle, so all three circles have the same area.

Shaded Area

Introduction

Often in fields like engineering, landscaping, interior design, architecture, and more, plane figures are combined to create new plane figures that meet the specific needs of a project. Figures need to be drawn carefully and areas might need to be added or subtracted to get the areas of the desired regions. The area formulas can be used and adapted to fit any region's requirements.

These problems are often called **shaded area problems**, since the region being analyzed is shaded for clarity. If you read any shaded area problems for which a diagram is not given, be sure to draw one. There could also be problems that require you to combine and adapt the circumference and area formulas.

Keep in mind that if any polygon is dissected and a new region is formed using all of the original dissected regions from the polygon in a different arrangement, the area of the newly formed figure is equal to the area of the original figure.

Example 1

A school is constructing a new synthetic running track and athletic field using artificial turf. It is composed of two semicircles of radius 36.5 m at each end of a rectangle whose length is 84.4 m. What is the area of the track and field to the nearest square meter?

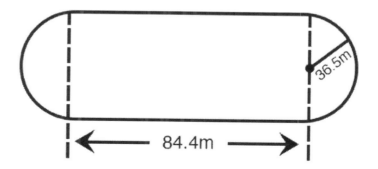

Solution 1

Notice that the width of the rectangle has the same length as the diameter of the semicircle, so the rectangle's width is 73 m. The area of the 73 m by 84.4 m rectangle is 6,161.2 square meters.

Rather than find the area of each separate semicircle, use the fact that they combine to form one full circle with radius 36.5. Use the formula $A = \pi r^2$ and substitute 36.5 for r.

$$A = \pi r^2$$

$$A = \pi \cdot 36.5^2$$

$$A \approx 3.14 \cdot 36.5^2 = 4{,}183.265 \text{ square meters.}$$

Add the areas of the two semicircles to the area of the rectangle.

$$6{,}161.2 + 4{,}183.265 = 10{,}344.465 \text{ square meters.}$$

Rounded to the nearest square meter, the area of the track and field is 10,344 square meters.

Example 2

A rectangle has area 90. It has length as shown in the diagram below. A triangle inside the rectangle creates two shaded regions. What is the total area of these two shaded regions?

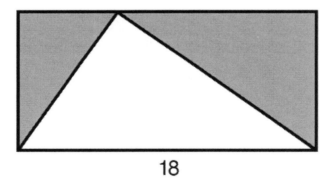

18

Solution 2

Divide 90 by 18 to find that the width of the rectangle is 5. Notice from the diagram that this is also the height of the triangle. So, the triangle has base 18 and height 5. Use the area of a triangle formula

$$A = \frac{1}{2}bh.$$

$$A = \frac{1}{2} \cdot 18 \cdot 5 = 45.$$

Subtract 45 from 90 to find that the shaded area is 45 square units.

Fill in the Blanks

The area of a semicircle can be found by using the circle area formula and dividing by

_____. If any polygon is dissected and a new region is formed using all of the original

dissected regions from the polygon, the area of the newly formed figure is _____ ____

the area of the original figure. You can use the diagram to determine if the shaded area

problem involves addition or _____.

Basic Problem

A rectangular plaza 200' by 80' is being constructed in a town square, as shown in the
diagram below. It will be covered with sod except for the area occupied by three circular
fountains. The larger fountain has a diameter of 40' and the smaller fountains have
diameters of 22'. How many square feet of sod are necessary to cover the sodded area?
Round to the nearest square foot.

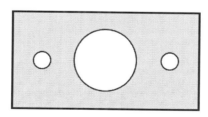

a) 13,984   b) 18,016   c) 16,044   d) 15,956

Intermediate Problem

An 8" by 10" photo is going to have a border (called a matte) around it. The matte is 2" in
width. What is the area of the matte?

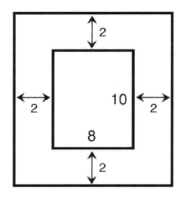

a) 168 sq. in.   b) 88 sq. in.   c) 80 sq. in.   d) 40 sq. in.

Challenging Problem

A circle with radius 20 is inscribed in a square. Find the area of the shaded region shown in the figure. Round to the nearest integer.

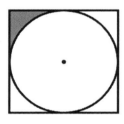

a) 86   b) 344   c) 274   d) 172

Numeric Entry Problem

What is the "perimeter" (distance around the outside) of the school track from Example 1? Round to the nearest integer.

Quantitative Comparison Problem

Compare Quantity A and Quantity B, using the information below.

Quantity A	Quantity B
The remaining area of a 14 x 20 rectangle with a 4 x 4 square inside of it removed.	The remaining area of a circle with radius 8 with a 4 x 3 rectangle inside of it removed.

Select one of the following answers.

a) Quantity A is greater.
b) Quantity B is greater.
c) The two quantities are equal.
d) The relationship cannot be determined from the information given.

Key Descriptors

shaded area problems, shaded region problems

Review/Renew

What is the solution set for the absolute value equation $|x + 7| = 17$?

a) {-24, -10}   b) {-10, 24}   c) {-24, 10}   d) {-17, -10}

DID YOU KNOW THAT?

In 2019, Po-Shen Loh created a new way to solve quadratic equations. Check out his video on the Internet!

$$ax^2 + bx + c = 0$$

Volume

Introduction

You have already seen that lines have one dimension, and you can measure their length. Plane figures have two dimensions, and the amount of space inside of a closed plane figure is its area, measured in square units. The amount of space inside a three-dimensional solid is called its **volume**. Volume is measured in **cubic units**. A cube is a six-sided solid with all right angles, congruent edges, and congruent faces. The volume of a solid is measured in 1 x 1 x 1-unit cubes. Look at the rectangular solid below. It has length 6, width 3, and height 4.

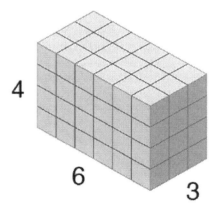

Imagine counting the 1 x 1 x 1 cubes (cubic units) that fill up the entire inside of the solid. You can see 6 x 4 = 24 cubes in the front face, and imagine two more sets of 24 cubes each behind the front face. The rectangular solid has a volume of 72 cubic units. The volume of a rectangular solid with length *l*, width *w*, and height *h* is

$$V = lwh.$$

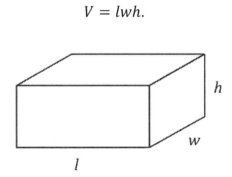

Here are the volume formulas for four other common solids.

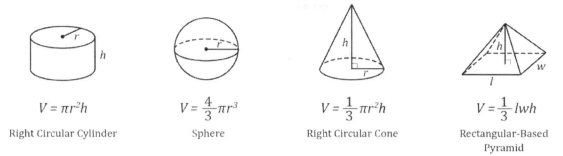

$V = \pi r^2 h$	$V = \frac{4}{3}\pi r^3$	$V = \frac{1}{3}\pi r^2 h$	$V = \frac{1}{3}lwh$
Right Circular Cylinder	Sphere	Right Circular Cone	Rectangular-Based Pyramid

Solids can be created by pairing these solids, or parts of them, similar to the way plane figures were combined to make some shaded area problems. For example, a silo is a hemisphere (half a sphere) placed on top of a right circular cylinder.

There are many more volume formulas for other solids, but these are the basic ones that you should know.

Example 1

Shipping containers can be loaded onto a truck bed and then hoisted by a crane off of the truck onto a ship. You've seen many trucks with these containers on the country's highways. A typical shipping container is a rectangular solid that is 53' long, 8.5' wide, and 9.5' high.

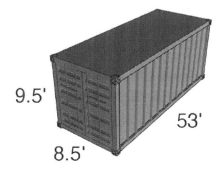

What is the volume of one of these shipping containers, to the nearest ten cubic feet?

Solution 1

Substitute $l = 53$, $w = 8.5$, and $h = 9.5$ into the volume formula

$$V = lwh.$$

$$V = 53 \cdot 8.5 \cdot 9.5 = 4{,}279.75 \text{ cubic feet.}$$

Rounded to the nearest ten square feet, the volume is 4,280 cubic feet.

Example 2

A silo has a hemispherical top sitting on a right circular cylinder. The diameter of the cylinder is 50 feet and the silo is 135 feet high. Find the volume of the silo to the nearest cubic foot.

Solution 2

The hemisphere is half of a sphere. The volume of a sphere is

$$V = \frac{4}{3}\pi r^3.$$

The diameter is 50 so the radius is 25. Substitute to find the volume of the full sphere.

$$V = \frac{4}{3}\pi \cdot 25^3$$

$$V = \tfrac{4}{3} \cdot 15{,}625\pi \approx 65{,}416.\overline{6}.$$

Divide by 2 to find the volume of the hemisphere.

$$65{,}416.\overline{6} \div 2 = 32{,}708.\overline{3}.$$

The volume of the cylinder can also be found by substituting. Be careful! The silo is 135 feet high, so the cylindrical part is 110 feet high, since the top 25 feet of the silo is from the radius of the hemisphere.

$$V = \pi r^2 h = \pi \cdot 25^2 \cdot 110 \approx 215{,}875.$$

Add $32{,}708.\overline{3}$ to 215,875 to find that the volume of the silo, rounded to the nearest cubic foot, is 248,583 cubic feet.

Fill in the Blanks

The amount of space inside of a three-dimensional solid is called its _____. While area is measured in _____ units, volume is measured in _____ units. A cube is a rectangular solid with six congruent square faces. If a cube has side length 7, its volume is _____ cubic units. The volume formula for a _____ is $V = \frac{4}{3}\pi r^3$.

Basic Problem

The Great Pyramid of Giza in Egypt has a square base, with sides 755.75'. Its height is 481.4'.

What is the volume of this pyramid, in cubic feet? Round to the nearest thousand cubic feet.

a) 91,652,000　　　　b) 137,478,000　　　c) 121,000　　d) 143,884,000

Intermediate Problem

What is the diameter of a sphere whose volume, in terms of π, is $7,776\pi$?

a) 18　　　　b) 36　　　　c) 1,944　　　d) 3,888

Challenging Problem

An industrial funnel filter is in the shape of an inverted cone at the bottom of a right circular cylinder. The cylinder gets filled with solid material which is collected as the fluid drips out through the filter.

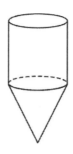

The height of the cylinder is 10' and the height of the cone is 6'. The diameter of the cylinder is 8'. What is the volume of this filter? Round to the nearest integer.

a) 603 cu. ft.   b) 452 cu. ft.   c) 151 cu. ft.   d) 955 cu. ft.

Numeric Entry Problem

Find the volume of a right circular cone with height 7, whose base has diameter 13. Round to the nearest integer.

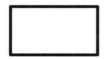

Multiple Choice with Multiple Answers Problem

Which of the following right circular cylinders have a volume greater than 50?

[a] $r = 1$; $h = 3$ [b] $r = 2$; $h = 4$ [c] $r = 4$; $h = 2$ [d] $r = 3$; $h = 3$

Key Descriptors

amount of space inside a three-dimensional solid, volume, volume of a cone, volume of a cylinder, volume of a rectangular prism, volume of a pyramid, volume of a solid

Review/Renew

Joelle got a new job with a starting salary of $52,500. Her salary increases 3% each year. What will her salary be in her fourth year? Round to the nearest dollar.

a) $55,697   b) $54,075   c) $59,089   d) $57,368

CORE CONCEPT 57
The Triangle Inequality

Introduction

You have often heard the expression, "The shortest distance between two points is a straight line." It makes sense when you look at a diagram.

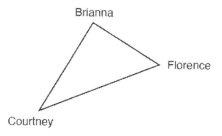

If Courtney is going straight to Florence's house, it is a shorter walk than if she goes to Brianna's house and then to Florence's house from Brianna's house. Mathematically, this concept is called the **triangle inequality**.

The sum of any two sides of a triangle is greater than the third side.

Can 30, 10 and 12 represent the sides of a triangle? Use the following picture to decide.

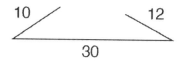

Even if the sides of 10 and 12 were placed end to end, they could not "cover" the side with length 30, so a closed figure cannot be formed. Since $10 + 12 < 30$, these lengths cannot represent the sides of a triangle. They violate the triangle inequality theorem.

Note that *all* pairs of sides must be greater than their remaining third side. If a triangle has side lengths a, b, and c, then

$$a + b > c \text{ and } a + c > b \text{ and } b + c > a \text{ must hold.}$$

Let's use these inequalities about the sums to form new inequalities about the differences:

- If $a + b > c$, then, subtracting a from both sides give us $b > c - a$.

- If $a + c > b$, then, subtracting a from both sides give us $c > b - a$.

- If $a + c > b$, then, subtracting c from both sides give us $a > b - c$.

Looking at the inequalities above, you can see that if you are given two side lengths of a triangle, x and y with $x > y$, the third side z must be between the sum and the positive difference between the two given sides.

$$x - y < z < x + y$$

Notice that all of these inequalities are "strict" inequalities that do not include "equal to."

Example

Two sides of a triangle measure 5 and 9. What are the possible measurements for the third side?

Solution

The third side z must be between the sum and the positive difference between the two given sides x and y.

$$x - y < z < x + y$$

Substitute.

$$9 - 5 < z < 9 + 5$$

$$4 < z < 14$$

The third side can be any real number between 4 and 14.

Fill in the Blanks

The triangle _____ theorem says that the _____ of any two sides of a triangle

must be _____ than the third side. As a result of this, the third side must be greater

than the _____ between the other two sides. If two sides of a triangle measure 11

and 30, the remaining side must have measure between _____ and _____.

Basic Problem

A triangle has sides 7 and 8. Which of the following could be the third side of the triangle?

a) 14.9   b) 16   c) 0.2   d) 15.7

Intermediate Problem

Two side lengths of a triangle are $x + y$ and y, where x and y are natural numbers. The third side is p. Which inequality represents possible values for p?

a) $x < p < 2y$ b) $x < p < y$ c) $x < p < x + y$ d) $x < p < x + 2y$

Challenging Problem

A triangle has side lengths 6, 8, and x. Which of the following, I, II, III, are true statements about x?

I.	$x < 8$
II.	$x < 13.9$
III.	$x > 2$

a) II only   b) II and III only   c) III only   d) I, II, and III

Numeric Entry Problem

Two sides of a triangle are the two largest prime numbers less than 20. The third side is the average of these two side lengths. What is the length of the third side?

Quantitative Comparison Problem

Compare Quantity A and Quantity B, using the information below.

	Quantity A		Quantity B

<table>
<tr><td><u>Quantity A</u></td><td><u>Quantity B</u></td></tr>
<tr><td>The perimeter of a triangle with sides 4, 5, and 6.</td><td>The perimeter of a triangle with two sides measuring 4 and 5.</td></tr>
</table>

Select one of the following answers.

a) Quantity A is greater.
b) Quantity B is greater.
c) The two quantities are equal.
d) The relationship cannot be determined from the information given.

Key Descriptors

shortest distance between two points, triangle inequality, triangle inequality theorem

Review/Renew

Find the value of x in the following proportion.

$$\frac{19}{7} = \frac{95}{x}$$

a) 5   b) 35   c) 665   d) 133

DID YOU KNOW THAT?

A pizza that has radius **z** and height **a** has volume

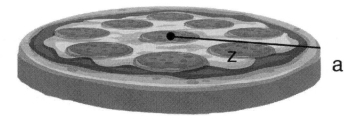

CORE CONCEPT 58
The Pythagorean Theorem

Introduction

If two intersecting lines form a right angle, they are called **perpendicular** lines. Perpendicular lines and 90-degree angles are often indicated by a little box at the angle's vertex, as shown in the right triangle below. If a triangle has a right angle, it is called a **right triangle**. The longest side, across from the right angle, is called the **hypotenuse**. The two perpendicular sides are called the **legs**. There is a special relationship between the legs and the hypotenuse of any right triangle. It is called the **Pythagorean theorem**.

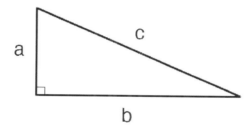

If a right triangle has legs with lengths a and b, and hypotenuse with length c, then

$$a^2 + b^2 = c^2.$$

The sum of the squares of the two legs of a right triangle is equal to the square of the hypotenuse.

If a triangle had legs of lengths 6 and 8, you could find the hypotenuse by substituting into the Pythagorean theorem.

$$6^2 + 8^2 = c^2$$

$$36 + 64 = c^2$$

$$100 = c^2$$

$$c = 10.$$

The hypotenuse has length 10. Since the three sides of this right triangle are each an integer, the set {6, 8, 10} is called a **Pythagorean triple**. Knowing some basic Pythagorean triples could save you time on your GRE. Here are three basic Pythagorean triples:

$$\{3, 4, 5\} \quad \{5, 12, 13\} \quad \{8, 15, 17\}$$

Since the Pythagorean theorem problems involve taking a square root, answers are often irrational numbers--nonterminating, nonrepeating decimals. If a triangle had legs of lengths 6 and 9, you could find the hypotenuse by substituting into the Pythagorean theorem.

$$6^2 + 9^2 = c^2$$

$$36 + 81 = c^2$$

$$117 = c^2$$

$$c = \sqrt{117} \approx 10.81665.$$

Of course, the triangle inequality holds for right triangles too.

Example 1

A rectangle has a diagonal with length 16, and width 5. What is the area of the rectangle? Round to the nearest integer.

Solution 1

Draw a diagram. Look for the right triangle and determine if the Pythagorean theorem can help.

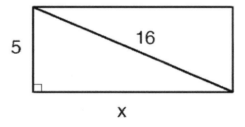

You'll need to find x to be able to compute the area. Use the Pythagorean theorem to get the length x.

$$a^2 + b^2 = c^2$$

Substitute.

$$5^2 + x^2 = 16^2$$

Subtract 25 from both sides.

$$25 + x^2 = 256$$

Take the square root of both sides.

$$x^2 = 231$$

$$x = \sqrt{231} \approx 15.199.$$

Multiply length times width to get the area.

$$15.199 \cdot 5 = 75.995 \approx 76 \text{ to the nearest integer.}$$

The area of the rectangle is approximately 76 square units.

Example 2

A rhombus has diagonals of length 6 and 8. What is the perimeter of the rhombus?

Solution 2

A rhombus is a parallelogram with four congruent sides. Remember these key facts about a rhombus:

- The diagonals of a rhombus bisect each other.
- The diagonals of a rhombus are perpendicular to each other.

Use these facts to label your diagram.

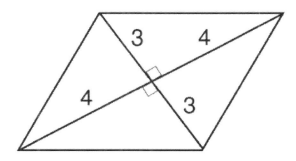

The perpendicular diagonals create four right triangles, and the fact that the diagonals bisect each other gives you the lengths of the legs of each of the four congruent right triangles.

Notice that the hypotenuse of each triangle is a side of the rhombus. Use the Pythagorean theorem to get the length of each side.

$$a^2 + b^2 = c^2$$

Substitute.

$$3^2 + 4^2 = c^2$$

$$9 + 16 = c^2$$

$$25 = c^2$$

$$c = 5.$$

The hypotenuse, c, is 5, so each side measures 5, and the perimeter of the rhombus is 20.

Fill in the Blanks

If one of the angles in a triangle measures 90 degrees, the triangle is called a _____ triangle. The two adjacent legs in a right triangle are _____ to each other. The _____ is the longest side and it is across from the right angle. The _____ theorem says that in a right triangle with legs x and y, and hypotenuse p, _____.

Basic Problem

A rectangle has length 15 and width 8. What is the length of the diagonal of the rectangle?

a) 17   b) 23   c) 49   d) 16

Intermediate Problem

A right triangle has a hypotenuse with length 41 and a leg with length 9. What is the perimeter of the right triangle?

a) 50   b) 40   c) 100   d) 90

Challenging Problem

An isosceles triangle has base 10. The two congruent sides each have measure 14. What is the area of the triangle, in square units, to the nearest tenth?

a) 70   b) 32.7   c) 65.4   d) 130.8

Numeric Entry Problem

A right angle with segments 5 and 11 is inscribed in a semicircle as shown. Find, to the nearest hundredth, the radius of the circle.

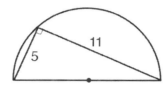

Multiple Choice with Multiple Answers Problem

Legs a and b are given for four right triangles. Which of the following right triangles has a perimeter less than 30?

[a] $a = 4$; $b = 3$ [b] $a = 5$; $b = 12$ [c] $a = 6$; $b = 8$ [d] $a = 12$; $b = 4$

Key Descriptors

diagonals of a rhombus, hypotenuse, legs of a right triangle, perpendicular lines, Pythagorean right triangles, Pythagorean theorem, Pythagorean triples

Review/Renew

The function ♦ is defined as $x ♦ y = 4x + y^2$. What is the value of 6 ♦ 3?

a) 33   b) 15   c) 729   d) 27

Angles in Triangles

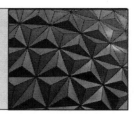

Introduction

An angle is composed of two rays with a common endpoint, its vertex. When you worked with the Pythagorean theorem, you were looking for right angles. An angle less than 90 degrees is called an **acute angle**. An angle that measures between 90 and 180 degrees is called an **obtuse angle**.

The sum of the angles of any triangle is 180 degrees. You can show this by using a ruler to draw a triangle, labeling the vertices *inside* the triangle, ripping off the angles, and arranging all three vertices on a common point on a line as shown below.

When labelling a triangle, use capital letters to denote vertices, and use lower case letters to represent the side lengths. Side *a* is opposite angle *A*, side *b* is opposite angle *B*, and side *c* is opposite angle *C*. This matters when interpreting word problems without a given diagram.

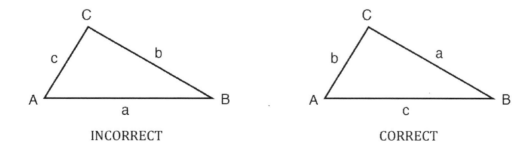

An angle is a geometric entity. The *measure* of an angle is a number. So, we should say "angle *A* measures 54 degrees" rather than saying "angle *A* equals 54 degrees." We will accept the formal and informal ways of addressing this. The context is clear either way.

Example 1

The largest angle in a triangle is five times the smallest. The mid-sized angle is ten less than four times the smallest. What is the measure of the largest angle?

Solution 1

Draw a diagram. Let x represent the smallest angle. Label the angle measures.

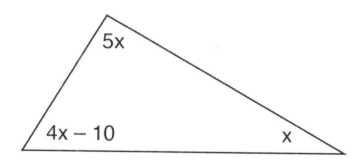

The sum of the angle measures is 180 degrees, so create an equation.

$$x + 4x - 10 + 5x = 180$$

$$10x - 10 = 180$$

$$10x = 190$$

$$x = 19.$$

Since x is positive, $5x$ is greater than $4x$ - 10. Substitute 19 for x in the representation for the largest angle, 5x.

$$5 \cdot 19 = 95$$

The largest angle measures 95 degrees.

Example 2

Triangle *ABC* below is **isosceles**. That means it has two congruent sides.
In this triangle,

$$\overline{AB} \cong \overline{AC}.$$

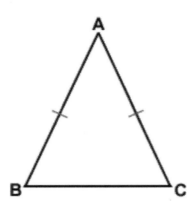

If angle *B* measures 50, degrees, how many degrees are in angle *A*?

Solution 2

The angle included by the congruent sides is called the **vertex angle**. The angles opposite the congruent sides of an isosceles triangle are called the **base angles**.

The base angles of an isosceles triangle are congruent.

In triangle *ABC*, angles *B* and *C* each measure 50 degrees, for a total of 100 degrees. Subtract from 180.

$$180 - 100 = 80$$

Vertex angle *A* measures 80 degrees.

Example 3

The exterior angle at vertex *C* of triangle *ABC* measures 112 degrees. If $\angle B = 40°$, find the measure of $\angle A$.

Solution 3

Draw a diagram.

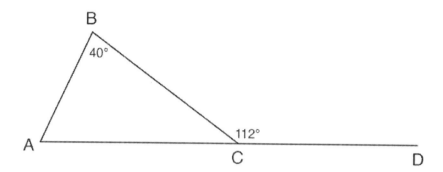

Angle *ACD* is a **straight angle** (180 degrees). If two angles have a segment in common and the other two segments form a straight angle, the angles are a **linear pair**. If two angles have measures totaling 180 degrees, we say they are **supplementary** angles.

Notice that ∡*BCA* is supplementary to ∡*BCD* since they form a linear pair. Subtract 112 from 180 to find that ∡*BCA* measures 68 degrees.

Now we'll use the fact that the sum of the interior angles of a triangle is 180 degrees.

$$∡B + ∡BCA + ∡A = 180$$

$$40 + 68 + ∡A = 180$$

$$108 + ∡A = 180$$

$$∡A = 72.$$

Notice that angle *A* and angle *B* sum to 112. This is not a coincidence.

- Since they are a linear pair, ∡*BCA* combines with ∡*BCD* to equal 180 degrees,
- ∡*A* and ∡*B* combine with ∡*BCA* to equal 180 since the sum of the angles in a triangle is 180.
- So, the measure of ∡*A* + ∡*B* is equal the measure of the exterior angle at *C*.

  An exterior angle of a triangle is equal to the sum of the two non-adjacent (remote) interior angles.

This is sometimes referred to as the **exterior angle theorem**.

Fill in the Blanks

The sum of the interior angles of a triangle is _____ degrees. An exterior angle to a triangle is equal to the sum of the two _____ - _____ interior angles. If two angles add up to 180 degrees, we say they are _____ angles. An obtuse angle is greater than _____ degrees but less than _____ degrees. Consequently, a triangle can have at most _____ obtuse angle(s). A triangle can have at most _____ acute angles.

Basic Problem

One of the acute angles in a right triangle is five times the measure of the other. What is the measure of the larger angle?

a) 15   b) 75   c) 18   d) 90

Intermediate Problem

In triangle *RST*, an exterior angle at *T* measures 123 degrees. Angle *R* is twice the measure of angle *S*. Find the measure of angle *R*.

a) 123   b) 57   c) 41   d) 82

Challenging Problem

The angle measures of a triangle are consecutive even integers. What is the measure of the largest angle?

a) 58   b) 62   c) 61   d) 59

Numeric Entry Problem

The three angles of a triangle are in the ratio 2:3:5. Find the number of degrees in the smallest angle.

Quantitative Comparison Problem

Compare Quantity A and Quantity B, using the information below.

<u>Quantity A</u>

The largest angle in a triangle whose angles are in the ratio 1:4:5.

<u>Quantity B</u>

The measure of the largest angle in a right triangle.

Select one of the following answers.

a) Quantity A is greater.
b) Quantity B is greater.
c) The two quantities are equal.
d) The relationship cannot be determined from the information given.

Key Descriptors

base angles of an isosceles triangle, exterior angle theorem, isosceles triangle, remote interior angles of a triangle, sum of angles of a triangle, supplementary angles, vertex angle

Review/Renew

Simplify the following rational expression:

$$\frac{8w^5 + 12w^3 - 10w^2 - 2w^{12}}{2w^2}$$

a) $4w^3 + 6w - 5 - w^{10}$

b) $4w^3 + 6w - 5w^2 - w^{10}$

c) $6w^3 + 10w - 8 - w^{10}$

d) $4w^3 + 6w - 5 - 2w^{10}$

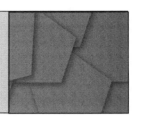

CORE CONCEPT 60
Angles in Polygons

Introduction

We know the angle sum of a triangle is 180 degrees. What about the interior angle sum for other polygons? Draw any polygon. Pick one vertex. Call it *A*. Connect that vertex to every other vertex to create triangles.

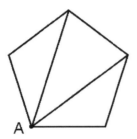

Pentagon

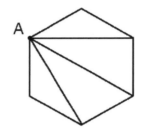

Hexagon

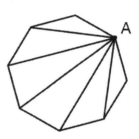

Octagon

Each triangle accounts for 180 degrees. Count the number of triangles. Do you see a pattern? The table below will unveil a pattern for the sum of the interior angles of an *n*-sided polygon. Look for a pattern relating the number of sides to the number of triangles.

Polygon	Number of Sides	Number of Triangles	Sum of Interior Angles
quadrilateral	4	2	$180(2) = 360$
pentagon	5	3	$180(3) = 540$
hexagon	6	4	$180(4) = 720$
heptagon	7	5	$180(5) = 900$
octagon	8	6	$180(6) = 1{,}080$
...	...	...	...
n-gon	*n*	*n* - 2	$180(n - 2)$

The sum of the interior angles of a *n*-sided polygon is 180(*n* - 2).

Example 1

Find the sum of the interior angles for baseball's home plate, which is an irregular pentagon.

Solution 1

Use the formula for the sum of the interior angles for a polygon.

$$\text{Sum} = 180(n - 2)$$

Substitute 5 for n.

$$\text{Sum} = 180(5 - 2) = 180(3) = 540.$$

The sum of the interior angles for home plate is 540 degrees.

Example 2

What is the measure of an interior angle of a regular decagon?

Solution 2

A decagon has 10 congruent sides and 10 congruent interior angles. Use the formula for the sum of the interior angles for a polygon and substitute 10 for n.

$$\text{Sum} = 180(10 - 2) = 180(8) = 1,440.$$

Divide 1,440 by 10 since there are 10 congruent angles. An interior angle of a regular decagon measures 144 degrees.

A general formula for the measure of an interior angle of an n-sided regular polygon would be

$$\frac{180(n - 2)}{n}.$$

Example 3

What is the measure of an exterior angle of a regular octagon?

Solution 3

An octagon has 8 congruent sides and 8 congruent interior angles. Use the formula for the sum of the interior angles for a polygon and substitute 8 for n.

$$\text{Sum} = 180(8 - 2) = 180(6) = 1{,}080.$$

Divide 1,080 by 8.

$$1{,}080 \div 8 = 135.$$

An interior angle of a regular octagon measures 135 degrees. An exterior angle is created by extending a side of the octagon, as shown in the figure below. Since the two angles are supplementary, subtract 135 from 180 to get the measure of the exterior angle.

$$180 - 135 = 45$$

An exterior angle of a regular octagon measures 45 degrees. Notice how it took three steps to arrive at this answer. There is a direct formula for the exterior angle of a regular polygon with n sides.

The measure of exterior angle of regular polygon with n sides is $\dfrac{360}{n}$.

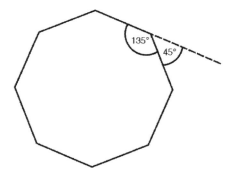

Notice that if you substitute 8 for n in the expression $\frac{360}{n}$ that you do get 45 degrees.

Fill in the Blanks

The sum of the interior angles of an *n*-sided polygon can be found using the formula

_____. The number of degrees in an interior angle of a regular *n*-sided

polygon is _____. The number of degrees in an exterior angle of a regular

n-sided polygon is _____. All of these formulas are based on the fact that the

sum of the measures of the angles in a _____ is 180 degrees.

Basic Problem

What is the measure of an interior angle of a regular nonagon (9 sides)?

a) 160°   b) 120°   c) 40°   d) 140°

Intermediate Problem

An exterior angle of a certain regular *n*-sided polygon measures 30 degrees. How many
sides does this polygon have?

a) 12   b) 10   c) 14   d) 36

Challenging Problem

An interior angle of a regular *n*-sided polygon measures 156 degrees. If each side measures
10", what is the perimeter of the polygon?

a) 150"   b) 170"   c) 156"   d) 130"

Numeric Entry Problem

What is the sum of the interior angles of a heptagon (7sides)?

Multiple Choice with Multiple Answers Problem

Which angles equal 20 degrees?

[a] The exterior angle of an 18-sided regular polygon.

[b] The smallest angle in a triangle whose angles are in the ratio 2:7:9.

[c] The largest acute angle in a right triangle with one acute angle measuring 50 degrees.

[d] The central angle of a sector that is $\frac{1}{8}$ of the circle.

Key Descriptors

exterior angle of a regular polygon, sum of the interior angles in a polygon

Review/Renew

An inch is equivalent to approximately 2.54 centimeters. How many inches are equivalent to 77 centimeters? Round to the nearest hundredth.

a) 30.31   b) 6.42   c) 195.58   d) 31

DID YOU KNOW THAT?

In general,

$$x^y \neq y^x.$$

However, for $x = 4$ and $y = 2$, it works!

$$4^2 = 2^4 = 16$$

Similar Polygons

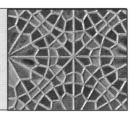

Introduction

Imagine that the door of your house is twice as tall as the window next to it. Imagine you took a picture of the front of your house with your phone camera. In the photo, which is a huge reduction in size, the door is still twice as tall as the window. If you zoomed out or zoomed in on your photo, the door would still be twice as high as the window. This is because the zoom feature keeps the original proportions intact.

You can think of **similar figures** as photographic enlargements, reductions, or zoomed in, zoomed out images. You studied **similar triangles** in geometry class. If two triangles are similar, their corresponding angles are congruent, and their corresponding sides are in proportion. The corresponding sides are across from the corresponding angles, and are labelled accordingly. See the figure in Example 1.

The ratio between any pair of corresponding sides in a set of similar triangles, or in a set of any similar polygons, is called the **ratio of similitude**. You can mathematically express the fact that triangle *ABC* is similar to triangle *DEF* by writing

$$\triangle ABC \sim \triangle DEF.$$

Note that the letters are written so the corresponding angles appear in the same order, in other words,

$$\angle A \cong \angle D \text{ and } \angle B \cong \angle E \text{ and } \angle C \cong \angle F.$$

Keep in mind that corresponding angles of similar polygons are congruent. Interestingly, if you zoom in or zoom out of a picture of an angle, the angle measure does not change!

Example 1

In the figure below, $\triangle ABC \sim \triangle DEF$. The side lengths are also shown. Find x and y.

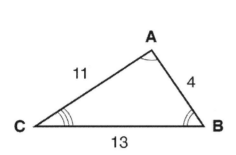
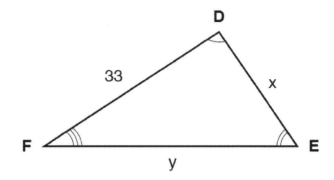

Solution 1

Since $\overline{AC}$ and $\overline{DF}$ are corresponding sides with lengths 11 and 33, the ratio of similitude is 11:33, which is written in fraction form as $\frac{11}{33}$. Remember that the corresponding sides are opposite congruent angles. Set up a proportion to find x.

$$\frac{11}{33} = \frac{4}{x}$$

Simplify.

$$\frac{1}{3} = \frac{4}{x}$$

Cross multiply.

$$x = 12$$

Side $\overline{DE}$ has length 12.

Set up a proportion to find y.

$$\frac{11}{33} = \frac{13}{y}$$

Simplify.

$$\frac{1}{3} = \frac{13}{y}$$

Cross multiply.

$$y = 39.$$

Side $\overline{FE}$ has length 39.

Example 2

The ratio of similitude between two similar triangles is 2:5. The perimeter of the larger triangle is 65. What is the perimeter of the smaller triangle?

Solution 2

The perimeter ratio is the same as the ratio of similitude for the sides since the perimeter is the sum of the sides. This relationship holds for any pair of similar polygons. Set up a proportion to find the perimeter p.

$$\frac{2}{5} = \frac{p}{65}$$

Cross multiply and divide by 5 to solve for p.

$$p = 26.$$

The perimeter of the smaller triangle is 26.

Example 3

Triangles XYZ and RST are similar. What is the area of $\triangle RST$?

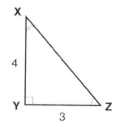 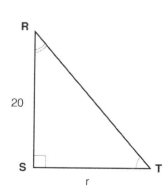

Solution 3

The triangle area formula is $A = \frac{1}{2}bh$. The ratio of similitude is 4:20. Set up a proportion to find r.

$$\frac{4}{20} = \frac{3}{r}$$

Simplify.

$$\frac{1}{5} = \frac{3}{r}$$

Cross multiply.

$$r = 15$$

Substitute into $A = \frac{1}{2}bh$ to find the area.

$$A = \frac{1}{2}bh.$$

$$A = \frac{1}{2} \cdot 15 \cdot 20.$$

The area is 150 square units. Notice that the area of $\triangle XYZ$ was 6 square units. The ratio of the areas is $\frac{6}{150} = \frac{1}{25}$. The ratio of similitude, $\frac{4}{20} = \frac{1}{5}$, is not equal to the ratio of the areas. The ratio of the areas is equal to the *square* of the ratio of similitude.

If the ratio of similitude between two similar polygons is $\frac{a}{b}$, the ratio of their areas is $\frac{a^2}{b^2}$.

In summary, if two polygons are similar, their perimeters and corresponding sides have the same ratio as the ratio of similitude. The ratio of their areas is the ratio of similitude squared.

Fill in the Blanks

Corresponding sides of _____ triangles are in proportion, and corresponding

angles of similar triangles are _____. The ratio between any pair of

corresponding sides is called the _____ of _____. The ratio of areas

between two similar polygons is the _____ of their ratio of similitude.

Basic Problem

Triangles *LMN* and *HJK*, shown below, are similar.

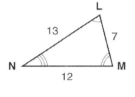
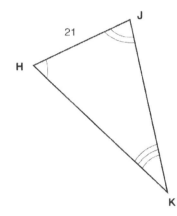

What is the length of side $\overline{JK}$?

a) 39   b) 36   c) 21   d) 25

Intermediate Problem

The ratio of similitude between two similar pentagons is 3:4. If the area of the smaller
pentagon is 90, what is the area of the larger pentagon?

a) 360   b) 160   c) 120   d) 270

Challenging Problem

Two hexagons are similar. The area of the larger hexagon is 225 and the area of the smaller
hexagon is 81. If the perimeter of the smaller hexagon is 45, what is the perimeter of the
larger hexagon?

a) 16.2   b) 405   c) 125   d) 75

Numeric Entry Problem

The ratio of similitude between two rectangles is 3:7. If the area of the smaller rectangle is 54, what is the area of the larger rectangle?

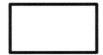

Quantitative Comparison Problem

Compare Quantity A and Quantity B, using the information below.

<u>Quantity A</u>

The ratio of the perimeters of two triangles if the ratio of their sides is 2:5.

<u>Quantity B</u>

The ratio of the areas of two triangles if the ratio of their perimeters is 2:5.

Select one of the following answers.

a) Quantity A is greater.
b) Quantity B is greater.
c) The two quantities are equal.
d) The relationship cannot be determined from the information given.

Key Descriptors

corresponding sides of similar triangles, ratio of area of similar polygons, ratio of similitude, similar triangles,

Review/Renew

What is the value of $8y^{-2}$ when $y = -6$?

a) -288   b) $\frac{2}{9}$ c) $-\frac{2}{9}$ d) $\frac{1}{288}$

CORE CONCEPT 62
The 30-60-90 Special Right Triangle

Introduction

Most trigonometry problems require you to use a calculator. There are two special right triangles that have angle measures that are so commonly used that anyone who uses mathematics in school or career often memorizes them. In Core Concept 62 we will look at the 30-60-90 triangle, and in Core Concept 63 we will look at the 45-45-90 triangle.

We can create the 30-60-90 triangle by dropping an altitude to the base of equilateral triangle *ABC* with side lengths 2.

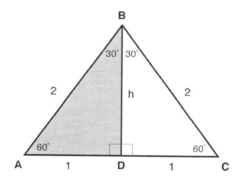

In an equilateral triangle, each interior angle is 60 degrees. Additionally, the altitude bisects an interior angle forming two 30-degree angles. Look at the shaded right triangle *ABD* above. It has angle measures of 30, 60, and 90 degrees and it is called a **30-60-90 triangle**.

We can use the Pythagorean theorem to find the height *h* of the triangle. This is the side opposite the 60-degree angle in the 30-60-90 triangle.

$$a^2 + b^2 = c^2$$

$$h^2 + 1^2 = 2^2$$

$$h^2 + 1 = 4$$

$$h^2 = 3$$

$$h = \sqrt{3}.$$

So, the sides of the shaded 30-60-90 triangle measure 1, $\sqrt{3}$, and 2. Since all 30-60-90 triangles are similar, their side lengths are a multiple of these lengths, and the three sides of any 30-60-90 triangle can be represented as

$$x, x\sqrt{3}, \text{and } 2x.$$

Knowing these proportions exist, you can find all three sides of a 30-60-90 triangle if you are given only one side. It is a good idea to find the short side length, x, first, and work from there.

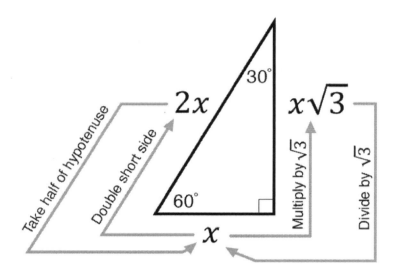

The GRE does not include any reference figures, so it is important to remember this diagram. You can draw this diagram on your test to use as reference.

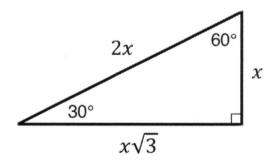

Make sure you can interpret the side relationships no matter how the triangle is rotated or oriented. If you use a decimal representation for $\sqrt{3}$, remember that $\sqrt{3}$ is irrational—it is a nonterminating, nonrepeating decimal, so your decimal representation is technically an approximation.

Example 1

In right triangle DEF, the right angle is at E and $\angle F = 60°$. If side DE measures $12\sqrt{3}$, find the length of the hypotenuse.

Solution 1

Draw and label a diagram for all 30-60-90 triangle problems.

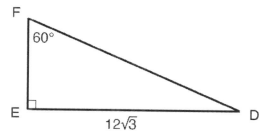

Leg EF, the shorter side, measures 12, the coefficient of $\sqrt{3}$, and the hypotenuse is twice the short side, so the hypotenuse has length 24.

Example 2

In right triangle PQR, the right angle is at Q. Angle P measures 60 degrees. If side QR has length 19, find the exact length of the hypotenuse.

Solution 2

The word 'exact' tells us not to use any decimal approximations or rounding. Draw a diagram first.

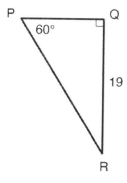

Since the side opposite the 60-degree angle is half the hypotenuse multiplied by $\sqrt{3}$, the hypotenuse is twice that longer leg, divided by $\sqrt{3}$. The exact length of the hypotenuse is

$$\frac{38}{\sqrt{3}}.$$

Knowing the 30-60-90 triangle's side proportions can be very helpful and time-saving.

Fill in the Blanks

If one acute angle of a right triangle measures 60 degrees, the other acute angle measures _____ degrees. A triangle with these three angle measures is called a _____ triangle. The shortest leg is opposite the _____ degree angle, and the hypotenuse is opposite the _____ degree angle. The hypotenuse measures _____ the length of the shortest leg. The shortest leg measures _____ the length of the hypotenuse.

Basic Problem

In right triangle LMN, the right angle is at M and $\angle L = 30°$. If the hypotenuse measures 52, find the length of leg MN.

a) 26　　　b) $26\sqrt{3}$　　　c) $52\sqrt{3}$　　　d) $\frac{52}{\sqrt{3}}$

Intermediate Problem

Right triangle XYZ has a right angle at Y. Leg XY measures 7 meters. Angle X measures 60 degrees. Find, to the nearest tenth, the perimeter of the triangle.

a) 24.2m　　　b) 26.1 m　　　c) 33.1 m　　　d) 21 m

Challenging Problem

What is the area, in square feet, of an equilateral triangle with perimeter 15 feet? Round to the nearest tenth.

a) 12.5 sq. ft.   b) 10.8 sq. ft.   c) 21.7 sq. ft.   d) 6.25 sq. ft.

Numeric Entry Problem

The hypotenuse of a 30-60-90 triangle has length 75. Express the length of the side opposite the 30-degree angle as a decimal. Round to the nearest tenth.

Multiple Choice with Multiple Answers Problem

Side lengths are given below for four 30-60-90 right triangles. Which of the following right triangles has a perimeter less than 24?

[a] short side = 5   [b] longer side = $8\sqrt{3}$ [c] hypotenuse = 12   [d] hypotenuse = 10

Key Descriptors

30-60-90 triangle, special right triangles

Review/Renew

A rectangle has a length that is 10 more than its width. Its perimeter is 180. What is its length?

a) 40   b) 50   c) 85   d) 170

CORE CONCEPT 63
The 45-45-90 Special Right Triangle

Introduction

You have seen the first of two special right triangles, the 30-60-90 triangle. Now we'll look at the second special right triangle--the **isosceles right triangle**. Imagine a right triangle with legs of length 1.

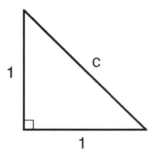

Since the base angles of an isosceles triangle are congruent, each acute angle measures 45 degrees. The isosceles right triangle is often referred to as the **45-45-90 triangle**.

We can use the Pythagorean theorem to find the hypotenuse c of the triangle.

$$a^2 + b^2 = c^2$$

$$1^2 + 1^2 = c^2$$

$$2 = c^2$$

$$c = \sqrt{2}.$$

So, the sides of the shaded 45-45-90 triangle measure 1, 1, and $\sqrt{2}$. Since all 45-45-90 triangles are similar, their side lengths are a multiple of these lengths, and the three sides of any 45-45-90 triangle can be represented as

$$x, x, \text{ and } x\sqrt{2}.$$

Knowing these proportions exist, you can find all three sides of a 45-45-90 triangle if you are given only one side.

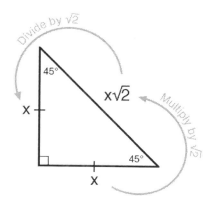

The GRE does not include any reference figures, so it is important to remember this diagram. You can draw this diagram on your test to use as a reference.

Make sure you can interpret the side relationships no matter how the triangle is rotated or oriented. If you use a decimal representation for $\sqrt{2}$, remember that $\sqrt{2}$ is irrational—it is a nonterminating, nonrepeating decimal, so your decimal representation is technically an approximation.

Example 1

An isosceles right triangle has legs with length 12. What is the perimeter of the triangle to the nearest hundredth?

Solution 1

Draw a diagram. Label all the side lengths based on what your learned above.

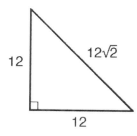

The perimeter is the sum of the sides, $12 + 12 + 12\sqrt{2}$. Enter this into your calculator and round to two decimal places.

$$40.97056 \text{ rounds to } 40.97.$$

The perimeter is approximately 40.97.

Example 2

What is the exact length of the diagonal of a square with area 100?

Solution 2

Draw a diagram. Since the area is 100, the sides measure 10. Note that the diagonal creates two isosceles right triangles.

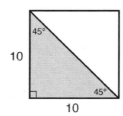

The diagonal is actually the hypotenuse of the 45-45-90 triangle, so its exact length is $10\sqrt{2}$.

Fill in the Blanks

The 45-45-90 triangle is often called the _____ _____ triangle. Since the

two legs have the same length, we say they are _____. If you are given the

length of the legs, you can find the hypotenuse by multiplying the leg length by _____. If

you are given the length of the hypotenuse, you can find the length of each leg by

_____ by $\sqrt{2}$.

Basic Problem

An isosceles right triangle has legs with length 20. What is the exact length of the hypotenuse?

a) 40   b) $40\sqrt{2}$ c) $20\sqrt{2}$ d) $10\sqrt{2}$

Intermediate Problem

What is the exact length of the diagonal of a square with perimeter 64?

a) $64\sqrt{2}$ b) $4\sqrt{2}$ c) $32\sqrt{2}$ d) $16\sqrt{2}$

Challenging Problem

A square has diagonal 10. What is its area?

a) 100   b) 50   c) 25   d) 200

Numeric Entry Problem

An isosceles right triangle has a hypotenuse with length 20. What is the length of one of the legs? Round to the nearest tenth.

Quantitative Comparison Problem

Compare Quantity A and Quantity B, using the information below.

<u>Quantity A</u>

The hypotenuse of a 45-45-90 triangle with area 8.

<u>Quantity B</u>

The perimeter of a 45-45-90 triangle whose legs have length 2.

Select one of the following answers.

a) Quantity A is greater.
b) Quantity B is greater.
c) The two quantities are equal.
d) The relationship cannot be determined from the information given.

Key Descriptors

45-45-90 triangle, isosceles right triangle, special right triangles

Review/Renew

Simplify $\sqrt{48}$ into simplest radical form.

a) $4\sqrt{3}$ b) $16\sqrt{3}$ c) $3\sqrt{16}$ d) $2\sqrt{12}$

CORE CONCEPT 64
Parallel Lines

Introduction

Parallel lines are lines in the same plane that are always the same distance apart--they never meet. When two or more parallel lines are cut by another line, that line is often called a **transversal**. The transversal and the parallel lines form angles which have certain names describing their position relative to the parallel lines and the transversal. In the figure below, line m is parallel to line p, and this can be written symbolically as

$$m \parallel p.$$

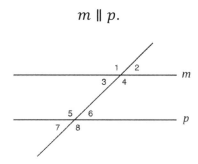

There are many angle relationships, some of which we have already reviewed.

- ∡1 and ∡2 form a linear pair, and are supplementary. In this figure, ∡1 is obtuse and ∡2 is acute. Note that ∡6 and ∡8 also form a linear pair. Look for several other linear pairs in the figure.
- ∡5 and ∡8 are vertical angles, and vertical angles are congruent.

The parallel lines create angles with special names.

- ∡3 and ∡6 are **alternate interior angles**, and if two parallel lines are cut by a transversal, alternate interior angles are congruent. Some people like to draw a 'Z' to help them see the alternate interior angles.

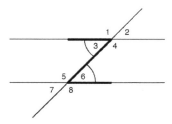

- ∡1 and ∡8 are **alternate exterior angles**, and if two parallel lines are cut by a transversal, alternate exterior angles are congruent. Notice that ∡2 and ∡7 are also alternate exterior angles.

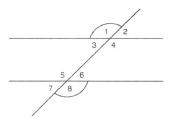

- ∡2 and ∡6 are **corresponding angles**, and if two parallel lines are cut by a transversal, corresponding angles are congruent. Notice that ∡3 and ∡7 are also corresponding angles. Some people like to draw an 'F' in any juxtaposition (mirror image, upside down, backwards, etc.) to help them see the corresponding angles.

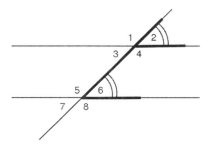

- ∡4 and ∡6 are **interior angles on the same side of the transversal**, and if two parallel lines are cut by a transversal, interior angles on the same side of the transversal are supplementary. Notice that ∡3 and ∡5 are also interior angles on the same side of the transversal. Some people like to draw a 'C' in any juxtaposition (mirror image, upside down, backwards, etc.) to help them see the interior angles on the same side of the transversal.

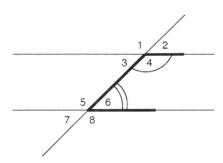

Note that if two lines are cut by a transversal and the alternate interior angles are *not* congruent, the lines are not parallel. If two lines are cut by a transversal and the corresponding angles are *not* congruent, the lines are not parallel. If two lines are cut by a transversal and the interior angles on the same side of the transversal are *not* supplementary, the lines are not parallel. If two lines are cut by a transversal and the alternate exterior angles are *not* congruent, the lines are not parallel.

Example 1

Two parallel lines are cut by a transversal, creating alternate interior angles with measures 2x + 7 and 3x - 16. Find the number of degrees in these angles.

Solution 1

Since these are alternate interior angles, they are congruent and have the same degree measure. Set up an equation.

$$2x + 7 = 3x - 16$$

$$x = 23$$

Substitute 23 for *x* in either angle's expression.

$$2(23) + 7 = 53.$$

The alternate interior angles each measure 53 degrees.

Example 2

In the figure below, $q \parallel p$ and they are cut by transversal *t*. An obtuse angle, ∡1, measures 126 degrees. Find the angle measures for ∡2 through ∡8.

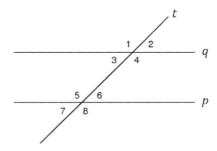

Solution 2

Due to the interdependence of all of these angle measures, there are usually several ways to find the measure of each of the angles. These are some possibilities:

$\angle 2 = 54°$ since it is supplementary to $\angle 1$.
$\angle 3 = 54°$ since it is a vertical angle with $\angle 2$.
$\angle 4 = 126°$ since it is a vertical angle with $\angle 1$.
$\angle 5 = 126°$ since it is a corresponding angle with $\angle 1$, or an
  interior angle on the same side of the transversal as $\angle 3$.
$\angle 6 = 54°$ since it is a corresponding angle with $\angle 2$.
$\angle 7 = 54°$ since it is a vertical angle with $\angle 6$.
$\angle 8 = 126°$ since it is a corresponding angle with $\angle 4$.

When parallel lines are embedded into more intricate figures, focus on the parallel lines and the transversal to find angle measures.

Fill in the Blanks

If two parallel lines are cut by a transversal, _____ interior angles are congruent. This

can be shown by superimposing a juxtaposition of the letter _____ over the diagram. If two

lines are cut by a transversal and the alternate interior angles are not congruent, the lines

are not_____. If two parallel lines are cut by a transversal, interior angles on the

same side of the transversal are_____.

Basic Problem

Two parallel lines are cut by a transversal, and interior angles on the same side of the transversal have measures represented by $x + 11$ and $4x + 24$. Find the number of degrees in the smaller angle.

a) 29   b) 140   c) 40   d) 43

Intermediate Problem

If lines *m* and *n* are parallel, which of the following, I, II, III, are true statements?

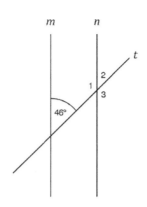

      I.   ∡1 is complementary to ∡2.
      II.   ∡1 is congruent to ∡3.
      III.   ∡2 measures 134°.

a) I only   b) I and II only   c) II only   d) III only

Challenging Problem

If $x, y, z,$ and w are degree measures of the angles shown in the figure below, find the value of $x + y + z + w$.

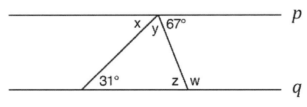

a) 293   b) 180   c) 144   d) 113

Numeric Entry Problem

Two interior angles on the same side of a transversal are consecutive odd integers. Find the number of degrees in the smaller angle.

Multiple Choice with Multiple Answers Problem

If $x = 4$, which could represent the degree measures of a pair of alternate interior angles for a set of parallel lines?

[a] $2x$ and $x + 4$ [b] x^2 and $164°$ [c] $5x + 20$ and $10x$ [d] x and $180 - x$

Key Descriptors

alternate exterior angles, alternate interior angles, corresponding angles, interior angles on the same side of a transversal, parallel lines cut by a transversal

Review/Renew

Simplify $\frac{x^2 - 25}{2x - 10}$.

a) $\frac{x + 5}{2}$ b) $\frac{x - 5}{2}$ c) $x + 5$ d) $\frac{x + 5}{x - 5}$

DID YOU KNOW THAT?

In 2020, two mathematicians solved a century-old geometry problem. They showed that any closed curve has the corners of a square somewhere on it.

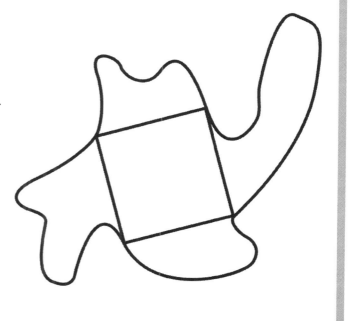

CORE CONCEPT 65
Proportions and Multiple Transversals

Introduction

In Core Concept 64 you reviewed many facts about parallel lines cut by transversals. What if a set of more than two parallel lines is cut by two transversals? In the figure below, parallel lines m, n, and p are cut by transversals t and u.

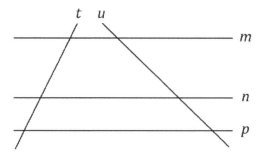

There is a relationship between segments of the two transversals themselves.

> *If two or more parallel lines are cut by two transversals, the segments on the transversals created by the parallel lines are in proportion.*

Let's label the segments and represent the proportions symbolically.

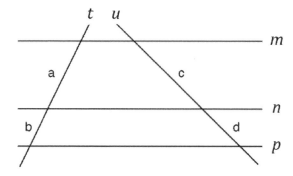

Algebraically this can be written as

$$\frac{a}{b} = \frac{c}{d}.$$

Keep in mind that if a set of several parallel lines is cut by two transversals, all of the angle relationships hold for the angles formed by each transversal individually.

Example

If lines *m*, *n*, and *p* are parallel, and they are cut by transversals *t* and *s*, find the value of the line segment with length *x*.

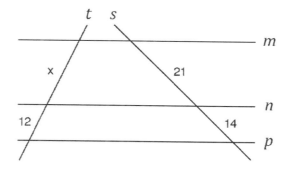

Solution

If two or more parallel lines are cut by two transversals, the segments on the transversals created by the parallel lines are in proportion. Set up a proportion.

$$\frac{x}{12} = \frac{21}{14}$$

Cross multiply and solve for *x*.

$$14x = 252$$

$$x = 18.$$

The segment has length 18.

Fill in the Blanks

There are many relationships between angles when two _____ lines are cut by a

_____. For example, when parallel lines are cut by a transversal, _____

exterior angles are congruent. If two or more parallel lines are cut by two

transversals, there are some additional segment relationships. The _____ on the

transversals created by the parallel lines are in proportion.

Basic Problem

If lines *m, n,* and *p* are parallel, and they are cut by transversals *a* and *b*, find the value of the line segment with length *y*.

a) 35 b) 20 c) 17 d) 15

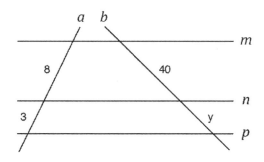

Intermediate Problem

If lines *a, b,* and *c* are parallel, and they are cut by transversals *t* and *s*, find the value of the line segment with length *x*.

a) 18 b) 28 c) 27 d) 21

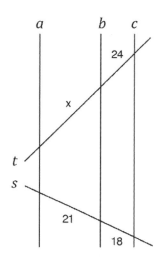

Challenging Problem

Lines *m, n,* and *p* are parallel, and they are cut by transversals *t* and *w*. Transversal *w* is perpendicular to the parallel lines, and both transversals intersect line *m* at point *K*. Lengths of segments are given. What is the value of *x*?

a) 2 b) 2.5 c) 5 d) 3

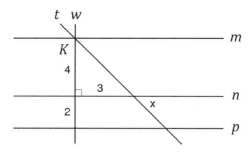

Numeric Entry Problem

Three parallel lines are cut by a transversal, and the segments yield the following proportion.

$$\frac{5}{8} = \frac{p}{20}$$

What is the value of p?

Quantitative Comparison Problem

Compare Quantity A and Quantity B, using the information below.

<u>Quantity A</u>   <u>Quantity B</u>

The value of y in the proportion $\frac{6}{y} = \frac{54}{45}$.

The value of k in the proportion $\frac{1}{17} = \frac{k}{85}$.

Select one of the following answers.

a) Quantity A is greater.
b) Quantity B is greater.
c) The two quantities are equal.
d) The relationship cannot be determined from the information given.

Key Descriptors

parallel lines cut by two transversals, parallel lines cutting transversals proportionally, proportions and parallel lines

Review/Renew

An arithmetic sequence has first term 3 and common difference 6. Find the 16th term.

a) 99   b) 96   c) 93   d) 90

Special Angles in Circles

Introduction

You have reviewed many relationships with angles, including interior and exterior angles of polygons, the sum of the angles in a triangle, linear pairs, supplementary and complementary angles, sectors, arc length, and the angles associated with parallel lines. There are many special angle relationships that occur in circles, and some of these will be discussed in Core Concept 66.

A **central angle** of a circle is composed of two radii, so its **vertex** is on the center of the circle. A central angle and the arc it intercepts can be measured in degrees. Angle *AOB* is a central angle in circle *O* below. It intercepts two arcs-**minor arc** *AB* and **major arc** *AB*. A central angle has the same degree measure as its intercepted arc. If angle *AOB* measures 51 degrees, then minor arc *AB* measures 51 degrees. (Keep in mind that 51 degrees is not the linear length of arc *AB*--you could bend a string around the arc to measure the linear length).

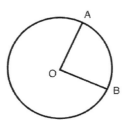

Look at angle *DEF* below. Its vertex is not on the center so it is not a central angle. Its vertex is on the actual circle, so this makes it an **inscribed angle**. An inscribed angle's measure is equal to the measure of *half* its intercepted arc. If intercepted arc *DF* measures 50 degrees, inscribed angle *DEF* measures 25 degrees. If inscribed angle *DEF* measures 20 degrees, then intercepted arc *DF* measures 40 degrees.

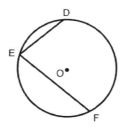

If a radius or diameter meets a tangent to a circle, the angle formed at the point of tangency is a right angle. If the center is at *A*, angles *ADB* and *ADC* below are right angles.

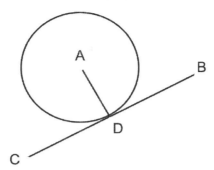

Many times, special angles in circles are "buried" or "masked" into more intricate diagrams, and you have to find them, or "isolate" them, to make computations.

Example 1

In circle *O*, obtuse central angle *DOF* has measure 164 degrees. What is the measure of inscribed angle *DEF* in the same circle?

Solution 1

Draw a diagram--it will really help--a picture is a thousand words!

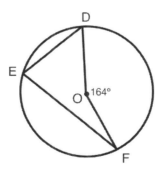

The arc intercepted by central angle *DOF* also measures 164 degrees. Notice that the inscribed angle *DEF* also intercepts the same arc *DF*. Therefore, angle *DEF* is half the measure of the intercepted arc.

$$164 \div 2 = 82.$$

Inscribed angle *DEF* measures 82 degrees.

Example 2

Angle ABC is inscribed in a circle. Vertex B is on the circle and points A and C are the endpoints of a diameter. Find the measure of ∢ABC.

Solution 2

Draw a diagram.

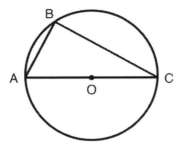

Since AC is a diameter, arc AC, which ∢B intercepts, measures 180 degrees. Since ∢B is inscribed, its measure is half of 180 degrees, so it is 90 degrees, and is a right angle. Any time an angle is inscribed in a semicircle, it is a right angle.

Example 3

Segment ST is tangent to a circle with center O at point R. If the circle has diameter 6, and RT has length 4, find the length of segment OT.

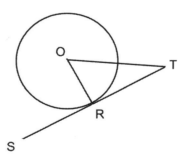

Solution 3

Since the tangent meets the radius at R, there is a right angle at R. Triangle ORT is a right triangle, so we can use the Pythagorean theorem. Since the diameter is 6, leg OR is 3. Substitute.

$$a^2 + b^2 = c^2$$

$$3^2 + 4^2 = OT^2 \text{ so, } OT = 5.$$

Fill in the Blanks

A central angle's degree measure is equal to the degree measure of its _____

_____. An inscribed angle's degree measure is equal to _____ its intercepted arc.

If an angle is inscribed in a semicircle, it is a _____ angle. Arcs and angles can be

measured in _____.

Basic Problem

Inscribed angle XYZ in circle O has vertex Y, and it intercepts an arc that measures 47 degrees. What is the measure of $\angle XYZ$?

a) 47°   b) 94°   c) 23.5°   d) 43°

Intermediate Problem

Quadrilateral $ABCD$ is inscribed in a circle. Angle DAB measures 80 degrees. What is the measure of angle DCB?

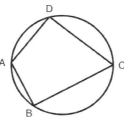

a) 80   b) 40   c) 160   d) 100

Challenging Problem

Triangle ABC in circle O has diameter AC and side lengths as labelled in the diagram below. What is the area of circle O? Leave answer in terms of π.

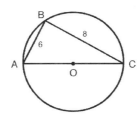

a) 25π b) 100π c) 10π d) 24π

Numeric Entry Problem

Central angle *DOF* in circle *O* measures 79 degrees. Find the degree measure of angle *DEF*.

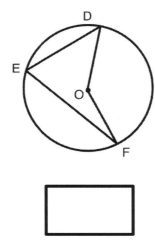

Multiple Choice with Multiple Answers Problem

In circle *O*, minor arc *AB* measures 60 degrees. Which of the following also measure 60 degrees?

[a] inscribed angle *AKB*   [b] central angle *AOB*

[c] angle *OAB* in triangle *AOB*   [d] angle *OBA* in triangle *AOB*

Key Descriptors

angle inscribed in a semicircle, central angle, inscribed angle, intercepted arcs, major arc, minor arc

Review/Renew

What is the solution set for the equation $|2x - 10| = 72$?

a) {41, -31}   b) {-41, 31}   c) {-41, -31}   d) {31, 41}

Bar Graphs, Line Graphs, Pie Charts and Pictographs

Introduction

Graphs tell a story. Most graphs do a more efficient job of telling that story than a few long paragraphs or lists would. You were formally introduced to graphs in elementary school. Perhaps, even before then, you saw graphs on television, online, and in newspapers and magazines.

Pictographs use pictures to represent quantities. They have less precision than the other types of graphs, but they make attractive graphics for newspaper and online articles. There is a **legend**, or **key**, to show what quantity each picture represents. The following pictograph shows how many Valentine's Day cards were sold by five local stores.

You can see how it is virtually impossible for this pictograph to display 23 Valentine's Day cards sold, because it would be difficult for a reader to discern the intent of a heart symbol that represented 23 cards if each symbol represented 50 cards.

Bar graphs use horizontal or vertical bars to represent quantities. They have two **axes**, which must be labeled carefully, so the graph can be read correctly. It is easy to rank the order of the quantities when you read a bar graph. The following bar graph shows sales of different color Stratosphere guitars at Smash Music Stores last year.

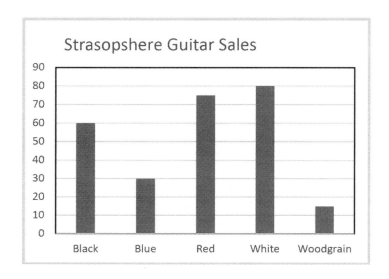

Pie Charts are also called **circle graphs**. They use sectors of a circle to show a percent breakdown. It is sometimes not as easy to rank the order using the sectors, if two of them are close in size. The circle graph below shows the percentage breakdown of how the Zimmer family used water last year. Keep in mind that the percentages must add up to 100% in any pie chart.

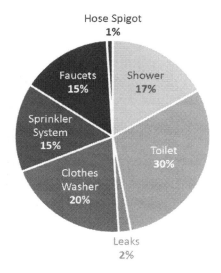

Line graphs are great for showing changes over a time period. You can see trends at a quick glance, and get very specific numerical information from them. It is also common to superimpose several line graphs on one set of axes to show even more information. The following **multiple line graph** shows monthly January-June temperatures for two selected cities last year.

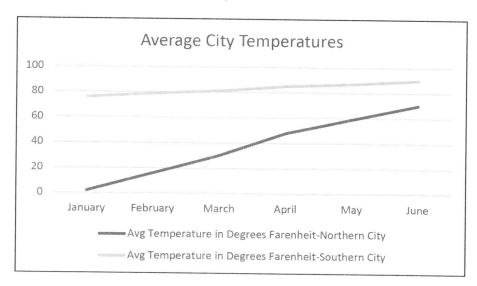

Read graph problems slowly and carefully---sometimes at first glance they could seem less complex than they are. Read the axes and legends just as carefully.

Example 1

In the pie chart above, if the Zimmer family used 7,400 cubic feet of water last year, how many cubic feet were wasted on leaks?

Solution 1

The circle graph shows 2% of water usage in the "leaks" category. Find 2% of 7,400 using the percent proportion.

$$\frac{2}{100} = \frac{x}{7,400}$$

Cross multiply and solve for x.

$$100x = 14,800$$

$$x = 148.$$

The Zimmer family wasted 148 cubic feet of water on leaks last year.

Example 2

In the pictograph above, how many Valentine's Day cards were sold by Frasier's?

Solution 2

The pictograph has 4.5 hearts next to Frasier's. Each heart represents 50 cards. Multiply 4.5 by 50.

$$4.5 \cdot 50 = 225.$$

Frasier's sold 225 Valentine's Day cards.

Example 3

In the line graph above, which month showed the greatest increase in average temperature for the Northern city?

Solution 3

This is a multiple line graph, so make sure you focus on the Northern city's data. Look at the graph for the steepest line segment. It occurs from March to April. The month of April showed the greatest increase over the previous month.

Example 4

Based on the bar graph above, what is the total number of Stratosphere guitars sold by Smash Music Stores last year?

Solution 4

Interpret the bars using the vertical axis, for each guitar color, and add.

Color	Number of Guitars Sold
Black	60
Blue	30
Red	75
White	80
Woodgrain	15

$$60 + 30 + 75 + 80 + 15 = 260.$$

Smash sold 260 Stratosphere guitars last year.

Fill in the Blanks

Since a picture is a thousand words, graphs can be very useful to display information. A pie chart, also called a _____ _____, uses _____ of a circle to show a percent breakdown of data. If two sectors of a circle are close in size, it is harder to rank the data than if it was presented in a _____ graph, which uses parallel, horizontal or vertical _____ to display data. Displaying changes over time is best accomplished using a _____ graph, and because of their artistic qualities, _____ are often used in magazines.

Basic Problem

In the bar graph above, what is the difference between the most popular and least popular colors of guitars sold?

a) 75   b) 60   c) 65   d) 45

Intermediate Problem

In the line graph above, approximately how much larger was the temperature differential between the two cities in January than in June?

a) 55   b) 20   c) 10   d) 80

Challenging Problem

Look at the bar graph above that shows sales of different color Stratosphere guitars at Smash Music Stores last year. If a pie chart was made out of this data, representing all of the Stratosphere guitar sales there, approximately how many degrees would be in the central angle of the sector for White guitars?

a) 81   b) 111   c) 41   d) 301

Numeric Entry Problem

If a sector of a circle graph is supposed to represent 15%, how many degrees would be in the central angle of that sector?

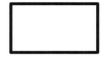

Quantitative Comparison Problem

Compare Quantity A and Quantity B, using the information below.

<u>Quantity A</u>   <u>Quantity B</u>

The number of ♦ symbols it would take to represent 550 diamonds if each ♦ represented 20 diamonds.

The number of π symbols it would take to represent 275 pizza pies sold if each π represented 10 pizzas.

Select one of the following answers.

a) Quantity A is greater.
b) Quantity B is greater.
c) The two quantities are equal.
d) The relationship cannot be determined from the information given.

Key Descriptors

axes, axis, bar graphs, circle graphs, line graphs, multiple line graph, pictographs, pie charts

Review/Renew

Using factoring, find the solution set for the quadratic equation $x^2 - 9x - 10 = 0$.

a) {-10, 1}   b) {10, -1}   c) {-10, -1}   d) {10, 1}

CORE CONCEPT 68
Graphing Lines in the Coordinate Plane

Introduction

You learned about graphing algebraic relationships in middle school and in high school algebra. Graphs are indispensable in statistics, trigonometry, geometry, analysis, and in solving problems that may have been too daunting to do algebraically. Sophisticated, widely available graphing software makes graphing a versatile problem-solving tool.

The most basic graph is the graph of a linear function. Consider the equation $3x + 2y = 12$. It has infinitely many solutions, so it would be impossible to list all of them. A point in the coordinate plane can represent a particular solution to the equation. The graph can be used to represent *all* of the solutions.

A point has two **coordinates**, forming an **ordered pair**. In the x and y plane, the x-coordinate is listed first and the y-coordinate is listed second. The intersection of the x and y axes is called the **origin**. It has coordinates $(0, 0)$. Parentheses around the points are the notations that it is an ordered pair. The point $(3, 5)$ is different than the point $(5, 3)$.

When plotting a point, the x-coordinate describes the horizontal direction and the y-coordinate describes the vertical movement. The signs of the coordinates tell you to move left or right and up or down to plot a given point. The four **quadrants**, with the signs of their coordinates, are numbered as follows.

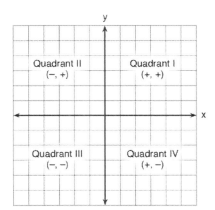

The relationship between a line, the points on the line, and the coordinates of those points allows graphs to be an integral component of algebra. If a point is on a line, then its x and y coordinates satisfy the equation of that line. If a point is *not* on a line, then its x and y coordinates will *not* satisfy the equation of that line. If a set of x and y coordinates satisfies a linear equation, then the point with those coordinates is on the graph of the equation of that line. If a set of x and y coordinates does *not* satisfy a linear equation, then the point with those coordinates is *not* on the graph of the equation of that line.

You won't be *drawing* graphs on the GRE, just reading and interpreting them. However, drawing graphs does give insight into interpreting them. The prevalence of graphing calculators, and free online graphing software give you instant access to using graphs to solve problems that may have been prohibitive when graphing with pencil and paper only.

Example 1

Fill in the following table with missing coordinates of points that are on the line $2x + 3y = 36$.

x	y
3	?
?	12
18	?
6	?
-3	?
?	6

Solution 1

If a point is on a line, then its x and y coordinates satisfy the equation of that line. Use the equation $2x + 3y = 36$ and substitute for x or y, depending on which coordinate was given, and solve for the missing coordinate.

x	y
3	10
0	12
18	0
6	8
-3	14
9	6

Example 2

Bippy's Fitness has a first-timers membership fee of $500. Annual dues are $100. Jupiter Fitness has a membership fee of $300, and annual dues of $140. After how many years will Bippy's Fitness be the better buy?

Solution 2

Let x represent the number of years and let y represent the total cost for all of those years. Create a system of two equations in two unknowns.

Bippy's: $y = 100x + 500$
Jupiter: $y = 140x + 300$

These two equations are entered into Desmos free online graphing software (www.desmos.com) and the following graph is produced.

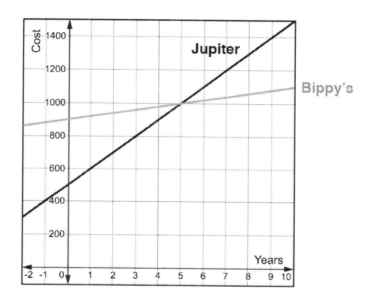

You can see the "breakeven point" at (5, 1000), which is the intersection of the two lines. The interpretation of this is that, at five years, the total cost of working out at Bippy's or Jupiter's is the same, $1,000. Look at the graph. After five years, Bippy's is the less expensive option since the costs, the y-coordinates, are below the costs for Jupiter. If you only planned to join for four years or less, Jupiter is the less expensive option.

Graphs are useful because they give tons of information at a glance.

Fill in the Blanks

A linear equation with two variables has infinitely many solutions, so you cannot put all of

the solutions in a _____. If the coordinates (2, 5) are substituted in the equation

$Ax + By = C$ and make it true, the point with those coordinates is on the _____ of the

_____ with that equation. If the coordinates do not satisfy the _____, then

the point with those coordinates is not on the _____ of the line.

Basic Problem

Which of the following points is not on the line with equation $5y - x = 1$?

a) $(19, 4)$ b) $(4, 19)$ c) $(14, 3)$ d) $(9, 2)$

Intermediate Problem

The sum of two numbers is 16. Chiara creates a linear graph to model this scenario. What quadrant will the line not pass through?

a) I   b) II   c) III   d) IV

Challenging Problem

The product of the two coordinates of point Q is 72. The x-coordinate is the additive inverse of the smallest prime number. What quadrant is the point in?

a) I   b) II   c) III   d) IV

Numeric Entry Problem

What is the x-coordinate of the point on the line whose graph is $2y = 3x - 7$ where $y = 4$?

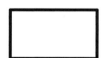

Multiple Choice with Multiple Answers Problem

Which if the following equations describe lines that go through the point $(-7, 3)$?

[a] $x + y = -4$ [b] $y = x + 10$ [c] $y = 2x + 9$ [d] $y = x - 4$

Key Descriptors

coordinate axes, coordinates of a point, graphing a line, graphing on a coordinate plane, graphing on the x and y axes

Review/Renew

Find the sum of the roots for the quadratic equation $x^2 + 4x - 21 = 0$.

a) 4   b) -4   c) 21   d) -21

DID YOU KNOW THAT?

This problem has a counterintuitive answer!

A steel band is placed around the earth snugly fit at the equator. (The equator is approximately 25,000 miles in circumference). The band is cut, and a 36-inch piec of string is spliced into the steel band. The new circular band is placed around the earth, centered off the earth surface, so its center coincides with the center of the earth. A gap is created between the earth and this circular band. How wide is this gap?

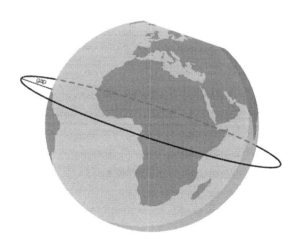

Answer: The gap is approximately 5.7 inches, regardless of the radius of the original circle!

Slope

Introduction

The **slope** of a line describes how steep, or slanted, it is. Let's look at two points, A and B, with coordinates (x_1, y_1) and (x_2, y_2), on a line.

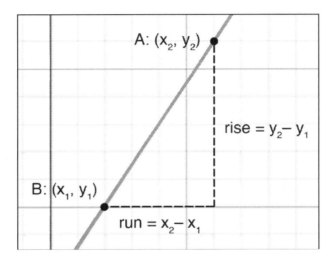

The **rise** is the vertical distance between two points, so it equals $y_2 - y_1$. The **run** is the horizontal distance between two points, so it equals $x_2 - x_1$. The rise is the change in the y-coordinates, and is abbreviated Δy. The run is the change in the x-coordinates, and is abbreviated Δx. When you read the Greek letter delta, (Δ), you can say "the change in."

Slope is often defined as $\frac{\text{rise}}{\text{run}}$. The letter '$m$' often represents slope; a popular thought is that it comes from the French word 'monter,' which means to climb.

The slope formula is

$$m = \frac{\text{rise}}{\text{run}} = \frac{\Delta y}{\Delta x} = \frac{y_2 - y_1}{x_2 - x_1}.$$

For example, the slope of the line that goes through the points $(3, 6)$ and $(5, 16)$ is 5, which can be found by substituting.

$$m = \frac{\text{rise}}{\text{run}} = \frac{\Delta y}{\Delta x} = \frac{16 - 6}{5 - 3} = \frac{10}{2} = 5.$$

Lines parallel to the *x*-axis are horizontal, and they have equations like $y = k$, where k is a constant. Lines with equations like $y = 3, y = -7,$ and $y = 113$ represent equations of horizontal lines. Lines parallel to the *x*-axis have a slope of 0. If you pick two points on the graph of $y = 7$, say $(3, 7)$ and $(11, 7)$, you can substitute into the slope formula and see why the slope is 0.

$$m = \frac{\Delta y}{\Delta x} = \frac{y_2 - y_1}{x_2 - x_1} = \frac{7 - 7}{11 - 3} = \frac{0}{8} = 0.$$

Lines parallel to the *y*-axis have an **undefined slope**. Lines with equations like $x = 7$, $x = -98,$ and $x = 82$ represent equations of vertical lines. We often say, "Vertical lines have no slope." If you pick two points on the graph of $x = 5$, say $(5, 6)$ and $(5, 19)$, you can substitute into the slope formula and see why the slope is undefined.

$$m = \frac{\Delta y}{\Delta x} = \frac{y_2 - y_1}{x_2 - x_1} = \frac{19 - 6}{5 - 5} = \frac{13}{0}.$$

Recall that fractions with a denominator of 0 are undefined. There is no real number that can be the slope of a vertical line.

You probably remember the **slope-intercept form** of the equation of a line, commonly known as

$$y = mx + b.$$

The **y-intercept** is the *y*-coordinate of the point where the line crosses the *y*-axis. Equations in this form allow you to "read" the slope and *y*-intercept at a glance. The **standard form of the equation of a line** is $Ax + By = C$, where $A, B,$ and C are constants. This form does not allow you to see the slope and *y*-intercept at a glance. You could algebraically change it to $y = mx + b$ form to find the slope and *y*-intercept.

Slopes can be any real number. Interestingly, if your variables have units like dollars, miles, hours, etc., then the slope, a ratio, is a rate with units like miles per hour, dollars per person, kilometers per liter, etc. You can always think of slope as a rate.

Example 1

Find the slope of the line that passes through the points (7, 11) and (-1, 13).

Solution 1

Use the slope formula and substitute. Either point can be considered (x_1, y_1). Just be consistent with the order of your subtractions.

$$m = \frac{\Delta y}{\Delta x} = \frac{y_2 - y_1}{x_2 - x_1} = \frac{11 - (13)}{7 - (-1)} = \frac{-2}{7 + 1} = \frac{-2}{8} = -\frac{1}{4} = -0.25.$$

The slope of the line is -0.25.

Example 2

Find the equation of the line that passes through the points (7, 11) and (-1, 13) in slope-intercept form.

Solution 2

Use the slope-intercept form of the equation, which is $y = mx + b$. We know, from Example 1 above, that the slope is -0.25. The equation now becomes

$$y = -0.25x + b.$$

We need to find the y-intercept b. Pick one of the points and substitute its coordinates for x and y. Our choice here is to pick (7, 11) to avoid using negatives.

$$11 = -0.25(7) + b$$

$$11 = -1.75 + b$$
$$b = 12.75.$$

Replace b with 12.75 in the slope-intercept form. The equation of the line is $y = -0.25 + 12.75$.

Example 3

Find the equation, in slope-intercept form, of the graph shown.

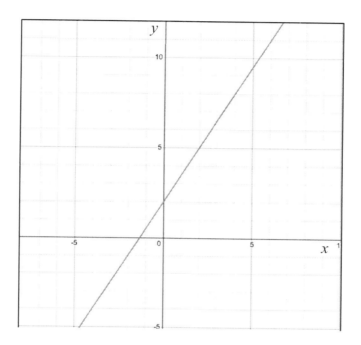

Solution 3

The y-intercept is 2 since the line crosses the y-axis at $(0, 2)$. The slope can be found by looking at two points with integer coordinates and using the slope formula, or visually counting to find $\frac{\text{rise}}{\text{run}}$. (If you don't use points with integer coordinates you can only approximate the coordinates). Two points with integer coordinates on the line are $(2, 5)$ and $(4, 8)$. First let's find the slope using the slope formula.

$$m = \frac{\Delta y}{\Delta x} = \frac{y_2 - y_1}{x_2 - x_1} = \frac{8 - 5}{4 - 2} = \frac{3}{2} = 1.5.$$

Let's find the slope visually, using the graph and $\frac{\text{rise}}{\text{run}}$.

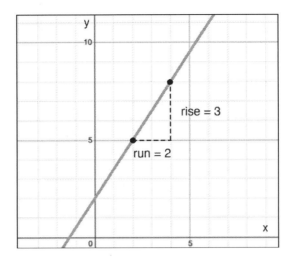

Notice that $\frac{\text{rise}}{\text{run}} = \frac{3}{2} = 1.5$ again. This confirms the slope.

The equation of the line is $y = 1.5x + 2$.

Fill in the Blanks

The _____ of a line describes how steep the line is. The slope of a line can be found

by dividing the rise by the _____. Slopes can be any real number, and lines parallel

to the ____-axis have a slope of 0. Lines _____ to the x-axis have an undefined

_____. The slope-intercept form of the equation of a line is _____.

Basic Problem

What is the slope of the line that passes through $(5, 7)$ and $(6, 11)$?

a) 4   b) 8   c) 2   d) −4

Intermediate Problem

What is the equation of the line $2x - 3y = 24$ in slope-intercept form?

a) $y = \frac{2}{3}x + 8$ b) $y = -\frac{2}{3}x - 8$ c) $y = \frac{3}{2}x - 8$ d) $y = \frac{2}{3}x - 8$

Challenging Problem

Which of the following equations describes a line with a slope of 4?

a) $y = 4x - 4$ b) $2y = 4x - 8$ c) $3y = 12x + 3$ d) $y = 4 + 11x$

Numeric Entry Problem

What is the y-intercept of the line with equation $5x + 2y = 12$?

Quantitative Comparison Problem

Compare Quantity A and Quantity B, using the information below.

Quantity A	Quantity B
The slope of the line whose equation is $y = 7 - 6x$.	**The y-intercept of the line whose equation is $y = 9x - 6$.**

Select one of the following answers.

a) Quantity A is greater.
b) Quantity B is greater.
c) The two quantities are equal.
d) The relationship cannot be determined from the information given.

Key Descriptors

rise over run, slope, slope formula, slope-intercept form of the equation of a line, standard form of the equation of a line, y-intercept

Review/Renew

Which of the following is equivalent to $\frac{17}{85}$?

a) 20%   b) 0.02   c) $\frac{2}{5}$ d) 0.20%

CORE CONCEPT 70
Slopes of Parallel and Perpendicular Lines

Introduction

The graph below has three lines drawn on it. The lines look parallel, and they are. Here are their equations:

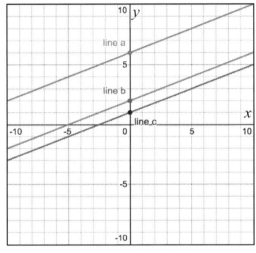

Line a has equation $y = \frac{2}{5}x + 6$.

Line b has equation $y = \frac{2}{5}x + 2$.

Line c has equation $y = \frac{2}{5}x + 1$.

Notice that the lines all have the same slope. If two lines are parallel, they have the same slope. If two lines have the same slope, they are parallel. Parallel lines also make congruent angles with the x-axis.

Look at Line d and Line e on the graph below. The lines look perpendicular, and they are. They form right angles where they meet.

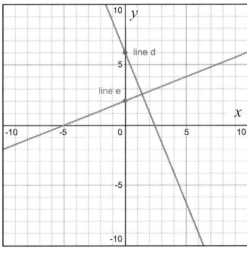

Line d has equation $y = -\frac{5}{2}x + 6$.

Line e has equation $y = \frac{2}{5}x + 2$.

Notice that the slopes are not quite reciprocals, they are **negative reciprocals**. The product of a number and its negative reciprocal is -1. If two lines are perpendicular, their slopes are negative reciprocals. If two lines have slopes that are negative reciprocals, the lines are perpendicular.

Keep in mind that there are infinitely many lines parallel or perpendicular to any given line.

Example 1

Find the slope of a line perpendicular to $7x - 3y = 11$.

Solution 1

Convert $7x - 3y = 11$ to slope-intercept form. Subtract $7x$ from both sides.

$$-3y = -7x + 11$$

Divide by -3.

$$y = \frac{7}{3}x - \frac{11}{3}$$

The slope is $\frac{7}{3}$. The slope of a line perpendicular to this line is the negative reciprocal, $-\frac{3}{7}$.

Example 2

Find, in slope-intercept form, the equation of the line parallel to $6x + 2y = 9$ that goes through $(3, 12)$.

Solution 2

Convert $6x + 2y = 9$ to slope-intercept form. Subtract $6x$ from both sides.

$$2y = -6x + 9$$

Divide by 2.

$$y = -3x + \frac{9}{2}$$

The slope is -3. The slope of a line parallel to this line is also -3. The line passes through $(3, 12)$, so substitute the slope and the point's coordinates into the slope-intercept form.

$$y = mx + b$$

$$12 = -3(3) + b$$

$$12 = -9 + b$$
$$b = 21.$$

The equation of the line parallel to $6x + 2y = 9$ that goes through $(3, 12)$ is $y = -3x + 21$.

Fill in the Blanks

If two lines are perpendicular, their slopes are _____ _____. The product of any number and its reciprocal is _____, and the product of any number and its negative reciprocal is _____. When two lines are _____, they have the same _____.

Basic Problem

Which of the following equations describes a line perpendicular to $5x = 3y + 13$?

a) $y = -\frac{3}{5}x + 2$ b) $y = \frac{3}{5}x + 1$ c) $y = -\frac{5}{3}x + 2$ d) $y = \frac{5}{3}x + 2$

Intermediate Problem

$\overleftrightarrow{AB}$ passes through the points $(1, 4)$ and $(7, 16)$. A line parallel to $\overleftrightarrow{AB}$, named $\overleftrightarrow{KL}$, passes through $(10, 1)$. What is the equation of $\overleftrightarrow{KL}$?

a) $y = \frac{1}{2}x + 1$ b) $y = 2x - 4$ c) $y = -\frac{1}{2}x - 4$ d) $y = 2x - 19$

Challenging Problem

Two lines, $\overleftrightarrow{AB}$ and $\overleftrightarrow{CD}$, are perpendicular to the line with equation $y = 5x - 17$. What is the product of the slopes of lines $\overleftrightarrow{AB}$ and $\overleftrightarrow{CD}$?

a) -1   b) 1   c) $\frac{1}{25}$ d) $-\frac{1}{25}$

Numeric Entry Problem

Find the slope of a line perpendicular to the line with equation $2y = -5x + 10$.

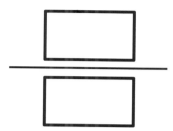

Multiple Choice with Multiple Answers Problem

Which of the following equations describe lines that are parallel to $y = 2x + 9$?

[a] $2x - y = 11$ [b] $y - 2x = 10$ [c] $y = -\frac{1}{2}x + 9$ [d] $y = \frac{1}{2}x + 9$

Key Descriptors

negative reciprocal slopes, slopes of parallel lines, slopes of perpendicular lines

Review/Renew

A triangle has side lengths that are consecutive even integers. The perimeter is 66. What is the length of the longest side?

a) 20   b) 24   c) 21   d) 33

DID YOU KNOW THAT?

A **numeric palindrome** is a number that reads the same forwards or backwards. Every positive integer is the sum of at most three numeric palindromes! For example,

$$389 = 22 + 44 + 323$$

Inequalities in the Coordinate Plane

Introduction

In Core Concept 28, you saw inequalities in one variable graphed on the number line. The graph was necessary because inequalities can have infinitely many solutions, and, as a result, the solutions cannot be listed.

Inequalities in two variables can also have infinitely many solutions, so graphs are well-suited to display the solutions in the **Cartesian**, or coordinate plane. Consider the inequality

$$y < 2x - 3.$$

The points with ordered pairs that satisfy this inequality can be shown on a graph. How? First, the inequality is changed to the equation $y = 2x - 3$ and that line is graphed.

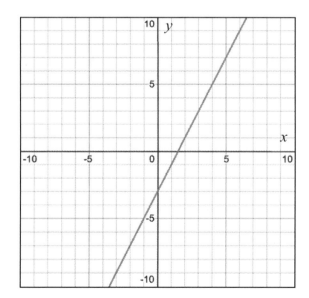

However, the line represents solutions to the equation $y = 2x - 3$. Those solutions do not satisfy the inequality, so the line is "dashed" to show that the points on the line do not solve the inequality. If the inequality used the $\leq$ or $\geq$ sign, the line would not be dashed.

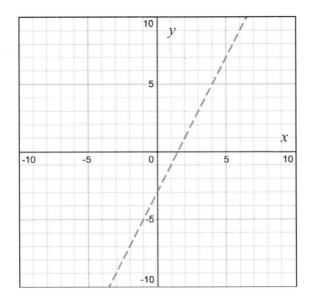

Next, a random point is chosen on one side of the dashed line, and that point's coordinates are substituted into the inequality to see if they make the inequality true.
Let's try the point (4, 3).

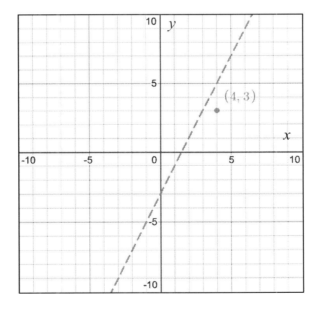

Substitute $x = 4$ and $y = 3$ into the inequality $y < 2x - 3$.

$$3 < 2(4) - 3$$

$3 < 5$, so the point $(4, 3)$ makes the inequality true.

This tells us that *all* of the points on this side of the inequality make the inequality true, so that side is shaded. That shaded area is called the **solution set**. The complete graph of $y < 2x - 3$ is shown below.

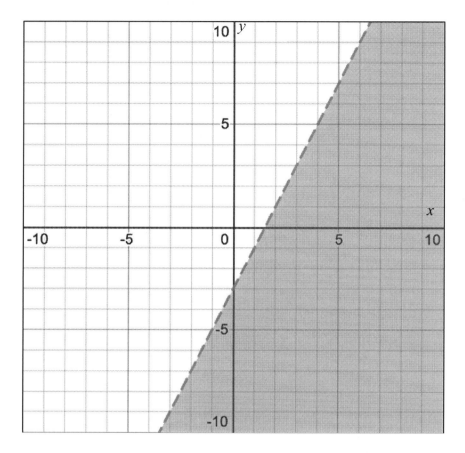

It is a good idea to test a point *not* in the solution set to make sure it *doesn't* satisfy the inequality, just to make sure you shaded correctly. Let's check the point $(1, 5)$ in the inequality

$$y < 2x - 3.$$

$$5 < 2(1) - 3$$

Since $5 < -1$ is false, the point $(1, 5)$ is not in the solution set.

A system of two inequalities in two unknowns can be solved by graphing both inequalities on the same set of axes. Often, the solution set to the system is labelled 'S.' You will not be graphing on your GRE, but you will need to interpret graphs that are given to you.

Example 1

Use the graph to determine if the point (5, 2) is a solution to the system of inequalities graphed below.

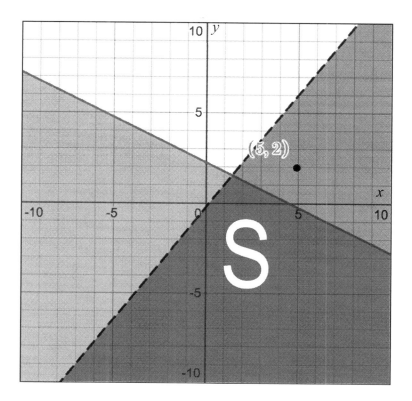

Solution 1

The point (5, 2) is plotted, and it is not in the solution set for the system. It does not satisfy *both* inequalities. Notice that it does satisfy *one* of the inequalities.

Fill in the Blanks

If you wanted to graph the solution to an inequality in two variables, you should change the

inequality to an _____ and graph the line. If the inequality is a "strict" inequality

(< or >), the graph of the line is a _____ line. If the graph of the line is not a

"strict" inequality (≤ or ≥), the graph is not a _____ line. A point is picked to

see which side of the line needs to be _____.

Basic Problem

The graph of the solution set of an inequality is shown below.

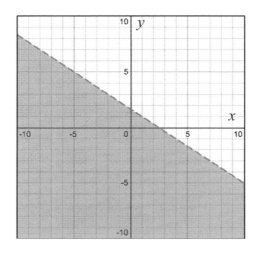

Which of the following points is a solution to the inequality?

a) (0, -4)   b) (6, -1)   c) (-2, 5)   d) (3, 1)

Intermediate Problem

The graph of a system of linear inequalities is shown below.

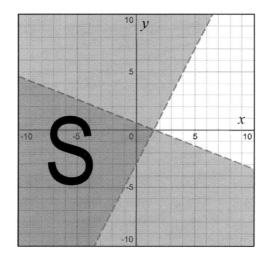

Which of the following points is in the solution set of the system?

a) (4, 1)   b) (3, -2)   c) (1, 5)   d) (-5, -3)

Challenging Problem

The graph of a system of linear inequalities is shown below.

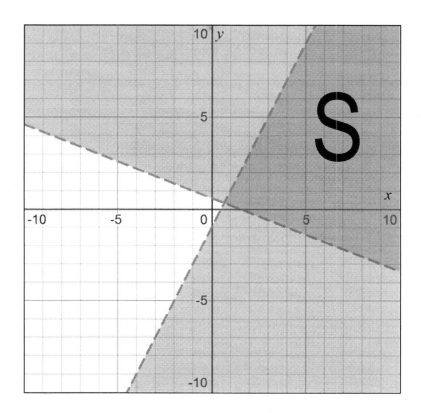

Which of the following points is not a solution to the system of inequalities shown in the graph, but is a solution to one of the inequalities?

a) (5, 0)   b) (-5, 1)   c) (1, 6)   d) (6, 1)

Numeric Entry Problem

If the point $(3, k)$ is in the solution set for the inequality $x + y \leq 7$, what is the maximum possible value of k?

Quantitative Comparison Problem

Compare Quantity A and Quantity B, using the information below.

Quantity A	Quantity B
The number of solutions to the inequality $y < x + 1$.	The number of solutions to the inequality $|x + y| < -5$.

Select one of the following answers.

a) Quantity A is greater.
b) Quantity B is greater.
c) The two quantities are equal.
d) The relationship cannot be determined from the information given.

Key Descriptors

graphing inequalities in the Cartesian plane, graphing inequalities in two dimensions, graphing systems of inequalities, solution sets for inequalities and systems of inequalities

Review/Renew

Twelve is 60% of what number?

a) 20   b) 100   c) 7.2   d) 72

DID YOU KNOW THAT?

A **zeptosecond** is a trillionth of a billionth of a second, or
0.000000000000000000001 of a second!

The Midpoint and Distance Formulas

Introduction

Let's say you are given two points in the coordinate plane, A and B. Their coordinates are

$$A: (x_1, y_1) \text{ and } B: (x_2, y_2).$$

They create a line segment denoted AB. It is common to need the length of AB and/or the midpoint of AB when doing geometrical analyses on the coordinate plane.

Let's first look at the midpoint formula. Let's find the midpoint of the segments with endpoints $(1, 3)$ and $(6, 15)$.

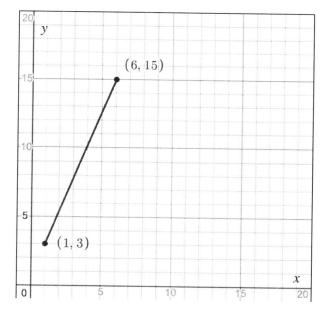

The midpoint of a segment with endpoints (x_1, y_1) and (x_2, y_2) is

$$\left(\frac{x_1 + x_2}{2}, \frac{y_1 + y_2}{2}\right).$$

Substitute.

$$\left(\frac{1 + 6}{2}, \frac{3 + 15}{2}\right) \text{ or } \left(\frac{7}{2}, \frac{18}{2}\right) \text{ or } (3.5, 9).$$

The midpoint's coordinates simplify to (3.5, 9). Look at the graph below. Notice that when this point is graphed on the segment it really looks like it is in the middle!

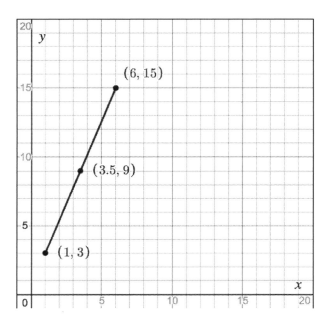

Now let's find the length of the same segment using the distance formula. The distance formula can be derived using the Pythagorean theorem, so it is no surprise that it has a square root in it. The length, d, of a segment with endpoints (x_1, y_1) and (x_2, y_2) is

$$d = \sqrt{(x_2 - x_1)^2 + (y_2 - y_1)^2}.$$

Substitute.

$$d = \sqrt{(6 - 1)^2 + (15 - 3)^2}$$

$$d = \sqrt{(5)^2 + (12)^2} = \sqrt{25 + 144} = \sqrt{169} = 13.$$

The length of segment *AB* is 13.

You can use the distance formula to verify that (3.5, 9) is indeed the midpoint. Let's call this midpoint *M*. If you find the lengths of segments *AM* and *MB* using the distance formula, they should each result in 6.5, which is half of 13. Try it!

Keep in mind that these two formulas are not given to you on the GRE so you need to memorize them.

Example 1

The midpoint M of line segment CD is $(2, 14)$. Point C has coordinates $(-3, 8)$. Find the coordinates of endpoint D.

Solution 1

Create two equations using the midpoint formula and substitute. First look at the x-coordinates.

$$\frac{x_1 + x_2}{2} = 2$$

Substitute, cross multiply, and solve for x_2.

$$\frac{-3 + x_2}{2} = 2$$

$$-3 + x_2 = 4$$

$$x_2 = 7.$$

Next, use the midpoint formula to find the y-coordinate of D.

$$\frac{y_1 + y_2}{2} = 14$$

Substitute, cross multiply, and solve for y_2.

$$\frac{8 + y_2}{2} = 14$$

$$8 + y_2 = 28$$

$$y_2 = 20.$$

The coordinates of endpoint D are $(7, 20)$.

Example 2

Find the perimeter, to the nearest hundredth, of right triangle ABC, which has these three vertices:

$$A: (1, 2) \qquad B: (6, 2) \qquad C: (6, 17)$$

Solution 2

A quick sketch can really help.

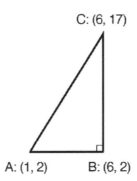

We need the length of the two legs and the hypotenuse. Leg AB is horizontal since A and B have the same y-coordinate. We can find its length by subtracting the x-coordinates.

$$6 - 1 = 5.$$

Leg BC is vertical since B and C have the same x-coordinate. We can find its length by subtracting the y-coordinates.

$$17 - 2 = 15.$$

Use the distance formula to find the length of the hypotenuse AC.

$$d = \sqrt{(x_2 - x_1)^2 + (y_2 - y_1)^2}$$

$$d = \sqrt{(6 - 1)^2 + (17 - 2)^2}$$

$$d = \sqrt{(5)^2 + (15)^2}$$

$$d = \sqrt{25 + 225} = \sqrt{250} \approx 15.811.$$

This is equal to 15.81 when rounded to the nearest hundredth.

Add the three side lengths to find the perimeter.

$$5 + 15 + 15.81 = 35.81.$$

The perimeter, to the nearest hundredth, of right triangle ABC, is 35.81.

Fill in the Blanks

The distance and midpoint formulas are _____ given on the GRE so they have to be memorized. The midpoint between two points (a, k) and (f, h) is _____. The distance between these two points is _____. If M is the midpoint of the segment PQ, the segment PM is _____ to segment MQ.

Basic Problem

What is the length of line segment KL if K has coordinates $(3, 7)$ and L has coordinates $(5, -9)$? Round to the nearest tenth.

a) 2.8   b) 17.9   c) 8.1   d) 16.1

Intermediate Problem

Point X has coordinates $(-2, 10)$ and point Y has coordinates $(10, 26)$. Find the distance between the midpoint of segment XY and point Y.

a) 16   b) 20   c) 10   d) 5

Challenging Problem

The midpoint of segment AB is $(8, 29)$. Point A has coordinates $(9, 42)$. What are the coordinates of point B?

a) (4.5, 21)   b) (7, 16)   c) (8.5, 35.5)   d) (4, 14.5)

Numeric Entry Problem

Find the distance between the points $(13, 7)$ and $(15, 21)$. Round to the nearest tenth.

Multiple Choice with Multiple Answers Problem

Which of the following points are located 5 units from $(1, 7)$?

[a] $(7, 6)$ [b] $(4, 11)$ [c] $(-2, 3)$ [d] $(6, 7)$

Key Descriptors

distance formula, midpoint formula, midpoint of a line segment in coordinate geometry

Review/Renew

Find the 5th term of a geometric sequence whose 7th term is 12,288 and whose 8th term is 49,152.

a) 768   b) 48   c) 3,072   d) 192

DID YOU KNOW THAT?

In the classic movie "The Wizard of Oz," when the scarecrow finally gets his "brains," he points to his head and famously mutters this incorrect version of the Pythagorean theorem:

"The sum of the square roots of any two sides of an isosceles triangle is equal to the square root of the remaining side."

Equations of Circles

Introduction

You have already reviewed many facts about circles, including area, circumference, arc length, areas of sectors, central and inscribed angles, and more. We will now look at circles graphed in the coordinate plane.

If you are given a circle that has center (h, k) and radius r, the **standard form of the equation of a circle** is

$$(x - h)^2 + (y - k)^2 = r^2.$$

So, the circle with center (-2, 6) and radius 7 has equation

$$(x + 2)^2 + (y - 6)^2 = 49.$$

Consequently, a circle with radius r that is centered on the origin has equation

$$x^2 + y^2 = r^2.$$

Remember how much information you could "read" from the slope-intercept form of the equation of a line $y = mx + b$? Similarly, you can "read" lots of information from the equation of a circle. For example, the circle with equation $(x - 9)^2 + (y + 4)^2 = 100$ has center (9, -4) and radius 10. Knowing the radius allows you to find the diameter, circumference, area, and much more information.

If we square the binomials in $(x - 9)^2 + (y + 4)^2 = 100$ we can create an alternate form for the equation of a circle.

$$(x - 9)^2 + (y + 4)^2 = 100$$

$$x^2 - 18x + 81 + y^2 + 8y + 16 = 100$$

Commute and combine like terms.

$$x^2 + y^2 - 18x + 8y + 97 = 100$$

Subtract 100 from both sides to set equal to 0.

$$x^2 + y^2 - 18x + 8y - 3 = 0.$$

The **general form for the equation of a circle** is

$$Ax^2 + By^2 + Cx + Dy + E = 0.$$

Examples 1, 2, and 3 will help you manipulate information about circles in the coordinate plane.

Example 1

The endpoints of the diameter of a circle are $(3, 8)$ and $(9, 16)$. Find the equation of the circle in standard form.

Solution 1

The midpoint of the diameter is the center of the circle. Substitute into the midpoint formula.

$$\left(\frac{x_1 + x_2}{2}, \frac{y_1 + y_2}{2}\right) = \left(\frac{3 + 9}{2}, \frac{8 + 16}{2}\right) = \left(\frac{12}{2}, \frac{24}{2}\right) = (6, 12).$$

The radius is the distance from the midpoint to one of the endpoints. Let's use the midpoint $(6, 12)$ and the endpoint $(3, 8)$. Substitute into the distance formula.

$$d = \sqrt{(x_2 - x_1)^2 + (y_2 - y_1)^2}$$

$$d = \sqrt{(6 - 3)^2 + (12 - 8)^2}$$

$$d = \sqrt{(3)^2 + (4)^2}$$

$$d = \sqrt{9 + 16} = \sqrt{25} = 5.$$

The radius is 5. Now that we have the center and the radius, we can write the equation of the circle in standard form.

$$(x - 6)^2 + (y - 12)^2 = 25.$$

Example 2

Find the center and the radius of the circle whose equation in general form is

$$x^2 + y^2 + 6x - 8y = 39.$$

Solution 2

It would be a good idea to review Core Concept 36, Example 3 before reading over this solution. You need to remember how to complete the square.

$$x^2 + y^2 + 6x - 8y = 39$$

Commute terms, and leave blank spaces to add in the constants.

$$x^2 + 6x + \underline{\hspace{1.5cm}} + y^2 - 8y + \underline{\hspace{1.5cm}} = 39$$

Use parentheses to group into two trinomials.

$$(x^2 + 6x + \underline{\hspace{1.5cm}}) + (y^2 - 8y + \underline{\hspace{1.5cm}}) = 39$$

In each trinomial, take half of the middle term, square it, and add it to both sides.

$$(x^2 + 6x + 9) + (y^2 - 8y + 16) = 39 + 9 + 16$$

Factor each trinomial. Combine like terms on the right side.

$$(x + 3)^2 + (y - 4)^2 = 64.$$

This is the equation of the circle in standard form. The center is (-3, 4) and the radius is 8.

Example 3

Find the standard form of the equation of the circle shown in the graph on the right.

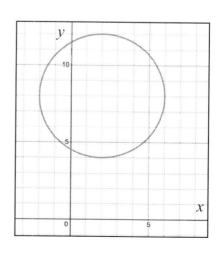

Solution 3

The center is $(2, 8)$. Count from this point to the point on the circle $(6, 8)$ to see that the radius is 4.

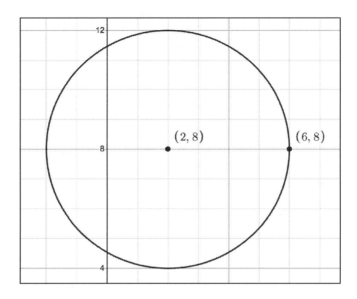

Substitute into the equation for a circle. The equation is

$$(x - 2)^2 + (y - 8)^2 = 16.$$

Fill in the Blanks

The standard form of the equation of a circle with center (d, k) and radius p is

_____. The standard form can be changed to the

_____ form by expanding the squared binomials, combining like terms, and

setting the equation equal to _____. If you wanted to change the general form to the

standard form, you would have to _____ _____ _____.

Basic Problem

What is the equation of a circle with center (-5, 1) and radius 10?

a) $(x + 5)^2 + (y - 1)^2 = 100$

b) $(x + 5)^2 + (y - 1)^2 = 25$

c) $(x - 5)^2 + (y - 1)^2 = 400$

d) $(x - 5)^2 + (y + 1)^2 = 100$

Intermediate Problem

The center of a circle is (-3, 11). If the circle has circumference 12π, what is the equation of the circle?

a) $(x + 3)^2 + (y - 11)^2 = 36$

b) $(x + 3)^2 + (y - 11)^2 = 12$

c) $(x - 3)^2 + (y - 11)^2 = 144$

d) $(x + 3)^2 + (y - 11)^2 = 144$

Challenging Problem

The point (12, 20) is on the circle with center (4, 5). Find the area of this circle in terms of π.

a) 8.5π b) 34π c) 289π d) 17π

Numeric Entry Problem

What is the diameter of a circle whose equation is $(x - 7)^2 + (y + 18)^2 = 40$? Round to the nearest tenth.

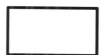

Quantitative Comparison Problem

Compare Quantity A and Quantity B, using the information below.

Quantity A	Quantity B
The number of points 5 units from (3, 14).	**The number of solutions to the inequality $\|x + y - 17\| < -99$.**

Select one of the following answers.

a) Quantity A is greater.
b) Quantity B is greater.
c) The two quantities are equal.
d) The relationship cannot be determined from the information given.

Key Descriptors

circles in coordinate geometry, equations of circles, general form of the equation of a circle, graphing circles from their equations, standard form of the equation of a circle

Review/Renew

What is the greatest integer between -18.4 and -6.5?

a) -18   b) -17   c) -6   d) -7

DID YOU KNOW THAT?

If a checkerboard-tiled floor is reflected in a chrome cylindrical mirror, we expect the reflection to be distorted because of the cylinder.

Surprisingly, there is a mathematical transformation called an **inversion in a circle**, in which a distorted picture in the plane creates a perfectly normal reflection in the cylinder! The prerequisite to understanding this transformation is regular high-school geometry. You can do an Internet search on inversions in a circle to learn more.

CORE CONCEPT 74
Graphing a Parabola

Introduction

In Core Concepts 35-37 you worked with quadratic expressions and equations. You might remember graphing quadratic equations as **parabolas**. Although a parabola looks "U-shaped," it has very specific qualities that make it a very unique U-shape that is relied on in hundreds of real-world applications.

Two parabolas are graphed below. The one on the left is **concave up** and the one on the right is **concave down**. The dashed line that divides each parabola symmetrically is called the **axis of symmetry**. The **vertex**, or **turning point**, of the parabola on the left is its minimum point, and the vertex of the parabola on the right is its maximum point. The y-intercept is the y-coordinate of the point where the parabola crosses the y-axis. The **roots** are the x-intercepts. Notice that the parabola on the left does not have any x-intercepts.

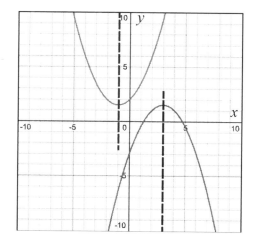

Let's first take a look at the **standard form of the equation of a parabola**,

$$y = ax^2 + bx + c.$$

Just like equations of lines and circles did, the standard form of the equation of a parabola allows you to "read" and compute lots of information about the parabola.

- If $a > 0$, the parabola faces concave up. If $a < 0$, the parabola faces concave down.
- The y-intercept of the parabola is c.

- The roots (*x*-intercepts) of the parabola can be found by setting the equation equal to 0 and solving, as you did in Core Concept 36.
- The axis of symmetry is the equation of the line that splits the parabola symmetrically. The equation of the axis of symmetry for the equation above is

$$x = -\frac{b}{2a}.$$

- The vertex, or turning point, is the intersection point of the axis of symmetry and the parabola. The *x*-coordinate of the vertex is $-\frac{b}{2a}$. The *y*-coordinate of the vertex can be found by substituting $-\frac{b}{2a}$ in for *x* in the equation.

Now let's look at the **vertex form of the equation of a parabola**,

$$y = a(x - h)^2 + k.$$

Vertex form got its name because the vertex of the parabola is (*h*, *k*) and this can be "read" right off of the equation. If *a* > 0, the parabola faces concave up. If *a* < 0, the parabola faces concave down. You can convert vertex form to standard form by squaring the binomial, distributing *a*, and combining like terms.

Example 1

Find the standard form of the parabola whose equation in vertex form is
$y = 3(x - 2)^2 - 5$.

Solution 1

Square the binomial first, distribute 3, and combine like terms.

$$y = 3(x - 2)^2 - 5$$

$$y = 3(x^2 - 4x + 4) - 5$$

$$y = 3x^2 - 12x + 12 - 5$$

The equation in standard form is $y = 3x^2 - 12x + 7$.

Example 2

What is the vertex form of the equation of the parabola whose equation is
$y + 2 = x^2 - 12x + 5$?

Solution 2

Subtract 5 from both sides.

$$y - 3 = x^2 - 12x$$

Complete the square on the right side. Take half of -12, which is -6, and square it, to get 36. Then add 36 to both sides.

$$y + 33 = x^2 - 12x + 36$$

Factor the right side.

$$y + 33 = (x - 6)^2$$

Subtract 33 from both sides.

$$y = (x - 6)^2 - 33.$$

The vertex form is $y = (x - 6)^2 - 33$ so the vertex of the parabola is (6, -33).

Example 3

A parabola has roots 2 and 5. What is the equation of its axis of symmetry?

Solution 3

There are many different parabolas with roots 2 and 5. Three possibilities are shown in the graph below, but note that they all have the same axis of symmetry.

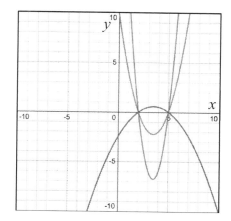

There are two ways to find the axis of symmetry. For any parabola, the axis of symmetry occurs midway between the roots. You can find the middle by finding the average of 2 and 5, which is 3.5. The axis of symmetry is $x = 3.5$.

Here's a second method. You could write the parabola as $y = k(x - 2)(x - 5)$ since the roots are 2 and 5, and then express it in standard form. Multiply the binomials.

$$y = k(x^2 - 7x + 10)$$

Distribute k.

$$y = kx^2 - 7kx + 10k$$

The equation of the axis of symmetry is $x = -\frac{b}{2a}$. Substitute.

$$x = -\frac{b}{2a} = \frac{-(-7k)}{2k} = \frac{7}{2} = 3.5.$$

The axis of symmetry is $x = 3.5$.

Fill in the Blanks

The equation of the axis of symmetry for the parabola $y = kx^2 + nx + h$ is _____. The y-intercept for this parabola is _____. Once you know the x-coordinate of the

_____ _____, you can write the equation of the axis of symmetry, since the turning point is on the _____ _____ _____. If k is a prime number, the parabola $y = kx^2 + nx + h$ faces concave _____, since prime numbers are always _____ numbers.

Basic Problem

What is the turning point of a parabola whose equation is $y = (x - 3)^2 - 2$?

a) (-3, 34)   b) (3, 2)   c) (-3, -2)   d) (3, -2)

Intermediate Problem

A parabola has axis of symmetry $x = -4$, and y-intercept 15. Which of the following could be its equation?

a) $y = x^2 + 8x + 30$ b) $y = x^2 - 4x + 15$

c) $y = x^2 - 8x + 15$ d) $y = x^2 + 8x + 15$

Challenging Problem

A parabola has equation $y = x^2 + kx + j$. The y-axis is its axis of symmetry. Its turning point is $(p, 19)$. What is the sum of k, j, and p?

a) 38   b) 19   c) 0   d) 57

Numeric Entry Problem

What is the y-intercept for the parabola whose equation is $2y = x^2 - 8x + 22$?

Key Descriptors

axis of symmetry, graphing parabolas, turning point of a parabola, vertex of a parabola, x-intercepts of a parabola, y-intercept of a parabola

Multiple Choice with Multiple Answers Problem

Which of the following points are located on the axis of symmetry for the parabola whose equation is $y = x^2 - 8x + 16$?

[a] $(-4, 6)$ [b] $(4, 7)$ [c] $(-4, 3)$ [d] $(4, -17)$

Review/Renew

What is $\frac{3}{7}$ of 280?

a) 40   b) 120   c) 80   d) 140

CORE CONCEPT 75
Transformations

Introduction

When a picture or graph is moved, or altered, we say a **transformation** has been made. In your high school math classes, you encountered several types of transformations, including line reflections, translations, dilations, and point reflections. We will review two of the most important ones here.

Below on the left are the graphs of two functions, $f(x)$ and $-f(x)$. Below on the right are the graphs of two functions, $g(x)$ and $-g(x)$.

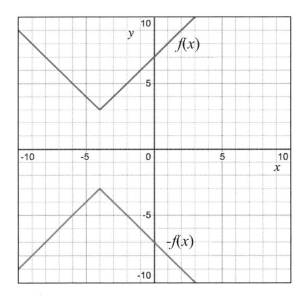

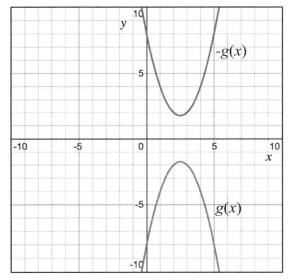

As you can see, if the entire function is negated, the graph is reflected in the x-axis.

On the next page, on the left, are the graphs of two functions, $h(x)$ and $h(-x)$. On the right are the graphs of two functions, $p(x)$ and $p(-x)$.

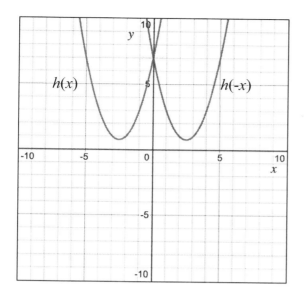 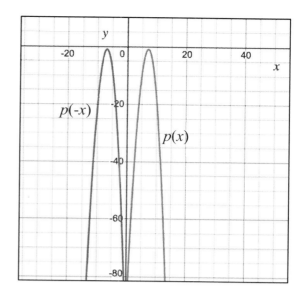

As you can see, if, in a function $f(x)$, x is replaced with $-x$, the graph is reflected in the y-axis.

What if x is replaced with $(x - k)$? How is the function transformed? Below is the graph of two functions, $f(x)$ and $f(x - 7)$. Notice how this moves the graph 7 places horizontally to the right. This is an example of a slide, or a **translation**. Think of a horizontal translation as just "sliding" the graph horizontally.

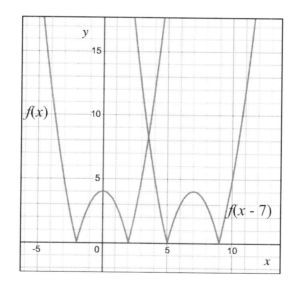

Below is the graph of two functions, $g(x)$ and $g(x + 10)$. Notice how this moves the graph 10 places horizontally to the left. This is another translation.

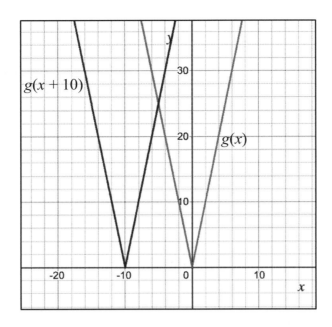

If x is replaced with $(x - k)$ in a function $f(x)$, then the graph moves horizontally to the right if $k > 0$, and to the left if $k < 0$.

Be careful! If x is replaced with $(x + 6)$, think of $(x + 6)$ as $(x - (-6))$, so $k < 0$ and the graph translates 6 units to the left!

How does the graph of $g(x) + k$ compare to the graph of $g(x)$?

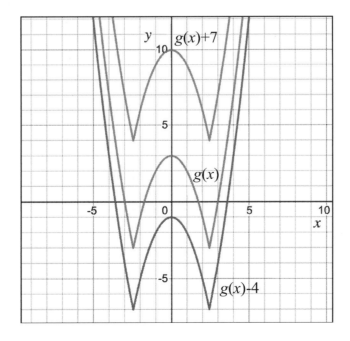

The graph of $g(x) + k$ represents a vertical shift of $g(x)$. If $k > 0$, the shift is up k units, and if $k < 0$, the graph shifts down k units.

Example 1

The following figure has the graph of $f(x)$, and three transformations of $f(x)$, labelled $g(x)$, $h(x)$, and $p(x)$.

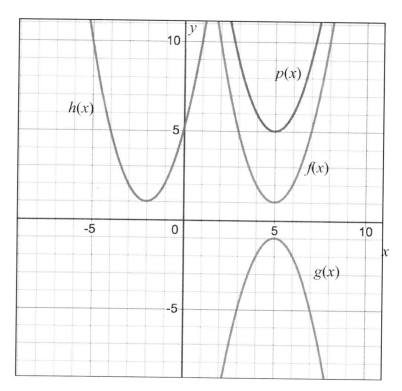

Describe each transformation.

Solution 1

Try to separate each curve as you compare it to $f(x)$.

The graph of $g(x)$ is a reflection in the x-axis. Notice the symmetry of $f(x)$ and $g(x)$ with respect to the line of reflection, the x-axis.

The graph of $h(x)$ is a translation of $f(x)$ that is 7 units to the left. The curve slides to the left. (Due to the symmetry of the parabola itself, it could also be viewed as a reflection in the vertical line $y = 1.5$).

The graph of $p(x)$ is a vertical translation of $f(x)$ that is 4 units up.

Example 2

The function $f(x)$ is graphed. The function $g(x)$ is also graphed on the same axes, where $g(x) = f(x - 3) + 5$. Describe the position of $g(x)$ compared to $f(x)$.

Solution 2

Use what you learned in the Introduction above. Notice that $(x - 3)$ replaced x, and this means that the graph shifts horizontally 3 units to the right. The '+5' indicates that the graph has shifted vertically, up 5 units. In summary, the graph of $g(x)$ is a translation of $f(x)$, 3 units to the right of, and 5 units up from, the graph of $f(x)$.

Fill in the Blanks

If, in a function $f(x)$, x is replaced with $-x$, the graph is reflected in the ____-axis. If x is

replaced with $(x + 9)$, the graph translates 9 units to the _____. If x is replaced with

$(x - 11)$, the graph translates 11 units to the _____. If $g(x) = f(x - 14) + 3$, the

graph of $g(x)$ is a _____ of the graph of $f(x)$.

Basic Problem

The function $f(x)$ is graphed. The function $g(x)$ is a translation of $f(x)$ on the same axes, 9 units to the right of, and 11 units higher than, the graph of $f(x)$. Which of the following is the function $g(x)$?

a) $g(x) = f(x - 9) + 11$ b) $g(x) = f(x + 9) - 11$

c) $g(x) = f(x - 11) + 9$ d) $g(x) = f(x + 11) - 9$

Intermediate Problem

The function $f(x)$ is graphed. The function $g(x)$ is graphed on the same axes, where $g(x) = f(x + 7) - 8$. Describe the position of $g(x)$ compared to $f(x)$.

a) $g(x)$ is 7 units to the right of, and 8 units down from, the graph of $f(x)$.

b) $g(x)$ is 7 units to the left of, and 8 units down from, the graph of $f(x)$.

c) $g(x)$ is 7 units to the right of, and 8 units up from, the graph of $f(x)$.

d) $g(x)$ is 7 units to the left of, and 8 units up from, the graph of $f(x)$.

Challenging Problem

The following figure has the graph of $f(x)$, and two transformations of $f(x)$, labelled $g(x)$ and $h(x)$.

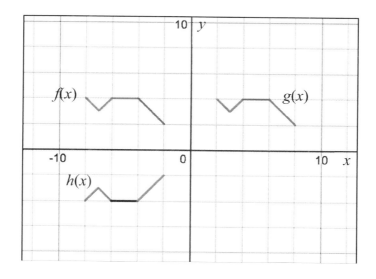

Which of the following statements correctly describes the transformations?

a) $g(x)$ is a translation of $f(x)$, and $h(x)$ is a reflection of $f(x)$

b) $g(x)$ is a translation of $f(x)$, and $h(x)$ is also a translation of $f(x)$

c) $g(x)$ is a reflection of $f(x)$, and $h(x)$ is a translation of $f(x)$

d) $g(x)$ is a reflection of $f(x)$, and $h(x)$ is also a reflection of $f(x)$

Numeric Entry Problem

The function $p(x)$ is graphed. The function $r(x)$ is graphed on the same axes, where $r(x) = p(x + 7) + 19$. Which number represents the amount of the vertical translation?

Key Descriptors

function transformation, line reflection, translation

Quantitative Comparison Problem

Compare Quantity A and Quantity B, using the information below.

<table>
<tr><td style="text-align:center">Quantity A</td><td style="text-align:center">Quantity B</td></tr>
<tr><td>The value of k if the graph of $f(x - k)$ is 7 units to the left of the graph of $f(x)$.</td><td>The value of h if the graph of $f(x) + h$ is 7 units higher than the graph of $f(x)$.</td></tr>
</table>

Select one of the following answers.

a) Quantity A is greater.
b) Quantity B is greater.
c) The two quantities are equal.
d) The relationship cannot be determined from the information given.

Review/Renew

The circumference of a circle, in terms of π, is 27π. What is the radius of the circle?

a) 27   b) 13.5   c) 54   d) $\sqrt{27}$

DID YOU KNOW THAT?

The shape of a TV satellite antenna is a **paraboloid**, which is a parabola spun on its axis of symmetry to create the three-dimensional "dish."

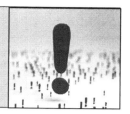

CORE CONCEPT 76
Permutations

Introduction

Let's say you had 6 books you wanted to place on a shelf. In how many different ways could they be placed? Clearly, the order is what makes each arrangement different. A **permutation** is an arrangement in which order matters.

The best way to look at this is to set up "slots" to depict the placement of each book. Since there are 6 books, we can set up 6 positions.

_____ _____ _____ _____ _____ _____

If one step of an experiment can result in m ways, and for each of those ways, a second step can occur in n ways, the two-step experiment has mn outcomes. This is the **multiplication principle of probability**, and it extends to more than two steps. So, we can place a multiplication symbol between each of the 6 slots.

_____ · _____ · _____ · _____ · _____ · _____

The first position on the shelf can be filled with any of the 6 books, so it can be filled in 6 different ways. We enter '6' in the first slot.

$$6 \cdot \underline{\quad} \cdot \underline{\quad} \cdot \underline{\quad} \cdot \underline{\quad} \cdot \underline{\quad}$$

For each way the first slot is filled, the second slot can be filled in 5 different ways, since one book was already placed on the shelf, and there are only 5 books remaining to be placed. We enter '5' in the second slot.

$$6 \cdot 5 \cdot \underline{\quad} \cdot \underline{\quad} \cdot \underline{\quad} \cdot \underline{\quad}$$

For each way the first and second slots are filled, the third slot can be filled in 4 different ways, since two books were already placed on the shelf. We enter '4' in the third slot.

$$6 \cdot 5 \cdot 4 \cdot \underline{\quad} \cdot \underline{\quad} \cdot \underline{\quad}$$

This line of logic continues for the remaining slots. Numbers are filled in and then multiplied all the way down to 1.

$$6 \cdot 5 \cdot 4 \cdot 3 \cdot 2 \cdot 1.$$

This operation is so common in mathematics that it was given a special symbol, the exclamation point (!). It is read as **factorial**.

$$6 \cdot 5 \cdot 4 \cdot 3 \cdot 2 \cdot 1 = 6!$$

You can multiply by hand or calculator, and many calculators have factorial keys or menu items. (The GRE online calculator does not have a factorial key).

$$6 \cdot 5 \cdot 4 \cdot 3 \cdot 2 \cdot 1 = 6! = 720.$$

The 6 books can be arranged in six factorial, or 720 different ways (720 different permutations). The slots will help you organize the way you count permutations.

Example 1

Let's say you had 16 books, and wanted to place just 4 on a shelf. In how many different ways could they be placed?

Solution 1

Set up four slots. The first position on the shelf can be filled with any of the 16 books, so it can be filled in 16 different ways. We enter '16' in the first slot. The second position can be filled with 15 books since one was already placed on the shelf. The same line of logic allows you to enter 14 and 13 in the remaining two slots.

$$16 \cdot 15 \cdot 14 \cdot 13$$

Notice that this does not multiply all the way down to 1, so it is not 16! You can just multiply to get the answer.

$$16 \cdot 15 \cdot 14 \cdot 13 = 43,680$$

That may seem like a surprisingly large number of different arrangements!

This operation can be considered a permutation of 4 objects taken from 16 objects, and it has a mathematical notation, 16P4. In general, the number of permutations of r objects taken from n objects has a mathematical notation, **nPr**. Look for this on your calculator.

Example 2

If you had 16 car models, and wanted to place 4 on a display shelf, in how many different ways could they be placed?

Solution 2

We need the number of arrangements, or permutations, of 4 items selected from 16 items. We could create slots as we did in Example 1 above. We can also use the permutations formula. The number of permutations of r objects taken from n objects is written as nPr, and the formula for computing this number is

$$nPr = \frac{n!}{(n-r)!}.$$

Let's substitute $n = 16$ and $r = 4$.

$$16P4 = \frac{16!}{(16-4)!} = \frac{16!}{12!}$$

We can simplify this fraction. We write the numerator's factors out until we hit 12!, so we can cancel the common factor 12!.

$$\frac{16!}{12!} = \frac{16 \cdot 15 \cdot 14 \cdot 13 \cdot 12!}{12!} = 16 \cdot 15 \cdot 14 \cdot 13 = 43{,}680.$$

Notice how the numbers in this problem, after the fraction is simplified, are the same as those found by using the slots in Example 1, and using the formula gave us the same answer.

Example 3

Noah has 8 different colors of socks, and 3 different colors of sneakers. How many different color arrangements of socks and sneakers can Noah create?

Solution 3

We won't use the *nPr* formula for this, because the scenario is different--we are selecting from two different sets of items, socks and sneakers. Set up two slots.

$$\underline{\hspace{2cm}} \cdot \underline{\hspace{2cm}}$$

The first slot can be filled with any of the sock colors, so it can be filled in 8 different ways. We enter '8' in the first slot. The second position can be filled with any of the 3 sneaker colors, so we place a '3' in the second slot.

$$8 \cdot 3$$

Noah can create 24 different sneaker/sock groups.

Fill in the Blanks

An arrangement in which order matters is called a _____. The

_____ principle is helpful when computing the number of different

arrangements. The importance of repeated multiplications in descending order, like

$5 \cdot 4 \cdot 3 \cdot 2 \cdot 1$, all the way down to 1, can be shortened by using _____notation,

which is an exclamation point after the original number.

Basic Problem

A class has 27 students in it. How many different slates of a President, Vice-President, Secretary and Treasurer can be created? (A student can hold only one office).

a) 24   b) 421,200   c) 105,300   d) 531,441

Intermediate Problem

Ken and Kerry's Ice Cream Parlor sells 22 flavors of ice cream, and offers 12 different toppings. Their sundaes come in 2 sizes. A sundae has one flavor and one topping. How many different sundaes can be created at Ken and Kerry's?

a) 528   b) 4!   c) 3!   d) 5,808

Challenging Problem

The chess club has 15 members. How many different groups of two chess players can be created from the 15 members?

a) 14   b) 30   c) 210   d) 105

Numeric Entry Problem

The Park Bake Shop has five different shapes of cookie cutters, two different kinds of sprinkles, and three different types of frosting. How many different kinds of cookies can they create if each cookie has one flavor of frosting and one type of sprinkles?

Multiple Choice with Multiple Answers Problem

Which of the following numbers of permutations are multiples of 10?

[a] 9P4   [b] 6P3   [c] 5P3   [d] 9P3

Key Descriptors

counting techniques, factorial, multiplication principle of probability, permutations

Review/Renew

If y is inversely proportional to x and $y = 2$ when $x = 36$, find x when $y = 12$.

a) 18   b) 24   c) 6   d) 72

CORE CONCEPT 77
Combinations

Introduction

In Core Concept 76, you learned about permutations. A permutation is an arrangement in which order matters. Sometimes order does not matter. If a teacher wants to select 5 students from a class of 32 to help with a food drive, the 32 names can be put on slips of paper in a hat, and 5 can be grabbed at once with one hand. There is no order or ranking of the 5 people; just a smaller group picked from a larger group. A group selected without regard to order is called a **combination**.

The number of combinations of r objects that can be taken from n objects is written as nCr, and the formula for computing this number is

$$nCr = \frac{n!}{r!\,(n-r)!}.$$

In Example 1 you will work with this formula. Notice its similarity to the nPr formula.

Note that if the teacher was selecting 5 students to fill out a slate of President, Vice President, Secretary, Treasurer, and Logistics Coordinator, that the number of slates possible from the 32 students is nPr, since the order of selection mattered.

Look at the photo near the above right corner of this page. You'll see a combination lock. Can you see why that is a misnomer? It should be called a permutation lock because the order in which numbers are entered matters!

Example

How many combinations of 5 students can be made from a group of 32 students?

Solution

We can use the combinations formula.

$$nCr = \frac{n!}{r!\,(n-r)!}$$

Let's substitute $n = 32$ and $r = 5$.

$$32C5 = \frac{32!}{5!\,(32-5)!} = \frac{32!}{5! \cdot 27!}$$

We can simplify this fraction. We write the numerator's factors out until we hit 27!, so we can cancel the common factor 27! from numerator and denominator.

$$\frac{32!}{5! \cdot 27!} = \frac{32 \cdot 31 \cdot 30 \cdot 29 \cdot 28 \cdot 27!}{5! \cdot 27!} = \frac{32 \cdot 31 \cdot 30 \cdot 29 \cdot 28 \cdot \cancel{27!}}{5! \cdot \cancel{27!}} = \frac{32 \cdot 31 \cdot 30 \cdot 29 \cdot 28}{5!}.$$

Now write out the 5! using its consecutive integer factors.

$$\frac{32 \cdot 31 \cdot 30 \cdot 29 \cdot 28}{5 \cdot 4 \cdot 3 \cdot 2 \cdot 1}.$$

We can divide numerator and denominator by common factors to simplify the computation. Look at the three fractions below as you read this bulleted list:

- Divide 30 and 5 by their common factor 5 to get 6 and 1--see first fraction.
- Divide 32 and 4 by their common factor 4 to get 8 and 1--see second fraction.
- Divide 6 and 3 · 2, which is 6, by their common factor 6, to get 1 and 1--see third fraction.

$$\frac{32 \cdot 31 \cdot \overset{6}{\cancel{30}} \cdot 29 \cdot 28}{\underset{1}{\cancel{5}} \cdot 4 \cdot 3 \cdot 2 \cdot 1} = \frac{\overset{8}{\cancel{32}} \cdot 31 \cdot \overset{6}{\cancel{30}} \cdot 29 \cdot 28}{\underset{1}{\cancel{5}} \cdot \underset{1}{\cancel{4}} \cdot 3 \cdot 2 \cdot 1} = \frac{\overset{8}{\cancel{32}} \cdot 31 \cdot \overset{\cancel{6}}{\cancel{30}} \cdot 29 \cdot 28}{\underset{1}{\cancel{5}} \cdot \underset{1}{\cancel{4}} \cdot \cancel{3} \cdot \underset{1}{2} \cdot 1}$$

The denominator is 1 and this will always be the case if you simplify completely. Multiply the numbers that remain in the numerator.

$$8 \cdot 31 \cdot 29 \cdot 28 = 201{,}376.$$

Incredible! If you are looking to make groups of 5 people from a class of 32 people, you can make 201,376 different groups! The number of combinations you can make if you take 5 objects from 32 objects is 201,376. Don't be surprised if you are surprised at how many different combinations you can make from a relatively small group.

Fill in the Blanks

An arrangement in which order matters is called a _____ while an arrangement in which order does not matter is called a _____. Both concepts have formulas which rely on _____, which are indicated by the exclamation point notation. The numerical difference between $12P5$ and $12C5$ is _____.

Basic Problem

The Kings Park Ice King sells 52 flavors of Italian ices. A Supreme cup consists of 4 different flavors. How many different groups of 4 flavors can be made from the 52 available flavors?

a) 13   b) 13!   c) 6,497,400   d) 270,725

Intermediate Problem

Simran is getting a Super Mega cup of ice cream from Marvel Ice Cream. They offer 31 flavors, and a Super Mega cup has scoops of 5 different flavors. Simran wants one of the scoops to be chocolate. How many different combinations of the Super Mega cup with chocolate can be created?

a) 1,699,911   b) 3,654   c) 27,405   d) $31C5$

Challenging Problem

Miguel is buying a lottery ticket. The ticket has 52 numbers on it and you need to pick 6 different numbers. If he buys one ticket, how many groups of 6 numbers will not match his?

a) $52P6$ b) $52C6$ c) $(52P6) - 1$ d) $(52C6) - 1$

Numeric Entry Problem

What is the value of r if $10Cr = 10$, and r is a positive integer less than 9?

Quantitative Comparison Problem

Compare Quantity A and Quantity B, using the information below.

<table>
<tr><td align="center"><u>Quantity A</u></td><td align="center"><u>Quantity B</u></td></tr>
<tr><td>The number of permutations you can make if you take 4 students from a group of 13 students.</td><td>The number of combinations you can make if you take 4 students from a group of 25 students.</td></tr>
</table>

Select one of the following answers.

a) Quantity A is greater.
b) Quantity B is greater.
c) The two quantities are equal.
d) The relationship cannot be determined from the information given.

Key Descriptors

combinations, combinations formula, permutations and combinations

Review/Renew

What is the perimeter of a square whose diagonal is $10\sqrt{2}$?

a) 100   b) 40   c) 20   d) $40\sqrt{2}$

DID YOU KNOW THAT?

If you assemble a room of just 23 randomly-selected people, the probability of having at least one pair with a matching birth date is over 50%. This is the famous "Birthday Problem" and you can do an Internet search to find out more about it!

CORE CONCEPT 78
Probability

Introduction

Your experience with **probability** dates back to playing board games as a child. The possible outcomes from an experiment are called **events**. Each event has a probability. The probability of an event is a fraction or decimal between 0 and 1 inclusive that describes how likely the event is to occur. Events can be named by capital letters. So, if you are flipping a coin, getting a head can be H, and the probability of getting a head can be written as $P(H)$.

Assume that all outcomes of an event are equally likely. The probability of event A occurring is

$$P(A) = \frac{\text{number of outcomes satisfying } A}{\text{total number of outcomes}}.$$

What is the probability of event A *not* occurring? The **complement** of an event A is denoted A'. Event A either occurs or it doesn't, so $P(A) + P(A') = 1$, and

$$P(A') = 1 - P(A).$$

There are two types of probability. **Theoretical probability** is based on the assumption that all outcomes have an equal chance of occurring. For example, if a coin is tossed, heads and tails are equally likely. If a die is tossed, outcomes 1, 2, 3, 4, 5, or 6 are all equally likely.

Empirical probability relies on observations from an experiment to determine the likelihood of an event. For example, let's say you tossed a thumbtack. It can land two different ways, as shown in the picture.

Does each way of landing have the same chance? It's hard to tell. The best way to assign a probability to each of these events is to toss the thumbtack many times, and use the data to assign a probability. If the tack is tossed 1,000 times and it lands on its base 441 times, we could assign the empirical probability of its landing on its base as $\frac{441}{1,000}$.

Probabilities can be expressed as decimals, fractions, or as a percent.

Example 1

There are 57 quarters, 15 pennies, 72 dimes and 33 nickels in the vending machine you loaned to a local carnival. If you open the machine and reach into the coin box and pull out one coin at random, what is the probability that it is a nickel?

Solution 1

There are $57 + 15 + 72 + 33 = 177$ coins in the box. That is the total number of outcomes from the experiment "pick one coin." That becomes the denominator. There are 33 nickels, so 33 is the numerator. We can represent the event "picks a nickel" as N.

$$P(N) = \frac{\text{number of coins satisfying } N}{\text{total number of coins}} = \frac{33}{177}.$$

The probability of randomly selecting a nickel is $\frac{33}{177}$. Note that the probability of the complement, *not* selecting a nickel, is

$$P(N') = 1 - \frac{33}{177} = \frac{144}{177}.$$

Example 2

The following Venn diagram depicts the number of seniors at North Shore High School who are on the football (F) and baseball (B) teams.

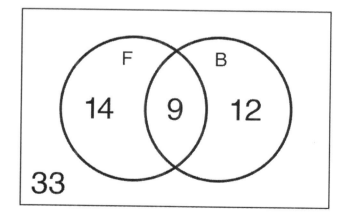

If a senior is selected at random, what is the probability they are on the football team?

Solution 2

The Venn diagram is just another way to display data, just like sets, tables and graphs. It has advantages due to its ability to use circles to display overlapping elements and distinct categories. Each circle is labelled with a title. From the Venn diagram above, at a glance, you have this data:

- There are $33 + 14 + 9 + 12 = 68$ seniors at North Shore High School.
- There are $14 + 9 = 23$ students on the football team.
- There are $9 + 12 = 21$ students on the baseball team.
- There are 9 students on both the football *and* baseball teams. This is the **intersection** of the two teams, indicated by the word 'and.'
- There are 14 football players who are not on the baseball team.
- There are 12 baseball players who are not on the football team.
- There are 33 seniors who are not on either of those two teams.
- There are $14 + 12 = 26$ students on the football or baseball team but not both.
- There are $14 + 9 + 12 = 35$ on the football *or* baseball teams. Note that if you are on both teams, you *are* on the football or baseball team. This is the **union** of the two events, indicated by the word 'or.'

Notice how the bullet list above is much more cumbersome in displaying information than the elegant, simple Venn diagram. We can use the data culled from the Venn diagram to answer the question. If a senior is selected at random, the probability they will be on the football team is

$$P(F) = \frac{23}{68}.$$

Note that the probability of the complement, *not* selecting a football team member, is

$$P(F') = 1 - \frac{23}{68} = \frac{45}{68}.$$

Probabilities can be expressed as fractions, decimals, or percents.

Fill in the Blanks

The probability of an event is a fraction, decimal or percent between the numbers _____ and _____ inclusive. The _____ of an event K is denoted _____ and it is the event that K does not occur. If $P(K)$ represents the probability of event K occurring, then $P(K')$ can be computed by subtracting _____ from 1.

Basic Problem

A single die is rolled. What is the probability of it not landing on an even prime number?

a) $\frac{1}{2}$ 　　　　 b) $\frac{1}{6}$ 　　　　 c) $\frac{2}{36}$ 　　　　 d) $\frac{5}{6}$

Intermediate Problem

The following Venn diagram describes the cars on the lot at the Nomad Chevrolet dealership.

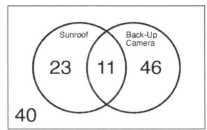

If a car was selected at random, what is the probability that it would have a sunroof?

a) $\frac{34}{80}$ 　　　　 b) $\frac{17}{60}$ 　　　　 c) $\frac{11}{30}$ 　　　　 d) $\frac{23}{120}$

Challenging Problem

The automobile license plate numbers for a certain state are two letters followed by three numbers. If a plate is randomly selected, what is the probably that it will have your initials?

a) $\frac{2}{26}$ 　　　　 b) $\frac{1}{676}$ 　　　　 c) $\frac{676}{1000}$ 　　　　 d) $\frac{1}{26}$

Numeric Entry Problem

An urn contains 3 green, 5 red, and 2 blue marbles. A red marble is picked without replacing it, and then another marble is selected. What is the probably that the second marble is blue?

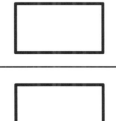

Multiple Choice with Multiple Answers Problem

A die is in the shaped of an **icosahedron**. It has 20 congruent faces, with the numbers 1 - 20 written on it, with one number on each face. What is the probability of the die landing on a prime number?

[a] $\frac{8}{20}$ 　　　　 [b] $\frac{7}{20}$ 　　　　 [c] $\frac{2}{5}$ 　　　　 [d] $\frac{9}{20}$

Key Descriptors

complement of a probability event, empirical probability, intersection of two events, probability, theoretical probability, union of two events

Review/Renew

How many kilograms are equivalent to 78,345 grams?

a) 78.345 kg 　　　　 b) 78,345,000 kg 　　　　 c) 0.078345 kg 　　　　 d) 7.8345 kg

DID YOU KNOW THAT?

There are infinitely many counting numbers. Consequently, the probability of randomly selecting a number, say 17, from all the counting numbers, is 0. However, it is *possible*, but highly *improbable*, to randomly select 17 from all the counting numbers. So, having a probability equal to 0, in this strange case, does not mean the event is impossible!

CORE CONCEPT 79
Two-Way Tables

Introduction

You have seen data presented in graph form, table form, and Venn diagram form. **Two-way tables** are an efficient way to display data for different levels of two variables, especially when the variables are non-numeric, or **categorical**. Variables like color, food, favorite sport or music, item purchases, etc., are examples of categorical variables. As with Venn diagrams, a ton of information can be presented in a form which is concise and clear. What exactly is a two-way table? Let's look. The following two-way table presents data on everyone at Jenneskio College who applied for a parking permit.

	SUV	Sedan	Pick-Up Truck	Motorcycle
Teachers	122	66	23	4
Students	545	13	77	9

The table displays a great deal of information. It is helpful to add a Totals row and Totals column if they are not already provided. Add to find the totals for each respective row or column.

	SUV	Sedan	Pick-Up Truck	Motorcycle	Totals
Teachers	122	66	23	4	215
Students	545	13	77	9	644
Totals	667	79	100	13	859

Note that the sum of the entries in the Totals row should equal the sum of the entries in the Totals column. That number is shown shaded in the bottom right cell.

Let's take a look at some of the information that this two-way table provides.

- Number of parking permits issued: 859
- Number of SUV's: 667
- Number of students who drive sedans: 13
- Number of students with parking passes: 644
- Number of teachers who have a motorcycle parking permit: 4
- The percent of students who drive a sedan: $\frac{13}{644} \approx 2\%$
- The percent of people at this college who drive a sedan: $\frac{79}{859} \approx 9\%$
- The percent of teachers who drive an SUV: $\frac{122}{215} \approx 57\%$

This is just the tip of the iceberg! A complete bulleted list could have dozens more facts found in the table. Notice how the statements have to be read very carefully so you can find the correct numbers you need to solve a given problem. The examples below will give you more practice on this.

Example 1

The Pennsy Creamery does a tremendous summer business. In fact, they have three lines leading to the counter: Cones, Shakes, and Cups. This makes their food preparation much more efficient.

They offer just one topping with each item. They are doing market research to plan future inventory. They collect this data on a summer week's sales:

	Sprinkles	Hot Fudge	Caramel	Cookies	Chocolate Chips	Nuts	Totals
Cones	112	4	1	88	121	33	359
Shakes	4	6	0	144	57	21	232
Cups	221	178	54	87	201	55	796
Totals	337	188	55	319	379	109	1,387

Based on this data, what is the probability that a randomly-selected person who is on the cup line will want sprinkles?

Solution 1

We know the person is on the cup line. Pennsy has data on 796 people who ordered cups, and 221 of them ordered sprinkles. Based on the data, the probability that a randomly-selected person on the cup line will want sprinkles is $\frac{221}{796}$.

Example 2

Based on the two-way table in Example 1, what percent of people who go to the Pennsy Creamery ordered a cone?

Solution 2

The data is based on 1,387 sales. The total in the Cone row is 359. Therefore, the percent of people who ordered cones is $\frac{359}{1,387} \approx 26\%$.

Example 3

A person represented by the data in the two-way table from Example 1 will be randomly selected. Given that they ordered hot fudge, what is the probability they ordered a shake?

Solution 3

Pennsy has data on 188 people who ordered hot fudge, and 6 of them ordered shakes. Based on the data, the probability that a randomly-selected person who ordered hot fudge ordered a shake is $\frac{6}{188} \approx 3\%$.

Fill in the Blanks

When you graph numerical quantities, you can put your entries in order, so you can use a graph with labeled axes. However, when you are displaying data about _____ variables like color, clothing, food, etc., you cannot order them, so _____-_____ tables are an efficient way to show the information. You need to read all questions carefully so you can find the correct row, column, or cell to create the _____ and denominator of the fraction required.

Basic Problem

The following two-way table displays how students at Melville Marra Middle School prefer to listen to recorded music.

	CD	Vinyl Record	File Download to MP3 Player	Streaming Service	Totals
Band Member	11	13	45	39	108
Orchestra Member	7	8	11	50	76
Neither Band nor Orchestra	44	23	66	121	254
Totals	62	44	122	210	438

How many more students prefer CDs over vinyl?

a) 2   b) 21   c) 18   d) 106

Intermediate Problem

Based on the table from the Basic Problem above, what percent of the students prefer using a streaming service? Round to the nearest percent.

a) 66%   b) 36%   c) 48%   d) 40%

Challenging Problem

Based on the table from the Basic Problem above, if a student who prefers vinyl was to be selected at random, what is the probability that the person was in the orchestra? Round to the nearest percent.

a) 58%   b) 17%   c) 18%   d) 18%

Numeric Entry Problem

Based on the table from the Basic Problem above, how many band members do not prefer streaming services?

Quantitative Comparison Problem

Compare Quantity A and Quantity B, using the information below and the table from the Basic Problem above.

Quantity A

The number of students at Melville Marra Middle School who prefer vinyl records.

Quantity B

The number of Band members at Melville Marra Middle School who prefer file downloads to MP3 players.

Select one of the following answers.

a) Quantity A is greater.
b) Quantity B is greater.
c) The two quantities are equal.
d) The relationship cannot be determined from the information given.

Key Descriptors

categorical variables, conditional probability from two-way tables, probability with two-way tables, qualitative variables

Review/Renew

What is the additive inverse of $-|2 - 9|$?

a) 7   b) -7   c) 11   d) -11

DID YOU KNOW THAT?

The only Shakespeare play to contain the word 'mathematics' is "The Taming of the Shrew."

Independent Events

Introduction

Imagine a two-step experiment in which you first flip a fair coin, and then roll a six-sided die. You can use shorthand to represent each possible outcome.

Let H = the coin lands on heads.   Let 3 = the die lands on 3.
Let T = the coin lands on tails.   Let 4 = the die lands on 4.
Let 1 = the die lands on 1.   Let 5 = the die lands on 5.
Let 2 = the die lands on 2.   Let 6 = the die lands on 6.

We know that

$$P(H) \ = \ P(T) = \frac{1}{2} \text{ and } P(1) \ = P(2) = P(3) = P(4) = P(5) = P(6) = \frac{1}{6}.$$

The probability of the die landing on 4 is $\frac{1}{6}$. It does not matter what the coin did in the first step of the experiment. When the probability of an event is not changed by the outcome of the previous step of the experiment, the two events are **independent events**.

You may wonder, before the experiment is started, what is the probability of getting, for instance, a tail and a 5? This can be written as $P(T \text{ and } 5)$. Since the events are independent, you can just multiply the probabilities.

$$P(T \text{ and } 5) = P(T) \cdot P(5) = \frac{1}{2} \cdot \frac{1}{6} = \frac{1}{12}.$$

- In general, if events A and B are independent events, $P(A \text{ and } B) = P(A) \cdot P(B)$.

- Conversely, if $P(C) \cdot P(D) = P(C \text{ and } D)$, C and D are independent events.

Remember, independent events are about the relationship between two events. It is about the *probability* of one event being affected by knowing the outcome of the other event. Read Examples 1 and 2 below carefully. If you find yourself having a little trouble understanding independent events, give it time. Everyone has trouble with it when they first learn it.

Example 1

What is the probability of picking out the king of diamonds if one card is randomly picked from a standard deck of 52 playing cards?

Solution 1

Think of a standard deck of 52 playing cards. There are 4 suits--hearts, diamonds, clubs and spades. There are 13 cards in each suit, as shown below.

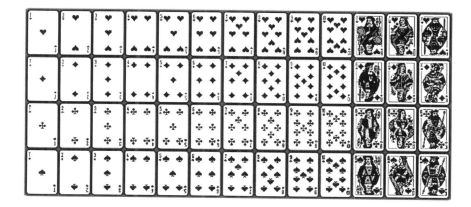

We are interested in two events; king and diamond.

    Let K = a king is chosen.
    Let D = a diamond is chosen.

Let's analyze this to get a better understanding of independent events. The probability of picking a king from the entire deck of 52 cards is

$$P(K) = \frac{4}{52} = \frac{1}{13}.$$

Now let's say the card is picked, and you are told it is a diamond. There are 13 diamond cards, with one king in that set. The probability of picking a king from the set of 13 diamonds is still $\frac{1}{13}$. *So, knowing the card was a diamond did not affect its probability of being a king.* As a result, king and diamond are independent events, and

$$P(K \text{ and } D) = P(K) \cdot P(D) = \frac{4}{52} \cdot \frac{13}{52} = \frac{1}{13} \cdot \frac{1}{4} = \frac{1}{52}.$$

This makes sense, since, out of the 52 cards, there is only one king of diamonds.

Example 2

A die is rolled and then a marble is picked out of a bin with 2 red, 6 blue, and 8 green marbles. What is the probability that the die lands on 3 and a red marble is picked?

Solution 2

The event "the die lands on 3" and the event "a red marble is picked" are independent events; the outcome on the die has no effect on the probability the marble comes up red.

Let 3 = the die lands on 3.
Let R = a red marble is picked.

$$P(3) \ = \ \frac{1}{6} \text{ and } P(R) = \frac{2}{16} = \frac{1}{8}.$$

Since the events are independent,

$$P(3 \text{ and } R) = P(3) \cdot P(R) = \frac{1}{6} \cdot \frac{1}{8} = \frac{1}{48}.$$

The probability that the die lands on 3 and a red marble is picked is $\frac{1}{48}$.

Fill in the Blanks

If the outcome of event X does not affect the probability of event Y occurring, we say that X and Y are _____ events. If the events A and B are independent, then $P(A) \cdot P(B)$ is equal to _____. So, to determine if two events K and L are independent, you need to compute three probabilities: _____, $P(L)$, and $P(K \text{ and } L)$.

Basic Problem

A summer baseball/softball camp surveys its 60 attendees to compile information about their meal program. The information appears in the two-way table below.

	Baseball (B)	Softball (S)	Total
Hot Dogs (H)	11	4	15
Chicken Fingers (C)	33	12	45
Total	44	16	60

What is the probability $P(C)$ that a camper prefers chicken?

a) $\frac{33}{44}$ b) $\frac{45}{60}$ c) $\frac{12}{16}$ d) $\frac{33}{45}$

Intermediate Problem

Using the two-way table from the Basic Problem above, what is the value of $P(C) \cdot P(B)$?

a) $\frac{33}{60}$ b) $\frac{45}{60}$ c) $\frac{11}{20}$ d) $\frac{33}{44}$

Challenging Problem

Using the two-way table from the Basic Problem above, what is the probability $P(C \text{ and } B)$ that a randomly-selected camper prefers baseball as a favorite sport *and* chicken as a favorite meal?

a) $\frac{11}{20}$ b) $\frac{45}{60}$ c) $\frac{11}{44}$ d) $\frac{33}{45}$

Numeric Entry Problem

Using the two-way table from the Basic Problem above, and your answers to the Basic problem, the Intermediate Problem, and the Challenging Problem, what is the difference between the probability $P(C \text{ and } B)$ and the probability $P(C) \cdot P(B)$?

Multiple Choice with Multiple Answers Problem

If R and T are independent events, and $P(R) = \frac{45}{60}$ and $P(T) = \frac{44}{60}$, which of the following expressions are equivalent to $P(R \text{ and } T)$?

[a] 0.55   [b] $\frac{33}{60}$ [c] 55%   [d] $\frac{11}{20}$

Key Descriptors

independent events in probability

Review/Renew

When written in scientific notation, how many significant digits does the number 4,071,000 have?

a) 3   b) 4   c) 5   d) 7

DID YOU KNOW THAT?

The surprising "Penny Doubled Every Day" problem can be modeled using exponential functions.

Imagine if you were asked to work for a 31-day month, and you would be paid every day. On the first day, you'd receive $0.01. On the second day that amount would be doubled and you'd receive $0.02. The third day's pay would be $0.04, and the fourth day's pay would be $0.08. Each day's pay is the double of the previous day's pay.

The tenth day's pay is just $10.24.

Amazingly, the 28th day's pay is over a million dollars, and the total pay for the 31 days is over 20 million dollars!

Mean, Median, Mode

Introduction

We have seen how graphs, tables, and Venn diagrams can summarize and display data. **Descriptive statistics** can also be used to describe, or summarize, data in a concise, convenient form. Imagine how cumbersome a list of everyone's income in the United States would be! Think of an old-fashioned telephone book for just your county--it is huge! Think of a list of every high school student in your state, everyone who visited a National Park last summer, every student who is taking the GRE, etc. Lists can be so long and cumbersome that you can't process or interpret any trends in the data. A list of data is sometimes called a **distribution** of data.

The most basic descriptive statistics are the **mean**, the **median**, and the **mode**. These three statistics are sometimes called **measures of central tendency**.

The mean is the arithmetic average. You add up all of the numbers and divide by the amount of numbers you added. It gives you the value everyone would have received if the sum of all of the values was distributed equally. Let's take a look at the mean using an example.

A college economics professor was polling 11 students in a study group about purchasing habits. She asked them how much cash they are currently carrying in their wallets, and received these responses, in dollars:

$$15, 20, 50, 5, 10, 12, 30, 10, 10, 18, 6.$$

The mean can be found by adding these eleven numbers and dividing by 11.

$$\frac{15 + 20 + 50 + 5 + 10 + 12 + 30 + 10 + 10 + 18 + 6}{11} = \frac{186}{11} \approx 16.91.$$

The mean, or average amount of cash students carry, is $16.91. This seems to be a somewhat "middle of the road" descriptive number for these eleven people. Let's change the numbers slightly.

On the day of the poll, one of the students got a month's pay from their job in cash, and had $1,112 dollars in his wallet. We'll replace the student who had the most money, $50, with this person. Let's find the mean of these eleven numbers:

$$15, 20, 1112, 5, 10, 12, 30, 10, 10, 18, 6.$$

Add and divide.

$$\frac{15 + 20 + 1112 + 5 + 10 + 12 + 30 + 10 + 10 + 18 + 6}{11} = \frac{1,248}{11} \approx 113.45.$$

The mean is now $113.45. This number is not representative of *anybody*! The mean was not **resistant** to the numerical effects of the highly extreme value of 1,112, making the mean a poor statistic to use to describe this data.

The median would be a better statistic for this data. The median is the middle value after the numbers are put in order. Let's order the numbers from the last two distributions, and find the median of each.

$$15, 20, 50, 5, 10, 12, 30, 10, 10, 18, 6$$

becomes

$$5, 6, 10, 10, 10, 12, 15, 18, 20, 30, 50.$$

The median of this set is the number in the middle, which is 12.

$$5, 6, 10, 10, 10, \boxed{12} 15, 18, 20, 30, 50.$$

Generally speaking, half of the numbers were below 12 and half were above. You can figure this out by counting, or crossing off numbers in pairs starting at each end. If you recall from before, the mean was 16.91. The numbers 12 and 16.91 seem to reasonably describe this set of numbers.

Let's look at the median of the distribution with the high extreme score of 1112.

$$15, 20, 1112, 5, 10, 12, 30, 10, 10, 18, 6$$

becomes

$$5, 6, 10, 10, 10, \boxed{12} 15, 18, 20, 30, 1112$$

The median is still 12, and recall that the mean was 113.45. The median is a better number to describe the students in this class than the mean is. The median *is* resistant to the numerical effect of extreme values.

What if you have an even number of values? What is considered the "middle" number? Let's look at this distribution of eight values:

$$11, 13, 14, 17, 21, 26, 26, 33.$$

The values 17 and 21 "sandwich" the middle of the distribution. To find the median, take the mean of the two middle numbers.

$$\frac{17 + 21}{2} = 19.$$

The median of these eight values is 19.

The mode is the value that occurs the most. The mode of these two distributions is 10. Keep in mind that the mode is not the majority. It is the most occurring case. For that reason, it is often used in situations involving categorical variables.

Let's say your school's 200 seniors were picking one of the school's 40 teachers for a yearbook dedication, and the teacher with the most votes wins. Theoretically, if the votes were evenly split, each teacher could get 5 votes. If 38 teachers got 5 votes, one teacher got 4 votes, and another got 6 votes, the teacher with the most votes is the teacher who got 6 votes! Notice that 6 votes constitute a very small minority of the 200 seniors.

There are many more statistics than just the mean, median and mode, but these statistics are a good way to start a description of a distribution of data.

Example 1

Find the sum of the mean and the median of the first five perfect squares.

Solution 1

The first five perfect squares are 1, 4, 9, 16, and 25. To find the average, add them and divide by 5.

$$\frac{1 + 4 + 9 + 16 + 25}{5} = \frac{55}{5} = 11$$

The mean of the first five perfect squares is 11.

The median of 1, 4, 9, 16, 25 is 9 since 9 is the middle number.

The sum of the mean and the median is 11 + 9 = 20.

Example 2

Twenty-five students take a test and the mean is 83. Two students were absent and take a make-up test. Their two grades are 79 and 99. What is the mean of the entire class? Round to the nearest percent.

Solution 2

Since we divide the total points by the number of students to get the mean, we multiply the mean by the number of students to get the total points. If the mean of the 25 students is 83, then the total number of points scored by all 25 students is

$$25 \cdot 83 = 2{,}075.$$

The two students who took make-up tests scored 79 and 99, which sum to 178. The class has 27 students, since 25 + 2 = 27. The total number of points scored by all 27 students is

$$2{,}075 + 178 = 2{,}253.$$

Divide the total points scored by the number of students to get the mean of the entire class.

$$\frac{2{,}075 + 178}{27} = \frac{2{,}253}{27} = 83.\overline{4}$$

The mean for the entire class is approximately 83.

Fill in the Blanks

The mean of a set of numbers is the _____ average and it can be found using

addition and _____. The _____ is the middle value once the numbers are put

in ascending or descending order. This statistic is not numerically affected much by

extremely high or low values. The case that occurs the most is called the _____.

Basic Problem

Find the mean of the following set of numbers:

$$25, 37, 3, 40, 65$$

a) 34   b) 37   c) 42.5   d) 12

Intermediate Problem

Find the mean of the first eight prime numbers.

a) 7.375   b) 9.625   c) 6.375   d) 7.125

Challenging Problem

Find the mean of the median and the mode for this set of data:

$$12, 12, 12, 13, 14, 17, 17, 21, 23,$$

a) $15.\overline{6}$ b) 14   c) 12   d) 13

Numeric Entry Problem

Find the product of the median and the mode for the following set of numbers:

$$6, 3, 2, 8, 7, 8, 9, 8, 1, 1, 12, 4, 11.$$

Quantitative Comparison Problem

Compare Quantity A and Quantity B, using the information below.

Quantity A	Quantity B
The mean of the first five prime numbers.	The median of the first five composite numbers.

Select one of the following answers.

a) Quantity A is greater.
b) Quantity B is greater.
c) The two quantities are equal.
d) The relationship cannot be determined from the information given.

Key Descriptors

descriptive statistics, distribution, mean, measures of central tendency, median, mode

Review/Renew

What is the product of $5 - 2x$ and $5 + 2x$?

a) $25 - 4x^2$ b) $25 - 4x$ c) $25 - 4x - 4x^2$ d) 10

DID YOU KNOW THAT?

A piece of photocopy paper is 0.004" thick. If it is repeatedly folded, each time the folded thickness would double. So, after one fold, it is 0.008" thick; after two folds it is 0.016" thick; etc. In just 51 folds, that thickness would reach from the Earth to the Sun, approximately 93 million miles!

Don't believe it?! It's another situation modeled by an exponential function, much like the penny-doubled-every-day problem from the Did You Know That? in Core Concept 80. Convert 93 million miles to inches and compute $0.004(2)^{51}$ and compare the results!

CORE CONCEPT 82
Frequency Distributions

Introduction

Imagine that your town government is taking a survey on how many cars each household has. The most common replies would be 0, 1, 2, and 3, but there could be thousands of households for each amount. Making a list of every household would be ridiculous! Let's say 1,213 households had 1 car. We say the **frequency** of 1-car households is 1,213.

When a distribution contains a large number of data points, it is impractical to list them, especially if many of the values are repeated. There is an efficient way to display large amounts of data using tables or bar graphs. We call these tables or graphs **frequency distributions**. A frequency distribution displays the number of responses for each possible outcome.

In Example 1 you will see how a frequency distribution can be displayed in table form. In Example 2 you will see how a frequency distribution can be displayed as a bar graph.

Example 1

The frequency table below shows results from a 60-point survey about the Bowe Corporation's customer service. The frequency column shows that 11 people rated the service as a 10, 7 people rated it as a 20, etc. If you add the numbers in the frequency column you can see that 46 people responded to the survey.

Score	Frequency
10	11
20	7
30	16
40	4
50	3
60	5

Find the mean, median and mode of this frequency distribution. Round to the nearest hundredth.

Solution 1

We are certainly not going to enter a score of 30 sixteen times! The chance of an error increases, and it is tedious and time-consuming. We use the table shown below. The bottom cell in the first column is blacked out--we never need to add those numbers, since they are not **weighted** by the frequency of that score. We can add the numbers in the Frequency column to get the Total Frequency. Since multiplication is repeated addition, we create a third column, the product of Score and Frequency, to compute the mean. The sum of the third column is the sum of all of the 46 scores.

Score	Frequency	(Score)·(Frequency)
10	11	110
20	7	140
30	16	480
40	4	160
50	3	150
60	5	300
	Total = 46	Total = 1,340

Add the numbers in the last column and make sure you divide by 46, even though you are only adding 6 numbers. You are really using a shorthand (multiplication) to add 46 numbers.

$$\frac{110 + 140 + 480 + 160 + 150 + 300}{46} = \frac{1,340}{46} \approx 29.13.$$

The mean is approximately 29.13.

The mode is again found by inspection. It is simply the score with the highest frequency, 30.

The median is the middle score. There are 46 data points, so the two middle scores must be averaged. They are the 23rd and 24th scores. Focus on the Frequency column, and use it to create a **Cumulative Frequency** column, so you can find where the 23rd and 24th scores are located. The Cumulative Frequency column is a running total of the frequencies. Look at the next table. From the Cumulative Frequency column you can see that the 23rd and 24th scores are each 30, so the average of the 23rd and 24th scores is 30.

Score	Frequency	Cumulative Frequency	(Score)·(Frequency)
10	11	11	110
20	7	18	140
30	16	34	480
40	4	38	160
50	3	41	150
60	5	46	300
	Total = 46		Total = 1,340

The median is 30.

In summary, the mean is 29.13, the median is 30, and the mode is 30.

Example 2

A college Psych professor gave a five-point quiz. The following bar graph gives the frequencies for each score. Find the mean, median, and mode. Round to the nearest hundredth.

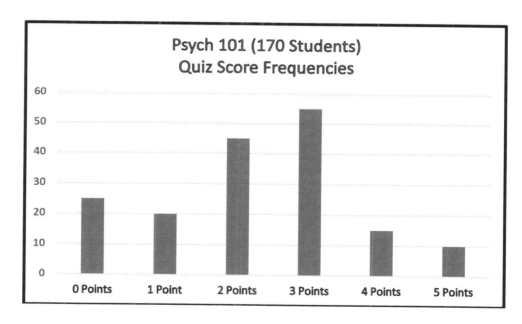

Solution 2

It looks like 55 students got a score of 3, and since that bar is the highest, the mode is 3. The most occurring case is a quiz score of 3 points.

The bar graph data can be turned into a table that will help you find the mean and the median.

Score	Frequency	Cumulative Frequency	(Score)·(Frequency)
0	25	25	0
1	20	45	20
2	45	90	90
3	55	145	165
4	15	160	60
5	10	170	50
	Total = 170		Total = 385

Divide 385 by 170 to find that the mean is 2.26 to the nearest hundredth.

Since there are 170 scores, the two middle scores are the 85th and 86th scores. The 85th and 86th scores are each 2, and the median is the average of these two middle scores. The median is 2.

In summary, the mean is 2.26, the mode is 3, and the median is 2.

Fill in the Blanks

A _____ _____ is a table or graph that is useful in displaying frequencies of outcomes when there is a large amount of data. The _____ frequency can be found by adding up all of the individual frequencies for each category. The mean, the _____, and the _____ can be computed using the information from a frequency distribution.

Basic Problem

Jordan's probability class is testing a typical six-sided die to see if it is fair. They record 500 rolls of the die, and display the results in the frequency distribution table below. Fill in the blank entries in the table.

Score	Frequency	(Score)·(Frequency)
1	82	
2	84	
3	83	
4	81	
5	85	
6	85	
	Total =	Total =

What is the exact mean for this frequency distribution?

a) 3   b) 83.$\overline{3}$ c) 3.5   d) 3.516

Intermediate Problem

A baseball scout rated the arm accuracy of kids on a travel team and filed this frequency distribution in bar graph form as part of his report. The vertical axis gives the frequency of each rating.

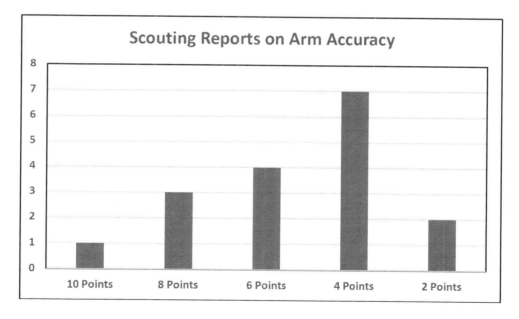

What is the mean rating, to the nearest tenth?

a) 6   b) 4   c) 5.3   d) 3.4

Challenging Problem

An elementary school nurse weighs 253 students and gets an average weight of 66 pounds. After all of that work, she finds out that the scale she was using under-weighed each person by 2 pounds. What is the correct mean?

a) 64   b) 66   c) 68   d) 33

Numeric Entry Problem

If 14 students score 80 on a test and 11 score 90, what is the mean score, to the nearest tenth, of all 25 students?

Multiple Choice with Multiple Answers Problem

Look at the table from Example 1. What fraction of the students scored 30?

[a] $\frac{480}{1,340}$ [b] $\frac{8}{23}$ [c] $\frac{34}{46}$ [d] $\frac{16}{46}$

Key Descriptors

cumulative frequency, frequency distributions, weighted mean

Review/Renew

Inscribed angle XYZ in circle O has vertex Y, and it intercepts an arc that measures 98 degrees. What is the measure of $\angle XYZ$?

a) 49°   b) 98°   c) 196°   d) 8°

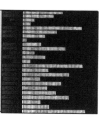

CORE CONCEPT 83
Relative Frequency

Introduction

Frequencies report raw numbers. A frequency is harder to interpret because, without the total frequency to compare a frequency to, the number is misleading or even meaningless.

Think back to the Covid-19 pandemic shutdown in March 2020. Data was reported endlessly about the number of cases in individual localities. If your county had a frequency of 10,000 cases, is that a problem? You have no idea, from this raw number, if there is a Covid-19 problem or not. If the county has a population of 15,000, there is a severe Covid-19 problem. If your county has a population of 3 million, there is not a severe Covid-19 problem. A frequency alone does not tell you this information immediately, but a **relative frequency** does. A relative frequency is a fraction that compares a frequency to the total frequency.

Example 1

The following table shows the frequencies of student scores on a five-point quiz.

Score	Frequency
0	25
1	20
2	45
3	55
4	15
5	10
	Total = 170

What is the relative frequency of a score of 5?

Solution 1

Let's create a Relative Frequency column. It will be composed of fractions that show that the frequency of each score is "out of" the total frequency of 170 students.

Score	Frequency	Relative Frequency
0	25	$\dfrac{25}{170}$
1	20	$\dfrac{20}{170}$
2	45	$\dfrac{45}{170}$
3	55	$\dfrac{55}{170}$
4	15	$\dfrac{15}{170}$
5	10	$\dfrac{10}{170}$
	Total = 170	Total = 1

The relative frequency of students who scored a 5 is $\dfrac{10}{170}$. The sum of the relative frequencies will always be 1. Relative frequencies can be converted to decimals and/or percents to make the interpretation even clearer. The relative frequency of $\dfrac{10}{170}$ is approximately 6%. So about 6% of the students scored a 5.

Example 2

The relative frequency of Smithtown South High School students who had perfect attendance last year is $\dfrac{2}{31}$. A student is to be chosen at random from a list of the 2,480 students at the school last year. What is the probability that the student who gets chosen will have perfect attendance?

Solution 2

Here you can see the relationship between relative frequency and probability. The fraction $\dfrac{2}{31}$ is approximately 6.5%. So, 6.5% of the students have perfect attendance. If you are choosing one student randomly from this group, the probability of choosing one who has perfect attendance is $\dfrac{2}{31}$.

Fill in the Blanks

If a frequency distribution has a relative frequency column, the sum of all the entries in that column must be _____. This is because that sum represents 100% of the _____ frequency. A relative frequency can also act as a _____ to assess how probable certain outcomes are.

Basic Problem

At Baldwinsville High School, 456 of the 611 students have a pet. What is the relative frequency of students who have a pet?

a) $\frac{1}{2}$ b) $\frac{147}{456}$ c) $\frac{456}{611}$ d) $\frac{147}{611}$

Intermediate Problem

Using the table from Example 1, what is the relative frequency of students who did not score 5 on the quiz?

a) $\frac{16}{170}$ b) $\frac{16}{17}$ c) $\frac{1}{17}$ d) $\frac{10}{170}$

Challenging Problem

The Venn diagram below shows how many children at Camp Camo visited the Baseball Hall of Fame (B), or Football Hall of Fame (F), both, or neither.

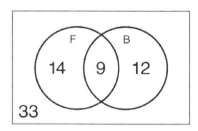

What is the relative frequency of children from the camp who attended exactly one of those Halls of Fame?

a) $\frac{13}{34}$ b) $\frac{35}{68}$ c) $\frac{9}{68}$ d) $\frac{33}{68}$

Numeric Entry Problem

Fifteen of the 144 members of the Hillside Middle School Honor Society missed the induction ceremony. What is the relative frequency of students who did attend the induction ceremony?

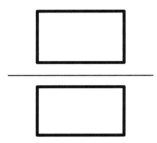

Quantitative Comparison Problem

Compare Quantity A and Quantity B, using the information below.

Quantity A

The relative frequency of students who take instrumental music courses at Elmira High School, if the frequency of students who take instrumental music is 177.

Quantity B

The relative frequency of students who do not take instrumental music courses at Elmira High School, if the frequency of students who take instrumental music is 177.

Select one of the following answers.

a) Quantity A is greater.
b) Quantity B is greater.
c) The two quantities are equal.
d) The relationship cannot be determined from the information given.

Key Descriptors

relative frequency, relative frequency as a probability

Review/Renew

A right triangle has a leg that measures 12 feet and a hypotenuse that measures 13 feet. What is the area of the triangle?

a) 78 sq. ft.   b) 156 sq. ft.   c) 60 sq. ft.   d) 30 sq. ft.

Expected Value

Introduction

Imagine you ran a carnival company. You'd have to make sure that you charged enough for each game to make a profit. You'd need to know the value of the prizes you gave players, and how often players won each possible prize. You'd have to know all of this in advance, to make sure your business did not suffer a loss. You don't care which specific player wins any given prize amount, just the "average" a player might win. Think of how this problem escalates for owners of a large casino!

Life insurance companies rely heavily on correctly anticipating average payouts, so they can predict the amount they will have to pay to policy holders in advance, and make sure they charge enough money for each policy.

The solutions to these types of problems are based on probability. Once the owners know how often each prize will be won, they can compute the total amount of the prizes they will have to give out. The probability can be used in advance as a relative frequency to predict the "average" payout. In mathematics, this is called the **expected value**. They use this to approximate the total payout to all winners.

Think about it. If the probability of picking a king from a standard deck of cards is $\frac{4}{52}$, which is equivalent to $\frac{1}{13}$, you'd expect the relative frequency of picking a king to be $\frac{1}{13}$. A relative frequency can be translated to a probability to allow you to predict what you *expect* to happen.

Let's look at an example of how expected value works.

Example 1

A spinning wheel at a carnival has four congruent sectors labelled $0, $1, $2, $5. You spin the wheel, and win the amount the spinner lands on. What is the expected value (the average prize payout) of playing this game?

Solution 1

The probability of landing on any specific sector is $\frac{1}{4}$, which is equal to 0.25. You set up a table listing each prize amount and the probability of that prize amount to solve an expected value problem.

Prize (x)	$0	$1	$2	$5
Probability P(x)	0.25	0.25	0.25	0.25

We'll call the expected value $E(x)$. To find the expected value, multiply each prize amount by its probability, and add those products. The capital Greek letter sigma (Σ) tells you to add all of the products together. The general formula is

$$E(X) = \sum x \cdot P(X).$$

Substitute to see how the formula works:

$$E(X) = 0(0.25) + 1(0.25) + 2(0.25) + 5(0.25)$$

$$E(X) = 2.$$

The expected value, which is the average payout, is $2 per game. You can see that if the carnival charges less than $2 to play this game, they will lose money. If they charge, say $3 to play the game, they will make an average of $1 per game. So, if attendees play the games 500 times in one day, they would make $500 profit for the day.

Example 2

A deck of cards contains a card labelled $10, two cards labelled $5, three cards labelled $3, four cards labelled $2, and five cards labelled $1. What is the minimum amount a carnival must charge to play this game so they can avoid losing money?

Solution 2

Let's set up another table listing each prize amount and the probability of that prize amount. There is a total of 15 cards in the deck.

Prize (x)	$10	$5	$3	$2	$1
Probability P(x)	$\frac{1}{15}$	$\frac{2}{15}$	$\frac{3}{15}$	$\frac{4}{15}$	$\frac{5}{15}$

Notice that the sum of all of the probabilities is equal to 1. This happens in every expected value table.

$$E(X) = 10\left(\frac{1}{15}\right) + 5\left(\frac{2}{15}\right) + 3\left(\frac{3}{15}\right) + 2\left(\frac{4}{15}\right) + 1\left(\frac{5}{15}\right) = \frac{10}{15} + \frac{10}{15} + \frac{9}{15} + \frac{8}{15} + \frac{5}{15} = \frac{42}{15}.$$

Convert $\frac{42}{15}$ to an equivalent decimal. The average payout for this game is approximately $2.80. That is the minimum that must be charged so the carnival breaks even or makes a profit on the game.

Fill in the Blanks

The _____ _____ can be thought of as the average of a series of outcomes from an experiment. The sum of the probabilities in a table set up to compute expected value is _____. The Geek letter _____ is used in the expected value formula to indicate that the products of the outcomes and their probabilities must be added.

Basic Problem

A high-priced charity dinner is raising money using a carnival spinning wheel. Based on the table below, what is the expected value? Round to the nearest cent.

Payout (x)	$5	$10	$20	$50
Probability P(x)	$\frac{9}{16}$	$\frac{1}{4}$	$\frac{1}{8}$	$\frac{1}{16}$

a) $10.14   b) $11.06   c) $21.25   d) $10.94

Intermediate Problem

The following table shows all five possible outcomes of a certain experiment, along with the probability of each outcome. What is the value of k?

Number Selected (x)	8	4	2	1	0
Probability P(x)	0.4	0.3	0.2	0.05	k

a) 0.1   b) 0.01   c) 0.05   d) 0.95

Challenging Problem

In Example 2 above, how much profit will the carnival company make if they charge $4 to play a game and 1,250 games are played during the carnival? Round to the nearest dollar.

a) $1,500   b) $5,000   c) $4,338   d) $588

Numeric Entry Problem

What is the expected value for rolling a typical, fair, six-sided die?

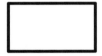

Multiple Choice with Multiple Answers Problem

What is the sum of the probabilities in the following table?

Payout (x)	$2	$4	$6	$25
Probability P(x)	$\frac{9}{16}$	$\frac{1}{4}$	$\frac{1}{8}$	$\frac{1}{16}$

[a] $\frac{15}{16}$ [b] $\frac{17}{16}$ [c] $\frac{16}{16}$ [d] 1

Key Descriptors

average value of random variable, expected value

Review/Renew

What is the value of $\left(\sqrt[5]{32}\right)^3$?

a) 16   b) 29   c) 8   d) 32

CORE CONCEPT 85
Box and Whisker Plots

Introduction

In Core Concept 81 you reviewed measures of central tendency, which included the mean, the median, and the mode. In Core Concepts 85 - 87 we will look at how the data in a distribution are spread out. This is often shown graphically since, as we have said before, a picture is a thousand words.

A **box and whisker plot**, or **boxplot**, is used to display the spread of quantitative data. (You could not create one for categorical data). It divides numerical data into sections, each of which represents 25% of the data. The numbers that divide the data into these four parts representing 25% each are called **quartiles**. A boxplot highlights five numbers, which make up **the five-number summary** for the boxplot:

- **Min**-the **minimum** value in the data set.
- Q_1-**the first quartile**. This is also the 25th **percentile**, since 25% of the scores are at or below this number.
- Q_2-**the second quartile**. This is also the 50th percentile, since 50% of the scores are at or below this number. This is also the median.
- Q_3-**the third quartile**. This is also the 75th percentile, since 75% of the scores are at or below this number.
- Q_4-**the fourth quartile**. This is also the 100th percentile, since 100% of the scores are at or below this number. This is also the **maximum (Max)**.

A boxplot is composed of a rectangle and two "whiskers" as shown below. Notice the placement of the five-number summary numbers.

The **range** of the data set is the difference between the highest and lowest score. You can subtract the minimum from the maximum to get the range. The "middle 50%" of a boxplot is shown by the rectangle, which is bordered by Q_1 and Q_3. Colleges often use this to describe data for a "typical" applicant. The quantity $Q_3 - Q_1$ is called the **interquartile range**, and abbreviated **IQR**.

You will not be drawing a boxplot on your GRE; you just need to know how to interpret one. Keep in mind that you cannot tell the value of the mean or the mode from a boxplot, but you can read the median from a boxplot.

Example 1

Using the data displayed in the boxplot below, what percent of the people scored between 35 and 56, inclusive?

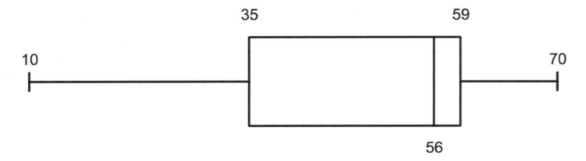

Solution 1

The score of 35 represents the first quartile Q_1 and the score of 56 represents the second quartile Q_2, which is also the median. Twenty-five percent of the scores occur in this interval, since the quartiles divide all of the scores (100% of them) into four parts, each representing 25% of the scores.

Example 2

If the boxplot in Example 1 represents data for 600 people, how many people scored at or below 59?

Solution 2

The boxplot shows that 59 is the 75th percentile, which means that 75% of the people scored at or below 59. Take 75% of 600 using the percent proportion or your calculator.

$$\frac{75}{100} = \frac{x}{600}$$

Cross multiply.

$$45,000 = 100x$$

Divide by 100.

$$x = 450.$$

Therefore, 450 people scored at or below 59.

Fill in the Blanks

A boxplot divides 100% of the data into four sections separated by _____. The fourth quartile is also the _____ and the second quartile is also the _____. Q_1 denotes the first quartile, which is the 25th _____. The key numbers in a box and whisker plot make up its _____-_____ _____.

Basic Problem

A box and whisker plot has a five-number summary of 11, 21, 25, 32, 55. What is its interquartile range?

a) 11   b) 44   c) 14   d) 7

Intermediate Problem

A box and whisker plot has a five-number summary of 21, 28, 35, 52, 65. What is its 75th percentile?

a) 24   b) 28   c) 65   d) 52

Challenging Problem

A box and whisker plot has a five-number summary of 21, 28, 35, 52, 65. Which of the following numbers could not be the mean of the data set?

a) 40   b) 19   c) 35   d) 34

Numeric Entry Problem

A teacher gave an easy 5-point quiz to help boost grades at the end of a marking period. Every student in the class scored a 5 on the quiz. What is the interquartile range for this distribution of scores?

Quantitative Comparison Problem

Compare Quantity A and Quantity B, using the information below.

Quantity A	Quantity B
The mean of the data from a boxplot with this five-number summary: 10, 14, 16, 21, 23.	**The value of Q_2 from a boxplot with this five-number summary: 13, 17, 28, 32, 41.**

Select one of the following answers.

a) Quantity A is greater.
b) Quantity B is greater.
c) The two quantities are equal.
d) The relationship cannot be determined from the information given.

Key Descriptors

box and whisker plots, boxplots, five-number summary, interquartile range, percentiles, quartiles, range

Review/Renew

A circle has circumference 20π. What is the area of a sector of the circle whose central angle measures 72 degrees? Round your answer to the nearest tenth.

a) 12.6   b) 62.8   c) 251.2   d) 78.5

Measures of Spread

Introduction

In Core Concept 85, you learned that the range tells you nothing about how the scores are distributed, since the range is computed using only the highest and lowest score. It ignores how the scores are distributed in between those two scores. Box and whisker plots show, to some degree, how data is spread out in between the minimum and maximum scores. However, in between the quartiles, you have no idea how the scores are spread out.

Usually we focus on how scores are spread out, or dispersed, around the mean. There is a statistic that measures spread that also takes *every* score in the distribution into account. It is called the **standard deviation**. You may remember it from a college statistics course. We will look at two standard deviation formulas. One is used if you are computing the spread around the mean for an entire population. The other is used for computing the spread around the mean of a sample, which is a *subset* of a population.

We will name each score x_i, where i represents, or names, each score. So x_1 represents the first score, x_2 represents the second, etc. The Greek letter μ represents the mean for a population. Let's say a population has n pieces of data. Let's look at the formula for the **population standard deviation**, which is denoted by the Greek letter lower-case sigma (σ).

$$\sigma = \sqrt{\frac{\sum (x_i - \mu)^2}{n}}$$

The upper-case sigma, Σ, on the right side of the formula, tells you to add all of the squared differences together. The steps used to figure out the population standard deviation σ are:

- Compute the mean μ.
- Find the difference between μ and each of the scores.
- Square each of the differences.
- Add up all of the squared differences.
- Divide by n to get the average of the squared differences.
- Take the square root of the quotient you just computed.

In a sample, the mean is denoted $\bar{x}$, and the standard deviation is called s. The **sample standard deviation** formula is

$$s = \sqrt{\frac{\sum(x_i - \bar{x})^2}{n - 1}}.$$

The steps used to figure out the sample standard deviation s are:

- Compute the mean $\bar{x}$.
- Find the difference between $\bar{x}$ and each of the scores.
- Square each of the differences.
- Add up all of the squared differences.
- Divide by $(n - 1)$.
- Take the square root of the quotient you just computed.

The seemingly subtle but important differences between the two standard deviation formulas would be explained in a statistics course. For your GRE, just notice if a problem is asking for a population standard deviation or a sample standard deviation.

Example 1

Find the standard deviation of the population with these scores:

12, 14, 16, 20, 23.

Solution 1

First compute the mean. The scores add to 85. Divide by 5 to get $\mu = 17$. Then organize all of this information into a table.

Score (x_i)	$(x_i - \mu)$	$(x_i - \mu)^2$
12	-5	25
14	-3	9
16	-1	1
20	3	9
23	6	36
Total = 85		Total = 80

The sum of the squared differences is 80. Divide by 5 to get 16. Take the square root to get 4. The standard deviation is 4.

Example 2

Distribution *A* has mean 24 and standard deviation 3.2. Distribution *B* has mean 24 and standard deviation 4.1. In which distribution are the scores more spread out?

Solution 2

The standard deviations can be compared. The distributions have the same mean, and since 4.1 > 3.2, Distribution *B* is more spread out.

Fill in the Blanks

The mean, median, and mode are measures of _____ _____. The range, interquartile range, and _____ _____ are measures of dispersion, or spread. They show how much the scores in the distribution are spread out around the _____.

Basic Problem

What is the population standard deviation for a distribution composed of the scores 5, 8, 10, 15, 22? Round to the nearest hundredth.

a) 12   b) 17   c) 5.97   d) 6.67

Intermediate Problem

Distribution *R* has mean 230 and standard deviation 1.5. Which of the following scores is least likely to be in the distribution?

a) 231   b) 229   c) 233   d) 278

Challenging Problem

A distribution has mean 61 and range 20. Which of the following scores cannot be in the distribution?

a) 82   b) 72   c) 62   d) 52

Numeric Entry Problem

Compute the sample standard deviation for the distribution composed of the scores 2, 4, 6, 8. Round to the nearest tenth.

Multiple Choice with Multiple Answers Problem

Which of the following data sets has a range of 18?

[a] 12, 15, 34, 31, 30   [b] 2, 6, 7, 8, 18

[c] 11, 13, 14, 21, 39   [d] 5, 18, 18, 21, 23

Key Descriptors

population standard deviation, sample standard deviation

Review/Renew

If 15% of a number is 135, what is 80% of that number?

a) 108   b) 60   c) 720   d) 16.2

DID YOU KNOW THAT?

In 1876, the 20th United States President, James A. Garfield, created an original proof of the Pythagorean theorem! It was based on the areas of three right triangles and a trapezoid.

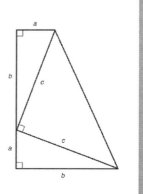

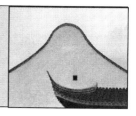

CORE CONCEPT 87
The Normal Distribution

Introduction

In Core Concepts 85 and 86 you learned about how the dispersion in a distribution can be reported. In this Core Concept, you will learn how the **normal curve**, or **bell curve**, can help describe spread for certain distributions, called **normal distributions**. The normal curve is symmetric, and centered around its mean, which is also equal to its median. The area under the curve represents 100% of the data in the distribution. Based on this, you can see that most of the scores tend to cluster around the mean. That is the way things "normally" happen in many real-life situations. Take a look at the shape of the curve.

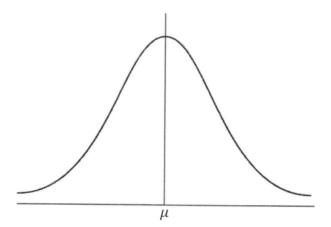

μ

Sections under the curve can then be used to represent specific intervals of data. You can shade the area under the curve in an interval, and the area of that section is the percent of the data that lies in that interval. Let's take a closer look at this concept.

The standard deviation σ is used in conjunction with the mean μ to mark off intervals on the horizontal axis. Look at the diagram below to convince yourself that:

- About 68% of the data occurs within 1 standard deviation of the mean.
- About 95% of the data occurs within 2 standard deviations of the mean.
- About 99.7%% of the data occurs within 3 standard deviations of the mean.

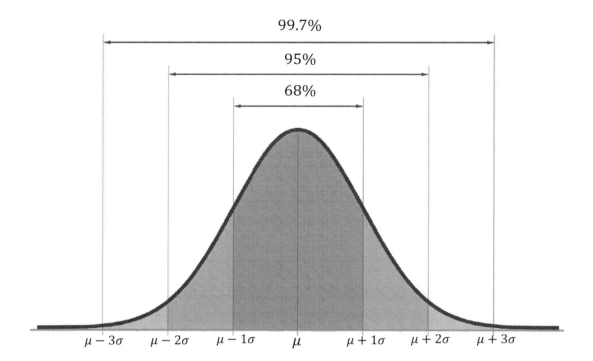

The symmetry about the mean will also help you compute percentages for certain areas under the curve. You will see this in Examples 1 and 2.

Example 1

The number of absences per student at Starr High School is normally distributed with mean 8 and standard deviation $\sigma = 1.5$. What is the percentile rank of a student who was absent 5 times?

Solution 1

Notice that 8 - 3 = 5. The score of 5 absences is 2 standard deviations below the mean of 8, since $\sigma = 1.5$ and 2(1.5) = 3. Draw a diagram and shade in the area below 5 absences.

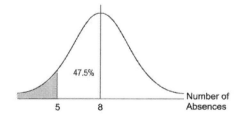

Since 95% of the data occurs within 2 standard deviations of the mean, 47.5% of the data occurs between the mean and 2 standard deviations below it. We know 50% of the data occurs to the left side of the mean, since the mean equals the median, so we subtract.

$$50\% - 47.5\% = 2.5\%$$

The percentile rank of a student with 5 absences is 2.5%.

Example 2

The summer salaries of the 150 Calvin High School students who worked are normally distributed with mean $1,241 and standard deviation $52. How many students earned $1,293 or more that summer?

Solution 2

The salary of $1,293 is 1 standard deviation above the mean. From the diagram we can see that 84% of the workers earned less than $1,293.

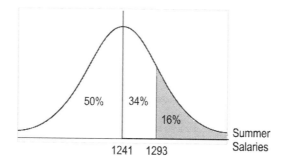

The area below the mean represents 50% of the data. The area between the mean and 1 standard deviation above the mean is half of 68%, which is 34%. Since the entire area under the curve represents 100% of the workers, we can subtract 84% from 100% to get that 16% of the students who worked earned more than $1,293. Use the percent proportion to find 16% of 150.

$$\frac{16}{100} = \frac{x}{150}$$

Solve to get that $x = 24$, so 24 students earned at least $1,293.

Fill in the Blanks

The normal curve is often called the _____ curve because of its shape. The area under the curve represents _____% of the data, and _____% of the scores occur within 3 standard deviations of the mean. The curve looks the same on both sides, which means it is _____ with respect to the mean.

Basic Problem

A normal distribution has mean 54 and standard deviation 6. Which of the following scores has a percentile rank closest to 84?

a) 48   b) 72   c) 60   d) 66

Intermediate Problem

Distribution X is normal, with mean 64 and standard deviation 5.2. Distribution Y is also normal, with mean 64 and standard deviation 7.1. Distribution Z is normal, with mean 24 and standard deviation 5.2. Distribution W is normal, with mean 24 and standard deviation 4. In which distribution are you most likely to find the score of 76?

a) Distribution X b) Distribution Y c) Distribution Z d) Distribution W

Challenging Problem

The mean and standard deviation of four normal distributions are given below. Which of the distributions is most likely to have a range of 20?

a) $\mu = 100$; $\sigma = 1.5$ b) $\mu = 90$; $\sigma = 3$ c) $\mu = 90$; $\sigma = 12$ d) $\mu = 20$; $\sigma = 1$

Numeric Entry Problem

A normal distribution has mean 54 and standard deviation 6. What score has a percentile rank closest to 16%? Round to the nearest integer.

Quantitative Comparison Problem

Compare Quantity A and Quantity B, using the information below.

Quantity A	Quantity B
The percentile rank of the third quartile Q_3.	**The percentile rank of a score in a normal distribution that is one standard deviation above the mean.**

Select one of the following answers.

a) Quantity A is greater.
b) Quantity B is greater.
c) The two quantities are equal.
d) The relationship cannot be determined from the information given.

Key Descriptors

bell curve, normal curve, normal distribution

Review/Renew

Find the number of degrees in an interior angle of a regular octagon.

a) 45°   b) 60°   c) 135°   d) 120°

DID YOU KNOW THAT?

The numbers on the opposite sides of a traditional six-sided die add to 7.

CORE CONCEPT 88
Scatterplots and Trend Lines

Introduction

Computing the mean, median, and mode involved getting a single piece of numerical information from each subject. If the data was categorical (eye color, hair color, favorite food) you can find frequencies and a mode, but you can't find a mean or median since the information is non-numeric and can't be ordered. When each subject only reports one piece of numerical information, we say we are working with **univariate** statistics--each subject is reporting on one variable.

Many times, each subject is asked for *two* pieces of numerical data. Researchers are interested in investigating a possible relationship between these two variables. In those cases, we are working with **bivariate** data. When you work with bivariate data, you can use the coordinate axes, with each axis representing one of the two variables reported by each subject. The two pieces of information reported by each subject can be plotted as a point in the plane, and that allows researchers to look for possible trends and patterns on how the two variables might be related.

You are very used to graphing lines, circles, parabolas, etc., on the coordinate axes. **Scatterplots** are not continuous lines or curves--they are separate, scattered points that represent bivariate data that was collected. The scatterplots allow you to make generalizations about trends based on the data, and they also allow you to make educated predictions assuming that the trend continues.

Just like measures of central tendency and measures of spread "summarize" a data set, you can draw a line on a scatterplot that fits the data points as closely as possible. This line has several names, including **linear regression line**, **line of best fit**, **least squares line**, and **trend line**. You can visually approximate the location of these lines somewhat by eye. Finding the equation of a trend line is a job for a graphing calculator. In Example 3, you will see how you can use the equation of the trend line to make predictions.

Example 1

The following scatterplot shows a food truck's water bottle sales graphed against the day's high temperature for the last week of last summer.

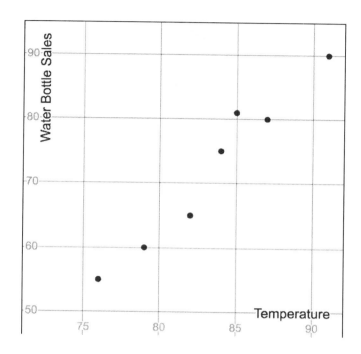

Describe the trend displayed by the scatterplot.

Solution 1

Notice how, as the temperature (x) increases, the water bottle sales (y) increase. We call this a positive association between x and y. When two variables are associated, it does not necessarily mean that changes in one variable *caused* the changes in the other; association does not imply causation. In this case, it does seem logical that, as the weather got hotter, more people wanted water.

Example 2

The following scatterplot shows the number of lifeguard rescues at Callahan's Beach graphed against coffee sales at the same beach.

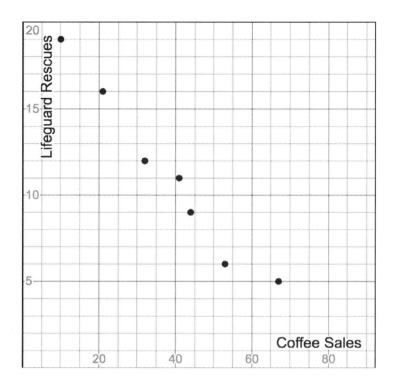

Describe the trend displayed by the scatterplot.

Solution 2

Notice how, as the coffee sales (x) increase, the lifeguard rescues (y) decrease. We call this a negative association between x and y. Recall that association does not imply causation. We are not saying that increased sales of coffee caused the need for less lifeguard rescues at the beach. In this case, it does seem logical that as the temperature decreased, more people wanted hot coffee, and, also due to the temperature decrease, less people went into the water, causing the need for less lifeguard rescues.

Example 3

Below is a scatterplot and trend line that looks at Patterson's Appliances video projector sales for the first ten weeks they were open. Let x represent the number of weeks and let y represent the number of projectors. The equation of the trend line is

$$y = 2.75x - 0.67.$$

Notice that you can tell if there is a positive or negative association between the variables from the slope of the regression line. In this case, the positive slope means that there is a positive association; as x increases y increases.

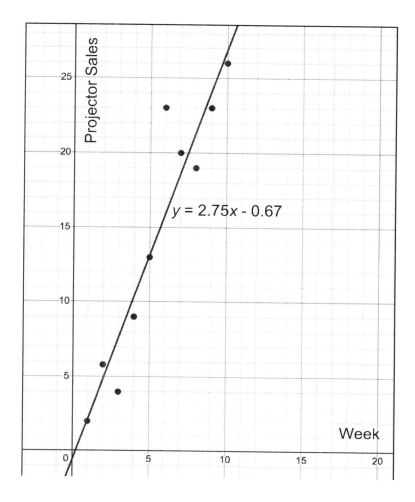

Based on this information, what could you predict for video projector sales for week 20? Round to the nearest integer.

Solution 3

Since the line seems to "hug," or approximate, the scatterplot points, we can substitute $x = 20$ into the regression equation that was given.

$$y = 2.75x - 0.67$$

$$y = 2.75(20) - 0.67$$

$$y = 54.33 \approx 54.$$

Patterson's, at this rate, could expect to sell 54 projectors during week 20.

Fill in the Blanks

When two pieces of numerical data are collected from subjects participating in an experiment, the data is called _____ and it can be graphed on the _____ axes using a _____. If the scatterplot shows that, as x increases, y increases, we say there is a _____ association between the variables. If the scatterplot shows that, as x increases, y decreases, we say there is a _____ association between the variables. In both cases, there is no _____ implied by the association. That is something that would have to be investigated. However, a trend line might help us _____ y-values for new x-values.

Basic Problem

Using the data from the scatterplot in Example 1, if the trend shown continued into the following week, what would be the best prediction for the number of water bottles sold if the temperature was 90 degrees?

a) 88   b) 62   c) 58   d) 55

Intermediate Problem

Using the data from the scatterplot in Example 2, if the trend shown continued into the following week, what would be the best prediction for the number of lifeguard rescues if that day's coffee sales was 80?

a) 9   b) 3   c) 14   d) 11

Challenging Problem

Dobby did research on the reading level of elementary school students. It turned out that there was a high positive association between reading level and the shoe size of these students. As shoe size increased, reading level generally increased. This was not causal--the researcher did not claim that bigger feet made somebody read better! Which of the following variables was likely "behind the scenes" of why these two variables had a positive association?

a) parents' salaries   b) age
c) time spent on homework weekly   d) ounces of water consumed daily

Numeric Entry Problem

Using the data from the scatterplot in Example 2, what is the number of lifeguard rescues associated with 10 coffees sold?

Multiple Choice with Multiple Answers Problem

Which of the following regression lines depict a negative association between the two variables?

[a] $y = 21 - 4x$ [b] $y = 1.6x - 3$ [c] $y = -5x + 21.6$ [d] $y = 2.2x - 42$

Key Descriptors

bivariate statistics, line of best fit, least squares line, linear regression, scatterplot, univariate statistics

Review/Renew

Which of the following is equivalent to -3^{-4} ?

a) -81   b) $\frac{1}{81}$ c) $-\frac{1}{81}$ d) $-\frac{1}{12}$

DID YOU KNOW THAT?

Actress Danica McKellar, who starred in a TV sitcom, "The Wonder Years," from 1988-1993, received her Ph.D. in mathematics from the University of Chicago, is the author of several books, and is a co-author of the Chayes-McKellar-Winn theorem.

PART 4

QUIZZES 1-25

5/5

Quiz 1
Date_ 05/30/22_____

---

1. Which of the following numbers is between 4 and -11?

a) -11.67   b) 4.001   (c) -8.2   d) -12

-11   4

CC 1

---

2. Which of the following expressions has the smallest value?

(a) -$|5 - 8|$ b) $|5 - 8|$ c) $|8 - 5|$ d) $|-2.9|$
-3   3   3   2.9

CC 2

---

3. Find the difference between the <u>smallest and largest prime factors</u> of 70.

a) 2   (b) 5   c) 3   d) 7

70   2,5,7, $\frac{2}{7}$

CC 3

---

4. The <u>additive inverse</u> of -5.66 is

(a) 5.66   b) 0   c) $\frac{1}{5.66}$ d) $-\frac{1}{5.66}$

CC 4

---

5. What is the <u>multiplicative inverse</u> of $\frac{22}{13}$?

a) 1   b) -$\frac{13}{22}$ c) -$\frac{22}{13}$ (d) $\frac{13}{22}$

CC 5

Quiz 2

Date_____ 6/1/22 _____

---

1. What value of x would make the fraction $\frac{4x - 12}{3x - 33}$ undefined?

a) 3   (b) 11   c) -11   d) -3

---

2. Find the value of $29 - (4^2 + 2) \div 2$.

a) 0   (b) 20   c) 9.5   d) 5.5

$29 - (16 + 2) \div 2 =$
$29 - 18 \div 2 =$
$29 - 9 = 20$

---

3. If $5\frac{2}{7}$ is expressed as an improper fraction, what is its reciprocal?

a) $\frac{37}{7}$ (b) $\frac{7}{37}$ c) $-\frac{7}{37}$ d) $-\frac{37}{7}$

$\frac{37}{7}$

---

4. The ratio of striped balloons to solid color balloons at the hot air balloon festival is 11:2. If there are 78 balloons in all, how may striped balloons are there?

(a) 66   b) 12   c) 6   d) 67

$11x + 2x = 78$
$13x = 78$ $x = 6$

$11x = 11 \times 6 = 66$

---

5. Twelve is what percent of 60?   12

$\frac{12}{60} \times 100 = 20\%$

a) 12%   b) 10%   (c) 20%   d) 0.2%

1. An GRE review program has 440 students this year. It is planning to expand, and increase the number of students 10% each year for the next three years. How many students will they have in that third year from now? Round to the nearest integer.

a) 586   b) 572   c) 484   d) 532

2. How many liters are equivalent to 678 cL?

a) 6.78 L   b) 0.00678 L   c) 67.8 L   d) 0.678 L

3. The function ♥ is defined as c ♥ $k = c^2 + 4k$. Find the value of 4 ♥ 7.

a) 65   b) 140   c) 44   d) 11

4. Simplify the following rational expression: $\frac{5x+9x^6}{x}$.

a) $5 + 9x^6$ b) $5 + 9x^5$ c) $5x + 9x^6$ d) $5x + 9x^5$

5. Which of the following expressions is equivalent to $7x^3 \cdot 3x^3$?

a) $10x^3$ b) $10x^6$ c) $21x^6$ d) $21x^3$

Quiz 4

Date_____

---

1. What is the measure of an interior angle of a regular octagon (8 sides)?

a) 160°   b) 135°   c) 22.5°   d) 45°

CC 60

---

2. The ratio of similitude between two similar hexagons is 2:5. If the area of the larger hexagon is 100, what is the area of the smaller hexagon?

a) 40   b) 4   c) 100   d) 16

CC 61

---

3. What is the measure of the other acute angle in a right triangle with acute angle 42 degrees?

a) 42°   b) 48°   c) 132°   d) 48°

CC 59

---

4. Which of the following is equivalent to $(2y^2)^4$?

a) $16y^8$ b) $16y^6$ c) $2y^8$ d) $8y^8$

CC 29

---

5. Find the least common multiple for the numbers 18 and 10.

a) 90   b) 60   c) 180   d) 2

CC 8

Quiz 5
Date_____

---

1. Express $\frac{2}{\sqrt{5}}$ as an equivalent fraction with a rational denominator.

a) $\frac{2\sqrt{5}}{5}$　　　b) $\frac{2}{5}$　　　c) $\frac{\sqrt{5}}{5}$　　　d) $\frac{10\sqrt{5}}{5}$

CC 34

---

2. Two trains at stations 600 miles apart leave at the same time and travel towards each other on parallel tracks. The faster train traveled an average of 10 mph faster than the slower train. They met each other after 5 hours. What was the speed of the slower train, in mph?

a) 55　　　b) 59　　　c) 69　　　d) 65

CC 49

---

3. One integer is 21 less than another. Their sum is 59. What is the smaller of the two numbers?

a) 40　　　b) 10.5　　　c) 19　　　d) 29

CC 48

---

4. The circumference of a circle, in terms of π, is 36π. What is the radius of the circle?

a) 18　　　b) 36　　　c) 9　　　d) 72

CC 52

---

5. A rectangle has length 40 and width 9. What is the length of the diagonal of the rectangle?

a) 49　　　b) 81　　　c) 41　　　d) 31

CC 58

Quiz 6

Date_____

---

1. Express the fraction $\frac{21}{35}$ in simplest form.

a) $\frac{1}{5}$ b) $\frac{3}{5}$ c) $\frac{3}{7}$ d) $\frac{7}{15}$

CC 11

---

2. The sum of three consecutive integers is 66. What is the largest of these three integers?

a) 21   b) 23   c) 65   d) 64

CC 49

---

3. One of the acute angles in a right triangle is four times the measure of the other. What is the measure of the larger angle?

a) 18   b) 72   c) 16   d) 90

CC 59

---

4. A circle has diameter 30. Find its area in terms of π.

a) 225π b) 900π c) 30π d) 15π

CC 54

---

5. What is the perimeter of a square whose area is 144 square feet?

a) 72'   b) 24'   c) 12'   d) 48'

CC 53

---

1. What is the greatest integer between -28.1 and -9.5?

a) -10   b) -29   c) -28   d) -9

CC 1

2. Inscribed angle XYZ in circle O has vertex Y, and it intercepts an arc that measures 50 degrees. What is the measure of $\angle XYZ$?

a) 50°   b) 25°   c) 100°   d) 10°

CC 66

3. What is the solution set for the equation $|2x + 11| = 71$?

a) {82, -60}   b) {30, -41}   c) {41, -30}   d) {-82, 60}

CC 38

4. Find the 19th term of the arithmetic sequence whose 17th term is 80 and 18th term is 86.

a) 94   b) 88   c) 90   d) 92

CC 39

5. If y is inversely proportional to x and $y = 10$ when $x = 8$, find x when $y = 16$.

a) 16   b) 5   c) 10   d) 80

CC 43

1. If the expression $5xk^2 + 6x^2k - 11xk^2 - 3x^2k$ has its like terms combined, what is the simplified expression?

a) $3x^2k - 6xk^2$ b) $3x^2k + 9xk^2$ c) $3x^2k + 6xk^2$ d) $3x^4k - 6xk^4$

CC 24

2. Triangle ABC has a right angle at C. Angle B measures 51 degrees. What is the difference between the degree measures of angle B and angle A?

a) 49   b) 90   c) 12   d) 39

CC 59

3. What is $\frac{7}{8}$ expressed as an equivalent decimal?

a) 1.125   b) 0.875   c) 87.5   d) 0.015

CC 15

4. Express $\sqrt[3]{11}^2$ using fractional exponents.

a) $11^{\frac{2}{3}}$ b) $11^{\frac{3}{2}}$ c) 11^6 d) $11^{\frac{3}{5}}$

CC 32

5. In right triangle MNP, the right angle is at N. If the legs measure 8 and 15, find the perimeter of the triangle.

a) 17   b) 23   c) 40   d) 30

CC 58

Quiz 9

Date_____

---

1. Big Boy's Book Club has 32 members. How many different slates of a President, Vice-President, and Secretary can be created? (A member can hold only one office).

a) 32   b) 29,760   c) 96   d) 32,768

CC 76

---

2. Which one of the following functions is an exponential function?

a) $y = 3x + 1$ b) $y = 4^x$ c) $y = 3x^2$ d) $y = x^2 - 7x + 12$

CC 41

---

3. Which of the following equations describes a linear graph with a slope of 3?

a) $3x + y = 10$ b) $2y = 3x - 6$ c) $y - 3x = 7$ d) $y = 3 - 7x$

CC 69

---

4. What is $\frac{3}{5}$ of 60?

a) 12   b) 36   c) 100   d) 24

CC 12

---

5. Find the sum of $\frac{7}{15}$ and $\frac{11}{25}$.

a) $\frac{43}{75}$ b) $\frac{68}{75}$ c) $\frac{18}{40}$ d) $\frac{9}{20}$ CC 14

Quiz 10

Date_____

1. If a sector of a circle graph is supposed to represent 35%, how many degrees would be in the central angle of that sector?

a) 35   b) 63   c) 126   d) 10.3

CC 67

2. Find the product of the roots for the quadratic equation $x^2 - 49 = 0$.

a) 14   b) 0   c) 49   d) -49

CC 37

3. Which of the following is equivalent to $25 + 15 \div 5$?

a) 8   b) 28   c) 22   d) 5

CC 7

4. A triangle has side lengths that are consecutive even integers. The perimeter is 72. What is the length of the longest side?

a) 26   b) 36   c) 22   d) 24

CC 51

5. A circle has area, in terms of π, of 64π. What is the diameter of the circle?

a) 8   b) 64   c) 16   d) 32

CC 54

1. What is the slope of a line that is perpendicular to the line with equation $2x + y = 13$?

a) 2   b) -2   c) $\frac{1}{2}$ d) $-\frac{1}{2}$

CC 70

2. How many prime numbers are there between 20 and 40?

a) 5   b) 4   c) 3   d) 6

CC 3

3. What is the additive inverse of $\frac{3}{7}$?

a) $-\frac{3}{7}$ b) $\frac{7}{3}$ c) $\frac{3}{7}$ d) $-\frac{7}{3}$

CC 4

4. What is the greatest common factor of 24 and 40?

a) 2   b) 4   c) 8   d) 12

CC 9

5. Express $5\frac{4}{7}$ as an improper fraction.

a) $\frac{25}{7}$ b) $\frac{35}{7}$ c) $\frac{27}{7}$ d) $\frac{39}{7}$

CC 10

1. The function $y = 4^x + 7$ crosses the y-axis at the point $(0, k)$. What is the value of k?

a) 1   b) 7   c) 8   d) 11

CC 29

2. An urn contains 4 green, 5 red, and 3 blue marbles. One marble is selected at random. What is the probability it is not red?

a) $\frac{1}{7}$ b) $\frac{7}{12}$ c) $\frac{4}{12}$ d) $\frac{5}{12}$

CC 78

3. Simplify $\sqrt{48}$ into simplest radical form.

a) $2\sqrt{12}$ b) $4\sqrt{12}$ c) $4\sqrt{12}$ d) $4\sqrt{3}$

CC 34

4. Find the sum of the roots for the quadratic equation $x^2 - 10x + 21 = 0$.

a) -10   b) 10   c) 7   d) 3

CC 36

5. What is the additive inverse of the reciprocal of 17?

a) -17   b) $\frac{1}{17}$ c) $-\frac{1}{17}$ d) 17

CC 5

1. If $f(x) = |x^2 - 5x|$, what is the closest prime number to $f(3)$ that is larger than $f(3)$?

a) 5　　　　b) 7　　　　c) 9　　　　d) 11

CC 23

2. The sum of two numbers, x and y, is 19. The difference $x - y$ is 9. What is the product of the numbers?

a) 90　　　　b) 70　　　　c) 95　　　　d) 171

CC 27

3. Which of the following expressions is equivalent to $6x^4 \cdot 5x^3$?

a) $30x^{12}$　　b) $30x^7$　　c) $11x^7$　　　　d) $11x^{12}$

CC 29

4. What is the product of $3 - 2x$ and $3 + 2x$?

a) $9 - 4x + 4x^2$　　　　b) 5　　　c) $9 - 4x^2$　　　d) $9 + 4x^2$

CC 37

5. What is the product if $1\frac{1}{5}$ is multiplied by $2\frac{1}{5}$?

a) $2\frac{16}{25}$　　b) $2\frac{1}{25}$　　c) $2\frac{1}{25}$　　d) $2\frac{1}{5}$

CC 12

Quiz 14

Date_____

---

1. The ratio of similitude between two similar triangles is 3:5. If a side of the smaller triangle is 12, what is the corresponding side of the larger triangle?

a) 96   b) 20   c) 80   d) 50

CC 61

---

2. What is the sum of the interior angles of a pentagon?

a) 540°   b) 360°   c) 900°   d) 180°

CC 60

---

3. What is the degree measure of the largest angle in a triangle with angles of 70 degrees and 30 degrees?

a) 100   b) 80   c) 70   d) 40

CC 59

---

4. In right triangle LMN, the right angle is at M and $\angle L = 60°$. If the hypotenuse measures 40, find the length of leg MN.

a) 20   b) $20\sqrt{3}$ c) $40\sqrt{3}$ d) $\frac{40}{\sqrt{3}}$

CC 62

---

5. A right triangle has one leg with length 15 and a hypotenuse with length 17. What is the length of the other leg?

a) 8   b) 2   c) 12   d) $\sqrt{514}$

CC 58

Quiz 15

Date_____

1. What is the solution set for the inequality $|2x + 5| + 1 < 26$?

a) $\{-10 < x < 15\}$

b) $\{-15 < x < 10\}$

c) $\{x < -15 \text{ or } x > 10\}$

d) $\{x < -10 \text{ or } x > 15\}$

CC 38

2. Find the 5th term of a geometric sequence whose 7th term is 8,192 and whose 8th term is 32,768.

a) 512   b) 2,048   c) 128   d) 32

CC 40

3. Find the mean of the first five positive integers.

a) 5   b) 3   c) 15   d) 2

CC 81

4. Find the quotient if $\frac{25}{8}$ is divided by $\frac{15}{16}$.

a) $\frac{2}{5}$ b) $\frac{15}{16}$ c) $1\frac{2}{3}$ d) $3\frac{1}{3}$

CC 13

5. Round 45.172399 to the nearest hundredth.

a) 45.18   b) 45.172   c) 45.17   d) 45.2

CC 16

1. Find the median of this distribution: 12, 34, 5, 7, 15, 35

a) 18   b) 13.5   c) 6   d) 11.5

CC 81

2. Find the perimeter of a regular pentagon whose side length is 13.

a) 52   b) 78   c) 65   d) 91

CC 51

3. A circle with radius 30 is inscribed in a square. What is the perimeter of the square?

a) 3,600   b) 225   c) 240   d) 900

CC 51

4. Find the value of y in the proportion $\frac{40}{y} = \frac{8}{11}$

a) 440   b) 66   c) 44   d) 55

CC 18

5. Eighteen is what percent of 150?

a) 20%   b) 10%   c) 12%   d) 0.12%

CC 20

1. Angles *A* and *B* are supplementary. If angle *A* measures 51 degrees, what is the difference between the degree measures of angle *A* and angle *B*?

a) 129°   b) 78°   c) 180°   d) 163°

CC 59

2. Which of the following equations describes a line perpendicular to $7x = 2y + 1$?

a) $y = -\frac{2}{7}x + 2$ b) $y = \frac{7}{2}x + 21$ c) $y = -\frac{7}{2}x + 2$ d) $y = \frac{2}{7}x + 2$

CC 70

3. What is the length of line segment *KL* if *K* has coordinates (2, 11) and *L* has coordinates (-5, 7)? Round to the nearest tenth.

a) 8.1   b) 5   c) 19.3   d) 18.2

CC 72

4. What is the turning point of a parabola whose equation is $y = (x - 5)^2 + 13$?

a) (-5, 15)   b) (5, 13)   c) (-5, -13)   d) (13, 5)

CC 74

5. What is the equation of a circle with center (-4, 3) and radius 12?

a) $(x + 4)^2 + (y + 3)^2 = 144$ b) $(x + 4)^2 + (y - 3)^2 = 36$

c) $(x + 4)^2 + (y - 3)^2 = 144$ d) $(x - 4)^2 + (y + 3)^2 = 36$

CC 73

Quiz 18

Date_____

1. Find the product of $\frac{x^2-49}{x^2+4x+4}$ and $\frac{x^2-4}{3x-21}$.

a) $\frac{x^2-5x-14}{3x-6}$ b) $\frac{x^2+5x-14}{3x+6}$ c) $\frac{x^2+5x-14}{3x-6}$ d) $\frac{x^2-5x+14}{3x+6}$

CC 45

2. What is the midpoint of the line segment whose endpoints are (-2, 11) and (12, 3)?

a) (7, 7)   b) (10, 14)   c) (5, 7)   d) (7, 5)

CC 72

3. The additive inverse of $\left|-13\right|$ is

a) 13   b) -13   c) 0   d) $\left|13\right|$

CC 4

4. The function ♣ is defined as x ♣ $y = (x + y)^2$. Find the additive inverse of 3 ♣ 1.

a) 16   b) -16   c) 4   d) -4

CC 23

5. If -5ab is subtracted from 19ab, what is the difference?

a) 14ab b) -14ab c) -24ab d) 24ab

CC 25

Quiz 19

Date_____

---

1. Which of the following graphs crosses the x-axis twice?

a) $y = x^2 + 4$ b) $y = x^2 - 4$ c) $y = x^2$ d) $y = 5x^2 + 4$

CC 74

---

2. Express $\frac{4}{9} a^{-3} b^2 c^{-7}$ as a rational expression using only positive exponents.

a) $\frac{4b^2}{9a^3c^7}$ b) $\frac{4}{9a^3b^2c^7}$ c) $\frac{4b^2c^7}{9a^3}$ d) $\frac{4a^3c^7}{9b^2}$

CC 31

---

3. What is the value of $4^{3.5}$?

a) 14   b) 128   c) 64   d) 28

CC 32

---

4. Which is the correct factorization of $x^2 - 9x + 20$?

a) $(x + 4)(x - 5)$ b) $(x - 4)(x + 5)$

c) $(x - 5)(x - 4)$ d) $(x - 10)(x - 2)$

CC 35

---

5. Find the roots of the equation $x^2 + 3x - 4 = 2$ to the nearest tenth.

a) {1.4, -4.4}   b) {-1.4, 4.4}   c) {4.4, -4.2}   d) {0.4, -3.4}

CC 36

1. A right triangle has hypotenuse 10 and one leg is 6. What is the area of the triangle?

a) 60   b) 30   c) 24   d) 48

CC 58

2. Which of the following points is on the line with equation $3y + x = 19$?

a) $(5, 4)$ b) $(4, 5)$ c) $(2, 11)$ d) $(3, 12)$

CC 68

3. Two lines are perpendicular. What is the product of their slopes?

a) 0   b) 1   c) -1   d) 90

CC 70

4. Which of the following points is a solution to the inequality $y > 4x - 1$?

a) $(0, 4)$ b) $(-1, -9)$ c) $(-2, -11)$ d) $(3, 1)$

CC 71

5. What is the circumference of a circle whose equation is $(x - 12)^2 + (y + 9)^2 = 64$? Leave answer in terms of π.

a) 8π b) 64π c) 16π d) 32π

CC 73

1. What is the sum of the solutions to $|x - 11| = 25$?

a) 36   b) -14   c) 50   d) 22

CC 38

2. Two angles of a triangle measure 34 and 50 degrees. What is the measure of the third angle?

a) 84   b) 6   c) 276   d) 96

CC 59

3. A rectangular solid has length 12', width 4' and height 6'. What is its volume?

a) 288 cu. ft.   b) 22 cu. ft.   c) 54 cu. ft.   d) 36 cu. ft.

CC 56

4. The sum of two positive integers is 44. One of the integers is 14 more than the other. What is the product of the integers?

a) 15   b) 29   c) 435   d) 1,276

CC 48

5. What is the sum, in degrees, of the interior angles of a nonagon (9 sides)?

a) 1, 620   b) 1,260   c) 1,980   d) 1,440

CC 60

Quiz 22

Date_____

---

1. Two parallel lines are cut by a transversal forming alternate interior angles of $2x + 1$ and $x + 9$ degrees. What is the measure of each of these angles?

a) 16°   b) 8°   c) 17°   d) 34°

CC 64

---

2. What is the equation of the axis of symmetry for the parabola $y = x^2 - 20x + 12$?

a) $x = 6$ b) $x - 6$ c) $x = 20$ d) $x = 10$

CC 74

---

3. A line with slope 4 goes through the point $(1, 17)$. What is the equation of this line?

a) $y = 4x + 17$ b) $y = 4x + 13$ c) $y = -\frac{1}{4}x + 13$ d) $y = -4x + 21$

CC 69

---

4. For what value of x is the fraction $\frac{x^2 - 1}{2x - 34}$ undefined?

a) 1   b) 17   c) -1   d) 0

CC 6

---

5. What is 109% of 50?

a) 54.5   b) 545   c) 0.00545   d) 5.45

CC 19

1. Find the y-intercept of the graph of $2y = x^2 - 6x + 18$.

a) 18   b) -3   c) 9   d) -9

CC 74

2. A pie chart has a sector that is supposed to represent 20%. How many degrees should be in the central angle of this sector?

a) 20   b) 36   c) 72   d) 54

CC 67

3. On yesterday's test, Ms. Mackin's 15 students had a mean of 84. One student was absent, and took a make-up today and received a grade of 72. What is the average of the entire class? Round to the nearest tenth.

a) 83.3   b) 84   c) 78   d) 83.9

CC 81

4. What is the least common multiple of the two smallest prime numbers?

a) 2   b) 3   c) 6   d) 12

CC 8

5. Julianne invested $3,000 into her retirement fund this year. She is planning to increase her annual investment 4% each year for the next five years. How much will she invest in the fifth year from now? Round to the nearest dollar.

a) $3,120   b) $3,600   c) $3,510   d) $3,650

CC 41

Quiz 24
Date_____

1. Find the quotient when $\frac{24}{35}$ is divided by $\frac{6}{5}$.

a) $\frac{5}{7}$ b) $\frac{7}{5}$ c) $\frac{7}{4}$ d) $\frac{4}{7}$

CC 13

2. How does the graph of $f(x) + 4$ compare to the graph of $f(x)$?

a) it is translated 4 units vertically up
b) it is translated vertically 4 units down
c) it is translated horizontally to the left 4 units
d) it is translated horizontally to the right 4 units

CC 75

3. How far will a train travelling at a speed of 72 mph go in 72 minutes?

a) 72 miles   b) 86.4 miles   c) 84 miles   d) 80.5 miles

CC 47

4. What is the correct factorization of $16x^2 - 25y^2$?

a) $(4x - 5y)(4x + 5y)$ b) $(4x - 5y)(4x - 5y)$

c) $(8x - 5y)(8x + 5y)$ d) $(4x + 5y)(4x + 5y)$

CC 37

5. Which expression is the square root of $36x^{16}$?

a) $6x^4$ b) $36x^8$ c) $6x^8$ d) $18x^8$

CC 29

Quiz 25

Date_____

---

1. What digit is in the 16th decimal place of the decimal $0.\overline{41295}$?

a) 4   b) 1   c) 2   d) 9

CC 15

---

2. Which of the following is not equivalent to 35%?

a) $\frac{35}{100}$ b) $\frac{7}{20}$ c) 0.35   d) 35

CC 17

---

3. A circle has diameter 12 inches. A sector with a central angle of 60 degrees is drawn in the circle. What is the length of the arc of the sector? Express your answer in terms of π.

a) 6π b) 2π c) 4π d) 3π

CC 52

---

4. Which of the following equations crosses the y-axis at $(0, 1)$?

a) $y = 3^x$ b) $y = 3^x + 1$ c) $y = 3^x - 1$ d) $y = -3^x$

CC 29

---

5. Find the multiplicative inverse of $f(9)$ if $f(x) = (x - 4)^2$.

a) $-\frac{1}{25}$ b) $\frac{1}{25}$ c) 25   d) -25

CC 23

PART 5

SOLUTIONS TO PROBLEMS FROM CORE CONCEPTS 1 - 88

Fill in the Blanks

On the number line, if number x is to the left of number y, then the number x is **less** than the number y. Any number to the left of 0 is **negative**, and any number to the right of 0 is **positive**, while **0** itself is neither positive nor negative. The number line never ends; it goes on infinitely in both directions.

Basic Problem

Which of the following numbers is between 5 and -9?   **c) -8.1**
Notice that -8.1 is to the right of -9 and to the left of 5.

Intermediate Problem

Which is a negative number between -7 and 3.3?   **d) -6**
Notice that -7.006 is slightly to the left of -7.

Challenging Problem

What is the greatest integer between -23.4 and -7.5?   **c) -8**
Look to the left of -7.5 to find the greatest integers less than -7.5, which is -8.

Numeric Entry Problem

Which of the numbers in the set {7, -2, -15, -19, 15, 11} is farthest from -3?   **15**

Quantitative Comparison

Compare Quantity A and Quantity B, using the information below. **b) Quantity B is greater.**

Quantity A	Quantity B
-79.11	**-79.0999**

Quantity B, -79.0999 is to the right of Quantity A, -79.11, on the number line.

Fill in the Blanks

The distance a signed number is from 0 on the number line is called its **absolute value** which can also be called the **magnitude** of the number. The absolute value of a number can never be **negative**, but it can be 0. A signed number can be viewed as a *directed* distance from the origin, and an absolute value can be viewed as an **undirected** distance from the origin.

Basic Problem

If -19 is added to its absolute value, what is the sum? **d) 0**

Intermediate Problem

Which of the following expressions has the smallest value? **a) -$|7 - 9|$**
Note that the other choices are all positive and **-$|7 - 9|$ = -2.**

Challenging Problem

If $x = -2$ and $y = -7$, which of the following expressions is equal to -5? **d) $|x| - |y|$**
Note that $|x| - |y|$ = 2 - 7 = -5.

Numeric Entry Problem

What is the absolute value of the difference between -132 and its absolute value?

$$\boxed{264}$$

The absolute value of -132 is 132. Put them on a number line to notice that one is 132 to the left of 0 and the other is 132 to the right of 0.

Multiple Choice with Multiple Answers Problem

Which of the following expressions is equal to 7?   **[b] $|8 - 1|$**   **[d] $|8| - |-1|$**

Fill in the Blanks

If a positive integer has exactly two divisors, it is called a **prime** number. Positive integers with more than two factors are called **composite** numbers. The only even prime number is **2** and all other even positive numbers are **composite**. The number 1 is not **prime** because it has only one factor, 1, and it is also not composite. There are **infinitely** many prime numbers.

Basic Problem

How many prime factors does the number 70 have?   **a) 3**
The three prime factors of 70 are 2, 5, and 7.

Intermediate Problem

Find the difference between the smallest and largest prime factors of 42.   **b) 5**
The prime factors of 42 are 2, 3, and 7, and 7 - 2 = 5.

Challenging Problem

What is the smallest number whose prime factors are 2, 3, 5, and 7?   **b) 210**
You'd have to multiply 2 × 3 × 5 × 7 to get a number that is divisible by all of those primes.

Numeric Entry Problem

If the largest prime factor of 35 is divided by the smallest prime factor of 35, express the answer as a fraction.

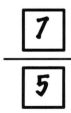

The largest prime factor of 35 is 7, and the smallest is 5, so the result is $\frac{7}{5}$ when they are divided.

Quantitative Comparison Problem

Compare Quantity A and Quantity B, using the information below. **b) Quantity B is greater**

Quantity A	Quantity B
The largest composite number less than 10.	**The sum of the three smallest prime numbers.**

The largest composite number less than 10 is 9, and the sum of the three smallest prime numbers, 2, 3, and 5, is 10.

CORE CONCEPT 4 SOLUTIONS: Additive Inverses

Fill in the Blanks

The additive inverse of a number is also called its **opposite**. You can create the additive inverse of any number by **multiplying** the number by **-1**. The sum of any number and its additive inverse is always **0**. The additive inverse of a positive number is **negative** and the additive inverse of a negative number is **positive**. The number 0 is also called the **additive inverse**, and, interestingly, the additive inverse of 0 is **0**.

Basic Problem

The additive inverse of -8.1 is   **d) 8.1**

Intermediate Problem

The additive inverse of $|-4|$ is   **b) -4**
Notice that the value of $|-4|$ is positive, so its additive inverse is negative.

Challenging Problem

What is the additive inverse of $-|5 - 11|$?   **a) 6**
Notice that the value of $-|5 - 11|$ is -6, so its additive inverse is positive.

Numeric Entry Problem

What is the additive inverse of $-\frac{5}{7}$?

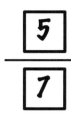

Multiple Choice with Multiple Answers Problem

Which two choices of the following represent the additive inverse of - 23?

[b] |-23| **[c] |-22| + |-1|**   (The additive inverse of -23 is 23).

CORE CONCEPT 5 SOLUTIONS: Multiplicative Inverses

Fill in the Blanks

The reciprocal of a number is also called its **multiplicative inverse**. When a negative or positive number is multiplied by its reciprocal, the result is **1**, which is also called the **multiplicative identity**. To find a multiplicative inverse, express the number as a fraction and flip the **numerator** and the **denominator**.

Basic Problem

What is the multiplicative inverse of $\frac{15}{7}$?   **a)** $\frac{7}{15}$

Intermediate Problem

What is the reciprocal of $\frac{1}{8}$?   **b) 8**

Challenging Problem

What is the additive inverse of the reciprocal of the only even prime number?   **b)** $-\frac{1}{2}$

The only even prime is 2. Its reciprocal is $\frac{1}{2}$, which has an additive inverse of $-\frac{1}{2}$.

Numeric Entry Problem

What is the reciprocal of the largest prime number less than 20?

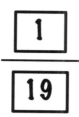

Note that the largest prime number less than 20 is 19.

Quantitative Comparison Problem

Compare Quantity A and Quantity B, using the information below.
c) The two quantities are equal.

Quantity A	Quantity B
The additive inverse of -3.	**The multiplicative inverse of $\frac{1}{3}$.**

Both quantities equal 3.

CORE CONCEPT 6 SOLUTIONS: Undefined Fractions

Fill in the Blanks

A rational number is the **quotient** of two integers, and it can be expressed as a fraction. If the denominator of a fraction is equal to **0**, we say the fraction is **undefined**.

Basic Problem

What value of x would make the fraction $\frac{5x - 10}{2x + 14}$ undefined? **c) -7**

Keep in mind that you work with the denominator only in this problem.

Intermediate Problem

For what value of p is the fraction $\frac{p+31}{p-2}$ undefined?　　**c) 2**

Challenging Problem

For what value(s) of k is the fraction $\frac{k+1.7}{(2-k)(k+4)}$ undefined?　　**c) 2, -4**

The denominator is 0 if $k = 2$ or $k = -4$.

Numeric Entry Problem

For what value of y is the fraction $\frac{y-3.2}{y-2.45}$ undefined?　　**2.45**

The denominator is 0 if $y = 2.45$.

Multiple Choice with Multiple Answers Problem

Which of the following fractions are undefined when $x = 12$?

[a] $\frac{5x-10}{2x-24}$　　　**[c]** $\frac{12x-12}{x-12}$　　　**[d]** $\frac{7x}{(x+2)(x-12)}$

In each fraction, if $x = 12$, the denominator is 0.

CORE CONCEPT 7 SOLUTIONS: Order of Operations

Fill in the Blanks

The order of operations requires you to do **parentheses** and **exponents** first. Then, you **multiply** and **divide** in order from left to right. Finally, you **add** and **subtract** in order from left to right. A mnemonic (trick) for remembering this is to use the initials **PEMDAS**.

Basic Problem

Find the value of $11 - (3^2 + 1) \div 2$.　　**d) 6**

The expression inside the parentheses yields 10, and $10 \div 2 = 5$. When 5 is subtracted from 11, the result is 6.

Intermediate Problem

Evaluate the expression $3^3 + 15 \div (6 - 3) \cdot 2^2 - 1$.   **a) 46**

Work on parentheses and exponents first to get $27 + 15 \div (3) \cdot 4 - 1$.

Then multiply and divide and then add and subtract: $27 + 5 \cdot 4 - 1 = 27 + 20 - 1 = 46$.

Challenging Problem

What is the value of the expression $21 \div (3^2 - 2) + 2^3 - 4^2 + 3(5 \cdot 2)$?   **c) 25**

Work on parentheses and exponents first to get $21 \div (7) + 8 - 16 + 3(10)$.

Then multiply and divide and then add and subtract: $3 + 8 - 16 + 30 = 25$.

Numeric Entry Problem

Express the value of the expression $7 \div (3 \cdot 23)$ as a fraction.

$$\frac{\boxed{7}}{\boxed{69}}$$

Work on parentheses and then divide left to right: $7 \div (3 \cdot 23) = \frac{7}{69}$.

Quantitative Comparison Problem

Compare Quantity A and Quantity B, using the information below. **a) Quantity A is greater.**

Quantity A	Quantity B
$30 - 4 \cdot 5 \div 2$	$24 \div 4 + 2 + 10$

Quantity A is equal to $30 - 4 \cdot 5 \div 2 = 30 - 20 \div 2 = 30 - 10 = 20$.
Quantity B is equal to $24 \div 4 + 2 + 10 = 6 + 2 + 10 = 18$.

Fill in the Blanks

The smallest positive integer that is a multiple of two or more given positive integers is called the **least common multiple**, and this is abbreviated as **LCM**. To find an LCM, you can make a **list** of the multiples of each integer, and look for the **smallest** multiple that the lists have **in common**.

Basic Problem

Find the least common multiple for the numbers 12 and 15.   **b) 60**

Intermediate Problem

What is the additive inverse of the least common multiple of 3, 5, and 10?   **c) -30**

Challenging Problem

What is the least common multiple of the three smallest prime numbers?   **a) 30**

The three smallest prime numbers are 2, 3, and 5.

Numeric Entry Problem

What is the multiplicative inverse of the lowest common multiple of the smallest four natural numbers?

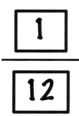

The smallest four natural numbers are 1, 2, 3, and 4, and their LCM is 12.

Multiple Choice with Multiple Answers Problem

Which of the following sets of numbers have a least common multiple of 60?

[a] {4, 15}   [c] {3, 4, 5}   [d] {5, 12}

Fill in the Blanks

The **greatest common factor** of a set of integers is the **largest** positive integer that divides **evenly** into the original given numbers. Dividing evenly into an integer means that, after dividing, there is no **remainder**. If you had a set of twenty different prime numbers, their GCF would be **1**.

Basic Problem

What is the greatest common factor of the integers 15 and 30? **c) 15**
Note that 5 is a *common* factor, but not the *greatest* common factor.

Intermediate Problem

Given the numbers 7 and 11. Which of the following statements, I, II, III, are true?
b) II and III only

> I. The GCF is 7.
> II. The LCM is 77.
> III. Both numbers are prime.

Note that the GCF is 1, so statement I is false.

Challenging Problem

Find the GCF of the four largest composite numbers less than 19.   **d) 1**

The four largest composite numbers less than 19 are 14, 15, 16, and 18, and their GCF is 1.

Numeric Entry Problem

Find the sum of the GCF and LCM for the integers 3 and 7. $\boxed{22}$

Note that the GCF = 1 and the LCM = 21, and 'sum' tells you to add.

Quantitative Comparison Problem

Compare Quantity A and Quantity B, using the information below. **b) Quantity B is greater.**

Quantity A	Quantity B
The GCF of 16 and 48.	**The LCM of 3 and 8.**

The GCF of 16 and 48 is 16, and the LCM of 3 and 8 is 24.

CORE CONCEPT 10 SOLUTIONS: Improper Fractions and Mixed Numbers

Fill in the Blanks

An improper fraction is a fraction that has its **numerator** greater than or equal to its **denominator**. Improper fractions can be expressed as **mixed numbers**, which are numbers that have an integer part and a fractional part. If a fraction has an equivalent, non-zero numerator and denominator, it is equal to **1**.

Basic Problem

Express $6\frac{3}{7}$ as an improper fraction.   **c)** $\frac{45}{7}$

Multiply 6 by 7 and add 3 to get the numerator. Denominator stays as 7.

Intermediate Problem

If $4\frac{2}{3}$ is expressed as an improper fraction, what is its reciprocal?   **b)** $\frac{3}{14}$

Multiply 4 by 3, and then add 2, to get the numerator. The mixed number is $\frac{14}{3}$ and flip to find the reciprocal.

Challenging Problem

Which of the following fractions has a prime numerator when it is converted to an improper fraction?   **a)** $2\frac{3}{5}$

The numerators for b), c), and d) are, respectively, 38, 65, and 93, which are all composite numbers. The numerator for $2\frac{3}{5}$ is 13.

Numeric Entry Problem

What is the value of $\left|-5\frac{3}{7}\right|$ when it is expressed as an improper fraction?

Multiply 5 by 7, and then add 3, to get the numerator.

Multiple Choice with Multiple Answers Problem

Which of the following mixed numbers has a composite number for the numerator when converted to an improper fraction?　　**[a]** $2\frac{5}{8}$　　　**[b]** $4\frac{2}{7}$

Note that $2\frac{5}{8} = \frac{21}{8}$ and $4\frac{2}{7} = \frac{30}{7}$, and 21 and 30 are composite (not prime) numbers.

CORE CONCEPT 11 SOLUTIONS: Simplifying Fractions

Fill in the Blanks

When a fraction is expressed in **simplest** form, the GCF of the **numerator** and the **denominator** is equal to **1**. If a fraction is not in simplest form, you can simplify it by dividing the numerator and the denominator by the **greatest** common factor.

Basic Problem

Express the fraction $\frac{12}{48}$ in simplest form.　　**a)** $\frac{1}{4}$

Divide numerator and denominator by the GCF, which is 12. Note that choices c) and d) are equivalent to $\frac{12}{48}$ but they are not in simplest form.

Intermediate Problem

Which of the following fractions is in simplest form?   **d)** $\frac{41}{60}$

Choice a) has a GCF of 19, choice b) has a GCF of 4, and choice c) has a GCF of 6.

Challenging Problem

Express the multiplicative inverse of $\frac{51}{60}$ in simplest form.   **d)** $\frac{20}{17}$

Flip the fraction and divide numerator and denominator by the GCF, 3.

Numeric Entry Problem

Express the reciprocal of $\frac{42}{60}$ as a mixed number in simplest form. $\boxed{1\frac{3}{7}}$

Flip the fraction, simplify using the GCF, 6, and change to a mixed number.

Quantitative Comparison Problem

Compare Quantity A and Quantity B, using the information below. **b) Quantity B is greater.**

Quantity A	Quantity B
The denominator of the fraction $\frac{52}{60}$ when it is written in simplest form.	**The numerator of the improper fraction, in simplest form, equivalent to the mixed number $5\frac{1}{3}$.**

Quantity A is 15 and Quantity B is 16.

CORE CONCEPT 12 SOLUTIONS: Multiplying Numeric Fractions

Fill in the Blanks

If you are asked to find the **product**, you need to multiply. When multiplying two fractions, it is a good idea to **simplify** first to make the computations easier. If you have to multiply mixed numbers, change each mixed number to an **improper fraction** first and then use the multiplying fractions procedure.

Basic Problem

What is the product if $3\frac{1}{7}$ is multiplied by $3\frac{1}{2}$? **d) 11**

Rewrite the problem using improper fractions as $\frac{22}{7} \cdot \frac{7}{2}$, and then simplify and multiply.

Intermediate Problem

What is $\frac{2}{3}$ of 210? **a) 140**

Write the problem as $\frac{2}{3} \cdot \frac{210}{1}$, and then simplify and multiply.

Challenging Problem

What is $\frac{5}{6}$ of the product of $2\frac{1}{2}$ and 12? **c) 25**

First rewrite the second part of the problem as

$$\frac{5}{2} \cdot \frac{12}{1}.$$

After simplifying and multiplying, the result is 30. Then take $\frac{5}{6}$ of 30 by multiplying

$$\frac{5}{6} \cdot \frac{30}{1}.$$

The result is 25.

Numeric Entry Problem

What is $\frac{2}{3}$ of $\frac{15}{22}$?

$$\frac{\boxed{5}}{\boxed{11}}$$

Write the problem as $\frac{2}{3} \cdot \frac{15}{22}$, and then simplify and multiply.

Multiple Choice with Multiple Answers Problem

Which of the following problems has an answer equivalent to $\frac{1}{2}$?

[c] $\frac{15}{7} \cdot \frac{7}{30} =$

Simplify and multiply to see that only [c] is equivalent to $\frac{1}{2}$. These Multiple Choice with Multiple Answers problems *can* have only 1 correct answer.

CORE CONCEPT 13 SOLUTIONS: Dividing Numeric Fractions

Fill in the Blanks

In the equation $x \div y = b$, x is called the **dividend**, y is called the **divisor** and b is called the **quotient**. If x and y are fractions, you can change the problem to a multiplication of fractions problem by using the **reciprocal** of the divisor, which is the second fraction. If x and y are mixed numbers, they need to be changed to **improper** fractions first.

Basic Problem

$\frac{5}{8} \div \frac{3}{4} =$ **c)** $\frac{5}{6}$

Write as $\frac{5}{8} \cdot \frac{4}{3}$, simplify, and multiply.

Intermediate Problem

Cameron needs to divide $7\frac{1}{3}$ cups of antifreeze equally into 11 test tubes for a chemistry experiment. How many cups of antifreeze should go into each test tube?   **a)** $\frac{2}{3}$

Change the mixed number $7\frac{1}{3}$ to the improper fraction $\frac{22}{3}$ first. Then use keep-change-flip.

Challenging Problem

The quotient of two fractions is $\frac{5}{3}$. The divisor is $\frac{12}{55}$. What is the dividend?   **b)** $\frac{4}{11}$

Multiply the divisor, $\frac{12}{55}$, by the quotient, $\frac{5}{3}$, to get the dividend, since multiplication is the inverse operation of division. (If the quotient was 10, and the divisor was 3, the dividend, 30, would be found by multiplying).

Numeric Entry Problem

Find the quotient when $\frac{42}{45}$ is divided by $\frac{7}{20}$. Express your answer as an improper fraction in simplest form.

Write as the multiplication problem $\frac{42}{45} \cdot \frac{20}{7}$, simplify, and multiply.

Quantitative Comparison Problem

Compare Quantity A and Quantity B, using the information below. **a) Quantity A is greater.**

Quantity A	Quantity B
The reciprocal of $\frac{4}{11}$.	The product of $\frac{4}{11}$ and its reciprocal.

The reciprocal of $\frac{4}{11}$ is $\frac{11}{4}$, which is greater than 1. The product of $\frac{4}{11}$ and $\frac{11}{4}$ is 1.

CORE CONCEPT 14 SOLUTIONS: Adding and Subtracting Numerical Fractions

Fill in the Blanks

When you are asked to find the **sum**, you add, and when you are asked to find the difference, you **subtract**. If the denominators are the same, the process is simpler than if the denominators are different. When the denominators are different, you need to find the **lowest common denominator**, which is the LCM for the denominators. Then you multiply the fractions by 1, where 1 is written in fractional form, engineered by you to yield the common denominator. This common denominator is also used in the answer, and the **numerators** can then be added or subtracted as indicated.

Basic Problem

Linda is mixing $7\frac{1}{2}$ cubic yards of mulch with $6\frac{1}{4}$ cubic yards of topsoil to create a mixture. How many cubic yards are in the mixture?   **d) $13\frac{3}{4}$**

Note that you need to find the sum using the lowest common denominator 4, and $7\frac{1}{2} = 7\frac{2}{4}$.

Intermediate Problem

$\frac{9}{16} + \frac{13}{24} =$ **d) $1\frac{5}{48}$**

Note that you need to use the lowest common denominator 48 and change the sum, $\frac{53}{48}$, an improper fraction, to a mixed number.

Challenging Problem

$15 - 2\frac{5}{8} =$ **b) $12\frac{3}{8}$**

You can express 15 as $14\frac{8}{8}$ to make the subtraction more straightforward.

Numeric Entry Problem

Find the difference between the sum and the product of $\frac{1}{2}$ and $\frac{1}{4}$.

$$\frac{\boxed{5}}{\boxed{8}}$$

The sum is $\frac{3}{4}$ and the product is $\frac{1}{8}$. Change $\frac{3}{4}$ to $\frac{6}{8}$ and subtract $\frac{1}{8}$ to get $\frac{5}{8}$.

Multiple Choice with Multiple Answers Problem

Which of the following problems has an answer greater than 1?   **[b] $\frac{11}{7} - \frac{1}{5}$ [c] $\frac{6}{7} + \frac{3}{7}$**

Choice [a] is equal to 1. Choice [b] is equal to $\frac{48}{35}$. Choice [c] is equal to $\frac{9}{7}$, which is greater than 1. Choice [d] equals $\frac{1}{8}$.

CORE CONCEPT 15 SOLUTIONS: Equivalent Fractions and Decimals

Fill in the Blanks

If you want to convert a fraction to an equivalent decimal, **divide** the **numerator** by the **denominator**. A decimal that ends after a finite number of places is called a **terminating** decimal and a decimal that repeats a group of digits in the same order, endlessly, is called a **repeating** decimal. Some non-terminating decimals do have patterns, like 0.12112111211112111112111112..., but since the pattern is not *repeating*, these decimals represent **irrational** numbers.

Basic Problem

What is $\frac{5}{8}$ expressed as an equivalent decimal?   **b) 0.625**

Divide 5 by 8 on a calculator or using long division.

Intermediate Problem

Which decimal is equivalent to $\frac{53}{99}$?   **c) $0.\overline{53}$**

Be careful to notice what digits repeat and to make sure the overbar is correctly placed.

Challenging Problem

A fraction that is equivalent to a repeating decimal is being created. The numerator is the largest prime number less than 10. The denominator is the smallest composite number greater than 16. How many digits are in the pattern that repeats?   **a) 1**

The fraction is $\frac{7}{18}$. When converted to a decimal, it is equal to $0.3\overline{8}$, so just the digit 8 repeats into infinity and the answer is 1.

Numeric Entry Problem

What digit is in the 13th decimal place of the decimal $0.\overline{53142}$?

1

Since five digits repeat, the first ten digits of the decimal expansion are 0.5314253142. Since we want the 13th digit, we need to go three digits into the next pattern of five digits, so the 13th digit is 1.

Quantitative Comparison Problem

Compare Quantity A and Quantity B, using the information below. **a) Quantity A is greater.**

Quantity A	Quantity B
$\dfrac{53}{99}$	$\dfrac{35}{66}$

Convert each to a decimal. Since $\frac{53}{99} = 0.\overline{53}$ and $\frac{35}{66} = 0.5\overline{30}$, Quantity A is greater.

CORE CONCEPT 16 SOLUTIONS: Rounding Decimals

Fill in the Blanks

A decimal with one decimal place can be written as a fraction with denominator **10**. A decimal with **two** decimal places can be written as a fraction with denominator 100. A decimal with four decimal places can be written as a fraction with denominator **10,000**. When a given decimal is rounded, the new rounded number is **not** equal to the given number; it is an **approximation** of the given number.

Basic Problem

Round 98.055 to the nearest tenth.   **b) 98.1**

Underline the 0 in the tenths place and circle the 5 to its right.

Intermediate Problem

Michael rounds the number 12.62684 to the nearest tenth and Courtney rounds it to the nearest thousandth. What is the sum of their rounded approximations?   **a) 25.227**

Michael rounds it to 12.6 and Courtney rounds it to 12.627. When adding decimals, remember to line up the decimal points.

Challenging Problem

Round $6.\overline{781}$ to the nearest ten-thousandth.   **c) 6.7818**

The nearest ten thousandth requires four decimal places. Expanding the repeating decimal to $6.781781\overline{781}$will make the solution clearer.

Numeric Entry Problem

Round $8.\overline{6}$ to the nearest hundredth.   **8.67**

Write it as 8.666... and notice the third '6' rounds the second '6' to a '7.'

Multiple Choice with Multiple Answers Problem

Which of the following decimals, when rounded to the nearest hundredth, is 23.74?

[a] 23.737   [c] $23.\overline{73}$

Look at the digit in the third decimal place, and use it to select the correct digit for the second decimal place. Note that [b] rounds to 23.75 and [d] rounds to 23.75.

CORE CONCEPT 17 SOLUTIONS: Interpreting Percent

Fill in the Blanks

Percent means "out of **100**." You can think of a percent as a fraction whose **denominator** is 100. These fractions can be converted directly to decimals. To change a percent to an equivalent decimal, you move the decimal point two places to the **left**, and drop the **percent** sign. To change a decimal to an equivalent percent, move the decimal point **two** places to the **right**, and add a percent sign.

Basic Problem

Which of the following is equivalent to 0.23?   **b) 23%**

Intermediate Problem

Which of the following, I, II, III, represent numbers that are equivalent to 45%?
b) I and II only

I. 0.45   II. $\frac{9}{20}$ III. $\frac{45}{100}$ %

Note that in III, the expression equals 0.45%, not 45%.

Challenging Problem

Which of the following represents $\frac{13}{250}$ as an equivalent percent?   **a) 5.2%**

As a decimal, $\frac{13}{250} = 0.052$, so when the decimal point is moved two spaces to the right, the result is 5.2%.

Numeric Entry Problem

Express 70% as a fraction in simplest form.

Using a GCF of 10, notice that $70\% = \frac{70}{100} = \frac{7}{10}$.

Quantitative Comparison Problem

Compare Quantity A and Quantity B, using the information below.
c) The two quantities are equal.

Quantity A	Quantity B
0.13	**13%**

When 13% is converted to an equivalent decimal, the "invisible" decimal point to the right of the '3' is moved two places to the left, forming 0.13.

Fill in the Blanks

Ratios can be expressed as fractions. If two **ratios** are set equal to each other, a **proportion** is formed. In the proportion $\frac{r}{s} = \frac{t}{u}$, s and t are the **means** and r and u are the **extremes**. In any proportion, the **product** of the means is equal to the **product** of the extremes, and this is often informally called **cross multiplying**.

Basic Problem

Find the value of y in the following proportion.   **b) 84.**

$$\frac{60}{y} = \frac{5}{7}$$

Cross multiply and solve the equation $5y = 420$.

Intermediate Problem

The ratio of cars to motorcycles at the Cruise Night parking lot is 9:2. If there are 132 vehicles in all, how may motorcycles are there?   **d) 24**

Represent the number of cars as $9x$ and the number of motorcycles as $2x$ and solve the equation $9x + 2x = 132$. Since $x = 12$, substitute 12 for x in $2x$ to get 24.

$$11x + 2x = 78$$
$$13x = 78$$
$$x = 6$$

Challenging Problem

There are 150 rookies (first year players) at the Florence Baseball Academy and 180 non-rookies. What is the ratio of rookies to total players expressed as a fraction in simplest form?

a) $\frac{5}{11}$

The total number of players is 330, so the ratio is $\frac{150}{330}$, which is $\frac{5}{11}$ in simplest form.

Numeric Entry Problem

What is the value of p in the following proportion?

$$\boxed{\mathbf{4}}$$

$$\frac{7.5}{6} = \frac{5}{p}$$

Cross multiply and solve the equation $7.5p = 30$.

Multiple Choice with Multiple Answers Problem

Which of the following proportions has the solution $p = 4$?   [a] $\frac{5}{20} = \frac{p}{16}$ [d] $\frac{7}{28} = \frac{1}{p}$

Cross multiply and solve each resulting equation. Choice [b] has solution $p = 12$ and choice [c] has solution $p = 24$.

CORE CONCEPT 19 SOLUTIONS: **Computations with Percent**

Fill in the Blanks

The **percent proportion** is useful in solving many percent problems. In this proportion, the ratio $\frac{\text{part}}{\text{whole}}$ is set equal to the ratio $\frac{\%}{100}$, which represents the percent written as a **fraction** with denominator **100**.

Basic Problem

Chloe buys a new car for $28,400. She is also charged 6% sales tax. How much sales tax must she pay?   **b) $1,704**

Set up the proportion $\frac{x}{28,400} = \frac{6}{100}$ and solve for x.

Intermediate Problem

Sixteen is what percent of 128?   **a) 12.5%**

Set up the proportion $\frac{16}{128} = \frac{x}{100}$ and solve for x.

Challenging Problem

Michelle sells audio equipment and is paid a commission for each month's sales. She receives 11% on her first $5,000 of sales and 5% on the rest of her sales. Last month she sold $6,300 worth of audio equipment. What was her commission?   **a) $615**

Find 11% of 5,000. The answer is $550. Subtract 5,000 from 6,300 to get 1,300. Find 5% of 1,300. The answer is $65. Add $550 and $65 to get $615.

Numeric Entry Problem

Ten is 62% of what number? Round your answer to the nearest tenth.

$$\boxed{16.1}$$

Set up the proportion $\frac{10}{x} = \frac{62}{100}$, solve for x, and round to the nearest tenth.

Quantitative Comparison Problem

Compare Quantity A and Quantity B, using the information below.
c) The two quantities are equal.

<u>Quantity A</u>   <u>Quantity B</u>

Fifteen percent   **Forty percent**
of forty.   **of fifteen.**

Set up percent proportions for each quantity. Quantity A becomes $\frac{x}{40} = \frac{15}{100}$ and Quantity B becomes $\frac{x}{15} = \frac{40}{100}$. Cross multiply, and solve the equation. Each quantity is equal to 6.

CORE CONCEPT 20 SOLUTIONS: Percent Change

Fill in the Blanks

A positive percent change represents an **increase** in quantity and a negative percent change represents a **decrease** in quantity. When you multiply by a percent over 100% you **increase** the original number and when you multiply by a percent under 100% you **decrease** the original number. If a quantity doubles, you can say it has *increased* **100**%.

Basic Problem

The Smithville School District's budget was $5,444,000 this year. Next year it will increase 2%. What will the budget be next year?   **b) $5,552,880**

Intermediate Problem

Camp Nittany has 550 campers this year. It is planning to expand, and increase the number of campers 8% each year for the next three years. How many campers will they have after those three years? Round to the nearest integer. **d) 693**

There will be three 8% increases from this year's 550, so compute $550(1.08)^3$.

Challenging Problem

Last year's orchestra budget was increased 12% to get this year's budget. This year's budget is $5,000. What was last year's budget? Round to the nearest cent.   **c) $4,464.29**

Let x = last year's budget. That increased 12% to get this year's budget. Solve the equation $1.12x = 5,000$.

Numeric Entry Problem

Express 101% as an equivalent decimal.   **1.01**

Move the decimal point two places to the left and removed the percent sign.

Multiple Choice with Multiple Answers Problem

Which of the following expressions represents a 17% change from 60?

[a] 60(1.00-0.17)   **[b] $60(1.17)$**   **[c] $60(1.00 + 0.17)$**

Choice [d] represents no change from 60 since 1.17 - 0.17 = 1.

CORE CONCEPT 21 SOLUTIONS: English System Measurement Conversions

Fill in the Blanks

You can use a **proportion** to convert units in the English measurement system. When setting up this proportion, the first fraction should be the **conversion ratio**, which is always equal to 1. Both numerators should have the same **units** and both denominators should have the same **units**.

Basic Problem

A roll of duct tape contains 60 yards of tape. How many feet of tape does the roll contain?

a) 180

Use the proportion with feet in the numerators and yards in the denominators (or vice versa). Use the fact that 3 feet = 1 yard to set up the conversion ratio.

Intermediate Problem

A drum of oil contains 55 gallons. An oil change for a car requires 5 quarts. How many oil changes can the drum of oil cover? **b) 44**

The drum holds 220 quarts. Since each oil change requires 5 quarts, divide 220 by 5.

Challenging Problem

Yoko is converting 2.1 miles into yards. Which of the following statements, I, II, III, are true?

I. The number of miles is more than the number of yards.
II. There are 1,760 yards in a mile.
III. The 2.1 miles equals more than 4,000 yards.

c) II only

There are 5,280 feet in a mile. Use the proportion to find that there are 1,760 yards in a mile. That makes II true. Since 2.1 miles is equivalent to 3,696 yards, I and III are not true.

Numeric Entry Problem

How many pounds are equivalent to 148 ounces?

9.25

Quantitative Comparison Problem

Compare Quantity A and Quantity B, using the information below. **a) Quantity A is greater.**

Quantity A	Quantity B
16.5 gallons	**65 quarts**

There are 4 quarts in a gallon, so 16.5 gallons is equal to 66 quarts.

CORE CONCEPT 22 SOLUTIONS: Metric System Measurement Conversions

---

Fill in the Blanks

The basic unit of weight in the metric system is the **gram**. A kilogram is **1,000** grams. The basic unit of length in the metric system is the **meter**, and there are 100 meters in a **hectometer**. The basic unit of liquid volume in the metric system is the **liter**, and a **milliliter** is equivalent to $\frac{1}{1000}$ of a liter.

Basic Problem

How many meters are equivalent to 2,345 km?   **d) 2,345,000 m**

Move the decimal point, which is to the right of the 5, three places to the right and add three zeroes.

Intermediate Problem

A liter is approximately 61.02 cubic inches. If a car engine is 427 cubic inches, how many liters is it? Round to the nearest tenth.   **a) 7 L**

Set up a proportion with cubic inches in the numerators and liters in the denominators. Solve the proportion $\frac{61.02}{1} = \frac{427}{x}$ and round the result.

Challenging Problem

The NextGen wireless router can cover a radius of 45.7m. The Big Boy wireless router can cover a radius of 23.1 m. The routers are located 100 meters from each other. A yard is approximately 0.9144m.

Which of the following statements, I, II, III, are true?   **a) I only**

> I. There is no location covered by both routers.
> II. The routers are approximately 60 yards apart.
> III. The NextGen router covers a radius of 457 cm.

The routers are 100 m apart, which is more than the sum of 45.7 and 23.1, so statement I is true. Statement II is false since 100 meters is approximately 110 yards. Statement III is false since the NextGen router covers a radius of 4,570 cm.

Numeric Entry Problem

A kilogram is approximately 2.2 pounds. How many kilograms are equivalent to 135 pounds? Round to the nearest tenth.

$$\boxed{61.4}$$

Set up a proportion with pounds in the numerators and kilograms in the denominators. Solve the proportion $\frac{2.2}{1} = \frac{135}{x}$ and round the result.

Multiple Choice with Multiple Answers Problem

Which of the following quantities are equivalent to 61,511 meters?

[a] 61.511 km   **[b] 6, 151, 100 cm**

Choice [c] is equivalent to 0.00061511 m and choice [d] is equivalent to 6,151,100 m.

Fill in the Blanks

A function is a mapping, or a **rule**, that assigns elements from the **domain** to elements of the **range**. If the notation $f(x)$ is used, x can be called the **input** variable, and a value of x is **substituted** into the function rule so $f(x)$ can be computed. For each value of x, the value of $f(x)$ is **unique**.

Basic Problem

The function ♥ is defined as a ♥ $b = a^2 - 3b$. Find the value of 5 ♥ 2.　　**b) 19**

Substitute 5 for x and 2 for y, so a ♥ $b = a^2 - 3b$ becomes 5 ♥ 2 = $5^2 - 3(2) = 25 - 6 = 19$.

Intermediate Problem

Find the additive inverse of $f(7)$ if $f(x) = (x+7)^2$.　　**a) -196**

By substitution, $f(7) = 196$, and the additive inverse of 196 is -196.

Challenging Problem

If $f(x) = |x^2 - 2x - 16|$, what is the closest prime number to $f(4)$?　　**b) 7**

By substitution, $f(4) = |4^2 - 2(4) - 16| = |-8| = 8$, so the closest prime number is 7.

Numeric Entry Problem

The function ♣ is defined as x ♣ $y = (2x - y)^2$. Find the value of 1.1 ♣ 1.　　$\boxed{\textbf{1.44}}$

By substitution, 1.1 ♣ 1 = $(2(1.1) - 1)^2 = (1.2)^2 = 1.44$.

Quantitative Comparison Problem

Compare Quantity A and Quantity B, using the information below.　**b) Quantity B is greater.**

Quantity A	Quantity B
$f(7)$, if $f(x) = 3x$	$g(7)$, if $g(x) = f(x) + 5$

Note that $f(7) = 21$ and $g(7) = 21 + 5 = 26$.

Fill in the Blanks

An algebraic expression with one term is called a **monomial** and an algebraic expression with more than one term is called a **polynomial**. You can simplify a polynomial by highlighting the **like** terms and using the **coefficients** of the like terms to combine them.

Basic Problem

If the expression $3xp^2 + 6x - 7xp^2 - 4x^2p$ has its like terms combined, what is the simplified expression?　　**d) $-4xp^2 - 4x^2p + 6x$**

Intermediate Problem

Simplify the expression $-2x^2y + 11xy^2 - 7x^2y^2 - x^2y + 3x^2y^2 - 12xy^2$ by combining like terms.　　**d) $-3x^2y - xy^2 - 4x^2y^2$**

Challenging Problem

Two like terms are being combined. The variable part is k^2mp^5. The two coefficients are the largest prime number less than 30 and the reciprocal of the smallest prime number. What is the simplest form after these two like terms are combined?　　**a) $29.5 \, k^2mp^5$**

The largest prime number less than 30 is 29 and the smallest prime number is 2. The reciprocal of 2 is $\frac{1}{2}$ which is 0.5 in decimal form.

Numeric Entry Problem

If the polynomial $9abc + 6ab - 7ab^2 - abc + 4ab - 12a^3b^2$ is simplified by combining like terms, what is the coefficient of the abc term?

$$\boxed{8}$$

Multiple Choice with Multiple Answers Problem

Which of the following expressions are equivalent to $19x^3$?

[a] $10x^3 + 9x^3$　　　**[b] $20x^3 - x^3$**　　　(Combine like terms).

Fill in the Blanks

Adding and subtracting polynomials requires the same skills as **combining like terms**. When subtracting, it is important to put parentheses around the **subtrahend** and place a 1 in front of the parentheses, so you remember to use the **distributive property** before combining like terms.

Basic Problem

Subtract $-2x^2 - 8x + 19$ from $3x^2 + 10x - 7$.   **c) $5x^2 + 18x - 26$**

$3x^2 + 10x - 7 - 1(-2x^2 - 8x + 19) = 3x^2 + 10x - 7 + 2x^2 + 8x - 19 = 5x^2 + 18x - 26$.

Intermediate Problem

If $-4kp$ is subtracted from $10kp$, what is the difference?   **a) $14kp$**

Be careful when subtracting a negative quantity: $10kp - (-4kp) = 10kp + 4kp = 14kp$.

Challenging Problem

If $14x^a y^3$ and $9x^5 y^b$ are like terms, what is the value of ab?   **b) 15**

If they are like terms, then $a = 5$ and $b = 3$, so $ab = 15$.

Numeric Entry Problem

If the following three binomials are combined, what is the coefficient of the $x^5 y^4$ term?

$$(14x^5 y^4 - 11) - (8x^5 y^4 - 1) + (2.5x^5 y^4 + 6.2)$$

$$\boxed{8.5}$$

Quantitative Comparison Problem

Compare Quantity A and Quantity B, using the information below.

Quantity A	Quantity B
3x + 7x - 2y	8x + 9x - y

d) The relationship cannot be determined from the information given.

The values of the quantities depend on the values of x and y, which can be positive or negative real numbers.

CORE CONCEPT 26 SOLUTIONS: Literal Equations

Fill in the Blanks

Equations that are made up primarily of letters are called **literal equations**. Many **formulas** you already know, like the Pythagorean theorem, or area and perimeter formulas, or the quadratic formula, are literal equations. Since a **literal equation** has several letters, it is possible to isolate, or solve for, any of the letters.

Basic Problem

Solve the equation $7a + 3b = \frac{5x}{4}$ for b.   **b)** $b = \frac{5x - 28a}{12}$

Cross multiply to get $28a + 12b = 5x$. Subtract $28a$ from both sides and divide both sides by 12.

Intermediate Problem

Solve the equation $x^2 - \frac{p^2}{4} = 5$ for p.   **a)** $p = \pm\sqrt{4x^2 - 20}$

Add $\frac{p^2}{4}$ to both sides: $x^2 = 5 + \frac{p^2}{4}$

Subtract 5 from both sides: $x^2 - 5 = \frac{p^2}{4}$

Multiply both sides by 4: $4x^2 - 20 = p^2$

Then take the square root of both sides.

Challenging Problem

If $5cx - 20x = 13r$ is solved for x, for what value of c is x undefined?   **c) 4**

Factor out x on the left side: $x(5c - 20) = 13r$. Then $x = \frac{13r}{5c-20}$. Set the denominator $5c$ - 20 equal to 0.

Numeric Entry Problem

If the equation $5x + 41y = 3z$ is solved for y, what is the denominator?

$$\boxed{41}$$

Subtract $5x$ from both sides and divide by 41 to get $y = \frac{3z-5x}{41}$.

Multiple Choice with Multiple Answers Problem

When solved for y, which of the following expressions is equivalent to $a + b$?

[b] $b + a - y = 0$ **[d]** $\frac{1}{a+b} = \frac{1}{y}$

Choice [a] yields $y = b - a$ and choice [c] yields $y = \frac{a}{b}$.

CORE CONCEPT 27 SOLUTIONS: Systems of Linear Equations

Fill in the Blanks

We reviewed two methods of solving a system of two linear equations in two unknowns. One method is the **elimination** method and the other is the **substitution** method. In the elimination method, one variable is eliminated because its coefficients were engineered to become **additive inverses**. In the **substitution** method, one variable is isolated and the expression it is equal to is substituted into the second equation.

Basic Problem

Solve the following system of equations and express the solution as an ordered pair (x, y).

$$2x - 3y = 1$$
$$4x + 3y = 29$$

a) (5, 3)

When the equations are added, the result $6x = 30$ gives us $x = 5$. Substitute 5 into either equation to get $y = 3$.

Intermediate Problem

If the following system of equations is solved, what is the multiplicative inverse of s?

$$r + 3s = 17$$
$$3r + 2s = 23$$

a) 0.25

In the first equation, subtract $3s$ from both sides to get $r = 17 - 3s$. Then use the substitution method. Using parentheses, replace r in the second equation with $(17 - 3s)$ to get $s = 4$. The multiplicative inverse (the reciprocal) is $\frac{1}{4}$ which is equivalent to 0.25.

Challenging Problem

The sum of two numbers x and y is 17. The difference $x - y$ is 7. What is the product of the numbers?   **c) 60**

Set up two equations, $x + y = 17$ and $x - y = 7$. Add them to eliminate y and you get $2x = 24$. Substitute $x = 12$ in either equation to get $y = 5$. Multiply 12 by 5 to get the product.

Numeric Entry Problem

If the following system is solved, what is the value of k, expressed as a decimal?

$$2k - 5m = -4$$
$$8k + 5m = 9$$

$$\boxed{0.5}$$

Add the equations to get $10k = 5$ and solve for k.

Quantitative Comparison Problem

Compare Quantity A and Quantity B, using the information below. **a) Quantity A is greater.**

Quantity A	Quantity B
The value of x in the solution to the system	**The value of y in the solution to the system**
$x + y = -2$	$x + y = -2$
$x - y = 8$	$x - y = 8$

Add the equations to get $2x = 6$ and solve to get $x = 3$. Substitute $x = 3$ into either equation to get $y = -5$.

CORE CONCEPT 28 SOLUTIONS: Inequalities

Fill in the Blanks

The **transitive** property states that if $a > d$ **and** $d > m$, then $a > m$. Algebraic inequalities can be solved much like equations can be solved, but since there could be infinitely many solutions, the solution set is shown using set notation or by graphing on the **number line**. Remember that when multiplying or dividing both sides of an inequality by a **negative** number, you must remember to reverse the direction of the inequality sign.

Basic Problem

Find the solution set of the inequality $2x + 15 < 49$.   **b) $\{x < 17\}$**

Subtract 15 from both sides and divide both sides by 2.

Intermediate Problem

Which is not a solution to the following system of inequalities? **a) 6.9**

$$3x - 1 \geq 20$$

$$-5x + 2 \geq -43$$

Solving both inequalities gives you $x \geq 7$ and $x \leq 9$, and 6.9 is not in this interval on the number line. You could have substituted all of the solutions into both inequalities, but that would be more time consuming.

Challenging Problem

If the literal inequality $-4x - b \geq k + 7$ is solved for x, what is the solution?

d) $x \leq \frac{b+k+7}{-4}$

Add b to both sides, and then divide both sides by -4, remembering to reverse the direction of the inequality sign since you are dividing by a negative number.

Numeric Entry Problem

What is the only solution to the following system of inequalities?

$$\boxed{x = 5}$$

$$2x \geq 10$$

$$x + 1 \leq 6$$

Solving both inequalities gives you $x \geq 5$ and $x \leq 5$, so the only solution is $x = 5$.

Multiple Choice with Multiple Answers Problem

Which of the following inequalities has 5 in its solution set?

[a] $x + 1 \leq 6$ **[b]** $-2x + 1 < 12$ **[c]** $3x + 1 > 15$ (Substitute 5 into each inequality).

CORE CONCEPT 29 SOLUTIONS: Laws of Exponents

Fill in the Blanks

In the expression $7x^{12}$, 7 is the **coefficient**, x is the **base** and 12 is the **exponent**. When multiplying powers of the same **base**, you keep the same base, and add their exponents to find the product. When dividing powers of the same base, you keep the same base and **subtract** their exponents to find the **quotient**. If a monomial is raised to a power, you can **multiply** the exponents to simplify. Be sure to remember that a monomial like x has an "invisible" exponent on the x that is equal to **1**.

Basic Problem

Which of the following expressions is equivalent to $4x^3 \cdot 5x^2$?   **a) $20x^5$**

Multiply the coefficients and add the exponents.

Intermediate Problem

Which monomial is equivalent to the expression $3x^5 + 2x^5 + 2x^2 \cdot 3x^3$ in simplified form?

b) $11x^5$

Follow the order of operations. First, multiply the monomials to get $6x^5$. Then add the like terms to get $11x^5$.

Challenging Problem

Simplify $\frac{5x^{11}y^3 \cdot 8x^2y^7}{(2x^3y^2)^3}$ using the laws of exponents.   **d) $5x^4y^4$**

The numerator simplifies to $40x^{13}y^{10}$. The denominator simplifies to $8x^9y^6$. Divide the coefficients and subtract the exponents.

Numeric Entry Problem

If the expression $(5m^5)^2$ is simplified using the laws of exponents, what is the product of the coefficient and the exponent?

$$\boxed{250}$$

The expression simplifies to $25m^{10}$ so the product is 250.

Quantitative Comparison Problem

Compare Quantity A and Quantity B, using the information below.

Quantity A	Quantity B
$3x^4 + 11$	$7x^5 + 25$

d) The relationship cannot be determined from the information given.

If x is negative, Quantity B could be smaller. If x is positive, Quantity B could be larger.

Fill in the Blanks

When dividing a polynomial by a monomial, you must remember to divide each **monomial** in the numerator by the denominator. You can break the original fraction into **separate** fractions and simplify each fraction, either physically, or in your head. These fractions can also be called **rational expressions**. Remember to follow the **laws of exponents** when simplifying.

Basic Problem

Simplify the following rational expression:

$$\frac{5w^4 + 7w^6 - 11w^8 - w^{12}}{w^2}$$

a) $5w^2 + 7w^4 - 11w^6 - w^{10}$

Divide the coefficients and subtract the exponents. Note that the coefficient is 1 if there is no coefficient shown.

Intermediate Problem

Simplify the rational expression $\frac{25x^{10}y^5 - 50x^5y^{15} + 250x^{20}y^{10}}{5(xy)^5}$.   **d) $5x^5 - 10y^{10} + 50x^{15}y^5$**

Note that the coefficient 5 in the denominator is not in the parentheses, so it is not being raised to any power. The denominator is equivalent to $5x^5y^5$.

Challenging Problem

If $x \neq 0$, for what value of m does the rational expression $\frac{x^{5m+7}}{x^{4m+10}}$ equal x?   **a) 4**

The exponent on x is 1. Subtract the exponents in the fraction and set that equal to 1. Be sure the put parentheses around the denominator so you remember to distribute when you subtract.

$$5m + 7 - (4m + 10) = 1$$

$$5m + 7 - 4m - 10 = 1$$

$$m - 3 = 1$$

$$m = 4.$$

Numeric Entry Problem

If the rational expression $\frac{12x^6 + 16x^5 + 8x^3}{4x^2}$ is simplified, what is the sum of the coefficients?

The fraction simplifies to $3x^4 + 4x^3 + 2x$, and the sum of the coefficients 3, 4, and 2, is 9.

Multiple Choice with Multiple Answers Problem

Which of the following fractions simplifies to $5x^2$?   **[c]** $\frac{20x^3}{4x}$ **[d]** $\frac{-20x^4}{-4x^2}$

Choice [a] simplifies to $5x^4$ and choice [b] simplifies to $5x^3$.

CORE CONCEPT 31 SOLUTIONS: Negative Exponents

Fill in the Blanks

Negative exponents are a somewhat **abstract** extension of the original notion of exponents. If negative exponent is a factor of the **numerator**, you can place it in the denominator with a positive exponent. If a negative exponent expression is a factor in the denominator, place it as a factor in the **numerator** with a positive exponent.

Basic Problem

Which of the following is equivalent to 2^{-3} ?   **b)** $\frac{1}{8}$

Rewrite as $\frac{1}{2^3}$ and $2^3 = 8$.

Intermediate Problem

Express $\frac{5}{8}a^{-2}b^5c^{-3}$ as a rational expression using only positive exponents.   **a)** $\frac{5b^5}{8a^2c^3}$

Challenging Problem

Which of the following is equivalent to $(2x^2)^{-3}$?   **c)** $\frac{1}{8x^6}$

Notice that 2 is also being raised to the -3 power, and $2^{-3} = \frac{1}{8}$.

Numeric Entry Problem

Find the value of $4x^{-2}$ when $x = -5$. Express your answer in decimal form.

$$\boxed{0.16}$$

Note that $\frac{4}{25} = 0.16$.

Quantitative Comparison Problem

Compare Quantity A and Quantity B, using the information below. **a) Quantity A is greater.**

Quantity A	Quantity B
$4x^{-3}$ **when** $x = 2$	$2x^{-2}$ **when** $x = -3$

Note that $\frac{4}{2^3} = \frac{1}{2}$ and $\frac{2}{3^2} = \frac{2}{9}$, which is less than $\frac{1}{2}$.

Fill in the Blanks

The original idea of using exponents to be a shorthand for repeated multiplication extends to a 0 exponent, a negative exponent, and a fractional exponent. In the expression $\sqrt[a]{x}^{-b}$, a is the **root** and b is the **exponent**, or power. When expressed using fractional coefficients, a becomes the **denominator** of the fractional exponent and b becomes the **numerator**.

Basic Problem

Express $\sqrt[5]{6}^{3}$ using fractional exponents.   **b) $6^{\frac{3}{5}}$**

Intermediate Problem

Find the sum of $16^{-\frac{1}{4}} + 16^{\frac{3}{2}}$.   **b) 64.5**

Note that $16^{-\frac{1}{4}} = \frac{1}{\sqrt[4]{16}}$ and the fourth root of 16 is 2, so $16^{-\frac{1}{4}} = \frac{1}{2} = 0.5$, and $16^{\frac{3}{2}} = \sqrt[2]{16}^{3} = 4^3 = 64$.

Challenging Problem

Find the sum of $4^{3.5}$ and $9^{2.5}$.   **c) 371**

Note that $4^{3.5} = 4^{\frac{7}{2}} = \sqrt[2]{4}^{7} = 2^7 = 128$. Similarly, $9^{2.5} = 9^{\frac{5}{2}} = \sqrt[2]{9}^{5} = 3^5 = 243$. Add 243 to 128.

Numeric Entry Problem

If $\sqrt[4]{36}^{5}$ is expressed using fractional exponents, what is the reciprocal of the exponent?

The exponent is $\frac{5}{4}$, so the reciprocal is $\frac{4}{5}$.

Multiple Choice with Multiple Answers Problem

Which of the following expressions simplifies to 8?   **[a] $2 \cdot \sqrt[3]{64}$ [d] $\dfrac{\sqrt[3]{64}^2}{2}$**

Choice [b] equals 16 since it is the cube root of 64, which is 4, squared. Choice [c] equals 64 since it is the square root of 16, which is 4, cubed.

CORE CONCEPT 33 SOLUTIONS: Scientific Notation

Fill in the Blanks

When expressing a number in scientific notation, you need to create **two** numbers that multiply to equal your original number. The first number is a decimal between **1** and **10**, and the digits of this number are called **significant digits**. The second number is written with an exponent as a power of **10**.

Basic Problem

Express the number 34,709,000,000 in scientific notation.   **d) 3.4709×10^{10}**

The decimal point was moved 10 places to the left to form the number consisting of the significant digits, which is 3.4709.

Intermediate Problem

Express the following quotient in scientific notation.   **b) 4.5×10^4**

$$\frac{5.85 \times 10^8}{1.3 \times 10^4}$$

Split into two fractions, and note that $\frac{5.85}{1.3} = 4.5$. Then use the laws of exponents for $\frac{10^8}{10^4}$ which is 10^4.

Challenging Problem

Find the product of (6.2×10^9) and (4.43×10^5) and express your answer in scientific notation.   **b) 2.7466×10^{15}**

Multiplying the powers of 10 gives 10^{14}. Multiplying 6.2 by 4.43 gives 27.466, but this is not a number between 1 and 10. The expression 27.466×10^{14} is not in scientific notation, so move the decimal point one place to the left and compensate by adding 1 to the exponent 14 on the 10.

Numeric Entry Problem

Express 3.41×10^{-3} as a decimal in standard notation.

$$\boxed{0.00341}$$

Move the decimal point 3 places to the left and add leading zeroes as placeholders.

Quantitative Comparison Problem

Compare Quantity A and Quantity B, using the information below. **b) Quantity B is greater.**

Quantity A	Quantity B
9.113×10^3	$\sqrt[3]{1000}^4$

Quantity A is 9,113. Quantity B is 10,000 since the cube root of 1,000 is 10 and $10^4 = 10,000$.

CORE CONCEPT 34 SOLUTIONS: Simplifying Radical Expressions

Fill in the Blanks

The square root of a non-perfect square is an **irrational** number, which means it is a non-terminating, non-repeating decimal. If the denominator of a fraction is a radical, you can **rationalize** the denominator by multiplying the fraction by 1 in a certain form. Combining **like** radicals is much like combining like **terms**, and simplifying a radical requires that one of the radicand's factors be a **perfect square**.

Basic Problem

Simplify $\sqrt{24}$ into simplest radical form. **a) $2\sqrt{6}$**

Factor $\sqrt{24}$ into $\sqrt{4} \cdot \sqrt{6}$.

Intermediate Problem

Express $9\sqrt{48} - 2\sqrt{12}$ in simplest radical form. **c) $32\sqrt{3}$**

Express $9\sqrt{48} - 2\sqrt{12}$ as $9\sqrt{16} \cdot \sqrt{3} - 2\sqrt{4} \cdot \sqrt{3}$. This is equal to $36\sqrt{3} - 4\sqrt{3}$.

Challenging Problem

Express $\dfrac{5+\sqrt{19}^2}{\sqrt{8}}$ in simplest form. **d) $6\sqrt{2}$**

Express $\dfrac{5+\sqrt{19}^2}{\sqrt{8}}$ as $\dfrac{5+19}{\sqrt{8}} = \dfrac{24}{\sqrt{8}} = \dfrac{24\sqrt{8}}{8} = 3\sqrt{8} = 3\sqrt{4}\sqrt{2} = 6\sqrt{2}$.

Numeric Entry Problem

What is the value of $\dfrac{2}{5}\sqrt{\dfrac{16}{9}}$ in simplest form?

$$\frac{8}{15}$$

Note that $\sqrt{\dfrac{16}{9}} = \dfrac{4}{3}$ and $\dfrac{2}{5} \cdot \dfrac{4}{3} = \dfrac{8}{15}$.

Multiple Choice with Multiple Answers Problem

Which of the following expressions simplifies to 3?   **[c]** $\dfrac{\sqrt{81}}{3}$ **[d]** $\dfrac{\sqrt{18}}{\sqrt{2}}$

Note that $\dfrac{\sqrt{81}}{3} = \dfrac{9}{3} = 3$ and $\dfrac{\sqrt{18}}{\sqrt{2}} = \dfrac{\sqrt{18}}{\sqrt{2}} \cdot \dfrac{\sqrt{2}}{\sqrt{2}} = \dfrac{\sqrt{36}}{2} = \dfrac{6}{2} = 3$.

Fill in the Blanks

When you multiply two binomials, you are finding their **product**. In certain cases, their product is a quadratic **trinomial**, which has **three** terms. When you **factor** a quadratic trinomial, you reverse the multiplication, and you should look first to see if you can factor out a **greatest common factor**. Whenever you factor a quadratic trinomial, check your result by multiplying the two binomials you came up with.

Basic Problem

Which is the correct factorization of $x^2 - x - 6$?   **b) $(x-3)(x+2)$**

Intermediate Problem

Which is the correct complete factorization of $3y^2 + 18y - 48$?   **b) $3(y-2)(y+8)$**

Factor out the GCF, which is 3, first, and then factor the remaining trinomial $y^2 + 6y - 16$ into $(y-2)(y+8)$.

Challenging Problem

Which is the correct complete factorization of $4m^2 - 18m - 10$?
b) $2(2m+1)(m-5)$

Factor out the GCF, which is 2, first, and then factor the remaining trinomial $2m^2 - 9m - 5$ into $(2m+1)(m-5)$.

Numeric Entry Problem

If $x^2 + 7x + 10$ is factored into the two binomial factors $(x+2)$ and $(x+k)$, what is the value of k?

$$\boxed{5}$$

Quantitative Comparison Problem

Compare Quantity A and Quantity B, using the information below. **b) Quantity B is greater.**

Quantity A	Quantity B
$(x + 2)(x + 5)$	$x^2 + 7x + 11$

Quantity A is equal to $x^2 + 7x + 10$, which is 1 less than Quantity B.

CORE CONCEPT 36 SOLUTIONS: Solving Quadratic Equations

Fill in the Blanks

If you have to solve a quadratic equation, there are three common methods. If the quadratic equation **factors**, you can solve it by **factoring**. You can use the **quadratic formula** to solve *any* quadratic equation, so it is a good idea to memorize it. Both of these methods require getting the equation into a form that is equal to 0. A third method, **completing the square**, does not require that the equation be set equal to 0.

Basic Problem

Using factoring, find the solution set for the quadratic equation $x^2 + 3x - 30 = -2$.

a) {-7, 4}

Add 2 to both sides to get $x^2 + 3x - 28 = 0$. This factors to $(x - 4)(x + 7) = 0$. Set each binomial factor equal to 0 to get the solution set.

Intermediate Problem

Find the roots of the equation $x^2 - 3x - 4 = 1$ to the nearest tenth.   **b) {4.2, -1.2}**

This quadratic does not factor, so use the quadratic formula. You must subtract 1 from both sides first, to get the equation equal to 0. It is now $x^2 - 3x - 5 = 0$ so you can identify a, b, and c.

Substitute into the quadratic formula to get $x = \frac{-b \pm \sqrt{b^2 - 4ac}}{2a} = \frac{3 \pm \sqrt{29}}{2}$. Use a calculator to compute $\frac{3+\sqrt{29}}{2}$ *and* $\frac{3-\sqrt{29}}{2}$ and round to the nearest tenth.

Challenging Problem

If the discriminant of the quadratic equation $x^2 + 8x + k = 0$ is 4, find the value of k.

a) 15

Substitute into the discriminant to get $b^2 - 4ac = 64 - 4k$. Set $64 - 4k = 4$. Solve for k.

Numeric Entry Problem

If the quadratic equation $x^2 - 10x = 11$ is solved by completing the square, what number must be added to both sides of the equation?

$$\boxed{25}$$

The b coefficient is -10. Half of that is -5. Square -5 to get 25.

Multiple Choice with Multiple Answers Problem

Which of the following are roots of the quadratic equation $x^2 - 6x + 10 = 2$?

[a] 2   [b] 4

Subtract 2 from both sides to get $x^2 - 6x + 8 = 0$, factor to $(x - 2)(x - 4) = 0$.

> ### CORE CONCEPT 37 SOLUTIONS: The Difference of Two Perfect Squares

Fill in the Blanks

When the binomials $(x + 7)$ and $(x - 6)$ are multiplied, the product, since it has three terms, is called a **trinomial**, and when the binomials $(x + 5)(x - 5)$ are multiplied, the answer is a binomial. The difference of two perfect squares factors into the **sum** and **difference** of two numbers, which are the square roots of the original squares. You can multiply the sum and difference between two numbers mentally, since the product of the outer terms and the product of the inner terms are **additive inverses**, and cancel out to 0.

Basic Problem

Find the product of $(2x - 5)$ and $(2x + 5)$.   **a) $4x^2 - 25$**

Intermediate Problem

Factor $81k^2 - 16m^2$.   **b) $(9k + 4m)(9k - 4m)$**

Challenging Problem

Find the solution set for the quadratic equation $3x^2 - 120 = 27$.   **c) {7, -7}**

Divide both sides by 3 to get $x^2 - 40 = 9$. Subtract 9 from both sides to get $x^2 - 49 = 0$. Factor to get $(x - 7)(x + 7) = 0$. Then set each factor equal to 0.

Numeric Entry Problem

If $x^2 - 4k$ factors into $(x + 10)(x - 10)$, find the value of k.

The product of the binomials is $x^2 - 100$, so $4k = 100$ and $k = 25$.

Quantitative Comparison Problem

Compare Quantity A and Quantity B, using the information below.
c) The two quantities are equal.

<u>Quantity A</u>   <u>Quantity B</u>

$$(3x + 7)(3x - 7)$$ $$9x^2 - 49$$

Fill in the Blanks

When solving an absolute value equation, first **isolate** the absolute value expression on one side of the equation. Then create **two** equations and solve each of them. When solving an absolute value inequality, isolate the absolute value expression on one side of the inequality. Then create two new **inequalities** and solve each of them.

Basic Problem

What is the solution set for the equation $|4x + 1| = 61$?   **a) {15, -15.5}**

Solve each of the equations $4x + 1 = 61$ and $4x + 1 = -61$ for x.

Intermediate Problem

What is the solution set for the inequality $|2x + 3| + 4 < 27$?   **a) $\{-13 < x < 10\}$**

Subtract 4 from both sides and then solve each of the inequalities
$2x + 3 < 23$ and $2x + 3 > -23$ for x.

Challenging Problem

What is the solution set for the inequality $|5 - 2x| - 7 \geq 20$?   **d) $\{x \leq -11 \text{ or } x \geq 16\}$**

Add 7 to both sides. Solve the inequalities $5 - 2x \geq 27$ and $5 - 2x \leq -27$ for x. Remember that when you divide both sides of an inequality by a negative number, the inequality sign is reversed.

Numeric Entry Problem

What is the sum of the solutions to $|x - 5| = 15$?   **10**

Solve each of the equations $x - 5 = 15$ and $x - 5 = -15$ for x.
The solutions are {-10, 20} and their sum is 10.

Multiple Choice with Multiple Answers Problem

Which of the following are solutions for the equation $|5x + 21| = 71$?   **[b]10**   **[c] -18.4**

Solve the equations $5x + 21 = 71$ and $5x + 21 = -71$.

CORE CONCEPT 39 SOLUTIONS: Arithmetic Sequences

Fill in the Blanks

The first term of an arithmetic sequence is usually denoted a_1. Successive terms are found by adding the **common difference** to the previous term. You can find any term in the sequence as long as you have the previous term and the **common difference**. There is a formula to find S_n, which is the **sum** of the first n terms of an arithmetic sequence.

Basic Problem

Find the 22nd term of the arithmetic sequence whose 20th term is 70 and 21st term is 78.

d) 86

Subtract to find that the common difference is 8. Add 8 to 78 to get 86.

Intermediate Problem

An arithmetic sequence has first term 4 and common difference 5. Find the sum of the first 21 terms.   **a) 1,134**

First find the 21st term: $4 + 20 \cdot 5 = 104$

Substitute into the sum formula: $S_n = \frac{n(a_1+a_n)}{2} = \frac{21(4+104)}{2} = \frac{21 \cdot 108}{2} = 1{,}134.$

Challenging Problem

In an arithmetic sequence, the first term is 2 and the 11th term is 72. What is the common difference?   **c) 7**

Use the formula to find the nth term: $a_n = a_1 + (n-1)d$

Substitute: $72 = 2 + (11-1)d$

Solve for d: $\qquad\qquad\qquad\qquad\qquad$ $70 = 10d$ so $d = 7$.

Numeric Entry Problem

The tenth term of an arithmetic sequence with common difference 3 is 46. What is the first term?

$$\boxed{\mathbf{19}}$$

Use the formula to find the nth term: $\qquad$ $a_n = a_1 + (n-1)d$

Substitute: $\qquad\qquad\qquad\qquad$ $46 = a_1 + (10-1)3$

Solve for a_1: $\qquad\qquad\qquad\qquad$ $46 = a_1 + 27,$ so $a_1 = 19$.

Quantitative Comparison Problem

Compare Quantity A and Quantity B, using the information below. **a) Quantity A is greater.**

Quantity A	Quantity B
The tenth term of the arithmetic sequence **1, 4, 7, 10...**	**The sixth term of the arithmetic sequence with first term 2 and common difference 5.**

Quantity A is 28, found by adding 3 nine times to 1 to get the tenth term. Quantity B is 27, found by adding 5 five times to 2 to get the sixth term.

CORE CONCEPT 40 SOLUTIONS: Geometric Sequences

Fill in the Blanks

Successive terms of a geometric sequence are found by multiplying the previous term by the **common ratio**. If you are given a geometric sequence, you can find the common ratio by **dividing** any given term by the previous term. There is a formula to find a_n, which is the nth term of the geometric sequence, and S_n, which is the **sum** of the first n terms of a geometric sequence.

Basic Problem

Find the 4th term of a geometric sequence whose 6th term is 486 and whose 7th term is 1,458.   **b) 54**

Divide 1,458 by 486 to find that the common ratio is 3. Use that to get the fifth term (162) and divide again by 3 to get the fourth term, 54.

Intermediate Problem

Find the sum of the first seven terms of the following geometric sequence: **a) 136,717**

$$1, 5, 25, ...$$

The common ratio is 5. Use the S_n formula to find the sum.

$$S_n = \frac{n(1 - r^n)}{1 - r} = \frac{7(1 - 5^7)}{1 - 5} = 136{,}717.$$

Challenging Problem

Which could be the missing term in the following geometric sequence?   **b) 12**

$$3, \underline{\hspace{1cm}}, 48, 192, ...$$

Let r be the common ratio. Divide 192 by 48 to get $r = 4$. To find the missing term, divide 48 by 4.

Numeric Entry Problem

Find the 7th term of the following geometric sequence: 4000, 2000, 1000, 500, ...

$$\boxed{62.5}$$

Divide 2,000 by 4,000 to get the common ratio 0.5. Use the formula for the nth term.

$$a_n = a_1 r^{n-1}$$

$$a_7 = (4{,}000)0.5^{7-1}$$

$$a_7 = 62.5.$$

Multiple Choice with Multiple Answers Problem

Which of the following are geometric sequences with common ratio 3?

[b] 4, 12, 36, 108, ...   **[c] 1, 3, 9, 27, ...**

Choice [a] is an arithmetic sequence. Choice [d] is not a geometric sequence (or an arithmetic sequence!).

CORE CONCEPT 41 SOLUTIONS: Appreciation and Depreciation

Fill in the Blanks

If something gains value as time passes, we say it **appreciates**, and if something loses value as time passes, we say it **depreciates**. If an item appreciates at a constant percent rate per year, we can model it using an **exponential** growth function. If it depreciates at a constant percent rate each year, we can model it using an exponential **decay** function.

Basic Problem

A record collection is currently valued at $1,000 and it increases annually. The following expression shows its value after 4 years.

$$1,000(1.045)^4$$

At what percent does the collection increase each year?   **b) 4.5%**

If you convert 1.045 to an equivalent percent by moving the decimal point two places to the right, you can see that the annual value is 104.5% of the previous year, so 4.5% is the increase.

Intermediate Problem

Apollo, age 66, is currently eligible to get $30,500 in Social Security each year. If she waits four years to take the benefits, until age 70, the benefits will increase 8% each year after age 66. What will her annual Social Security benefit be if she waits until age 70 to take it? Round to the nearest dollar.   **d) $41,495**

Let S represent the value in four years. Use the exponential growth function

$$S = 30,500(1.08)^4.$$

Challenging Problem

Imagine a $2,000,000 property investment that is projected to grow at a rate of 8.5% annually. In how many years will it double in value at this rate?
b) between 8 and 9 years

Let V represent the value. Use the exponential growth function $V = 2,000,000(1.085)^k$ and try different values of k from the answer choices.

If $k = 8$, the value had not yet doubled, and if $k = 9$, the value had more than doubled.

Numeric Entry Problem

Noah has a vintage baseball card that was worth $90 eight years ago, but it depreciated at the rate of 2% per year since then. What is its current value? Round to the nearest dollar.

$$\boxed{77}$$

Let V represent the value in four years. Use the exponential growth function

$$V = 90(0.98)^8 \approx 76.57 \approx 77.$$

Quantitative Comparison Problem

Compare Quantity A and Quantity B, using the information below. **a) Quantity A is greater.**

Quantity A	Quantity B
The value of a $1000 collectible that will increase 4% each year, in three years.	**The value of a $1500 collectible that will decrease 5% each year, in six years.**

Quantity A equals $1000(1.04)^3 \approx \$1,125$. Quantity B equals $1500(0.95)^6 \approx \$1,103$.

Fill in the Blanks

When you put your money in a bank, the bank pays **interest** for the use of that money. The amount you deposit is called the **principal**. Simple interest is based only on the original principal deposited into the account, while **compound interest** is based on the principal amount and the interest that has already been added to the account.

Basic Problem

How much simple interest does $8,000 earn at an annual rate of 1% after three years?
a) $240
Substitute $p = 8,000$, $r = 0.01$, and $t = 3$ into $I = prt$.

Intermediate Problem

What is the balance after six years if $10,000 is deposited in an account that compounds interest semiannually at an annual rate of 3%? Round to the nearest dollar.
d) $11,956

Use the compound interest formula: $B = 10,000 \left(1 + \frac{0.03}{2}\right)^{2(6)}$. Notice that the question asks for the balance, not the interest.

Challenging Problem

A college's endowment fund has $100 million dollars in it. How much less would it earn in one year at 3.5% simple interest compared to 3.5% interest compounded daily? Round to the nearest dollar.   **c) $61,797**

For the simple interest, substitute $p = 100,000,000$, $r = 0.035$, and $t = 1$ into $I = prt$ to get $3,500,000 as the interest. Add to $100,000,000 to get a balance of $103,500,000.

For the compound interest, use the compound interest formula and round to the nearest dollar:

$$B = 100,000,000 \left(1 + \frac{0.035}{365}\right)^{365(1)} \approx 103,561,797.$$

This is the balance. Subtract the two balances to get a difference of $61,797.

Numeric Entry Problem

A simple interest savings account that paid 4% annual interest earned $300 after three years. What was the principal, in dollars?

$$\boxed{2{,}500}$$

Substitute $I = 300$, $r = 0.04$, and $t = 3$ into $I = prt$. Solve for p.

Multiple Choice with Multiple Answers Problem

Which of the following equations represents the balance B on an account that compounds interest at an annual rate of 5.2%?

[b] $B = 6{,}000 \left(1 + \frac{0.052}{12}\right)^{12(3)}$ **[d]** $B = 6{,}000 \left(1 + \frac{0.052}{4}\right)^{4(8)}$

Notice where the interest rate r appears in the compound interest formula, in the numerator of the fraction:

$$B = P\left(1 + \frac{r}{n}\right)^{n(t)}$$

Remember that the interest rate is annual, and is expressed as a decimal.

CORE CONCEPT 43 SOLUTIONS: Direct and Inverse Variation

Fill in the Blanks

If x varies directly with y, y is a constant **multiple** of x. If $y = kx$ and $k > 1$, as x increases, y increases. We can say that y is **directly proportional** to x. If y varies inversely with x, the product xy is a **constant**, and we can say that y is **inversely proportional** to x. Since the equation $xy = k$ models an inverse proportion, if x and its corresponding y were negative, k would be **positive**.

Basic Problem

If y is inversely proportional to x and $y = 16$ when $x = 3$, find x when $y = 24$.   **d) 2**

Use the equation $xy = k$ and substitute $x = 3$ and $y = 16$ to find that $k = 48$. Then use the equation $xy = 48$ and substitute $y = 24$ to find that $x = 2$.

Intermediate Problem

Variables y and x vary inversely as depicted in the following table.

x	y
2	12
3	8
4	6
6	4
8	3

What is the value of x when $y = 2.4$?   **c) 10**

Use the equation $xy = k$ and substitute $x = 2$ and $y = 12$ to find that $k = 24$. Then use the equation $xy = 24$ and substitute $y = 2.4$ to find that $x = 10$.

Challenging Problem

If y is directly proportional to x^2, and $y = 12$ when $x = 2$, find y when $x = 5$.   **b) 75**

Notice that y is directly proportional to x^2, so the two quantities that make up the directly proportional equation are k, y, and x^2.

$$y = kx^2$$

Substitute. Note that $x^2 = 4$ since $x = 2$.

$$12 = k \cdot 4$$

$$k = 3.$$

Knowing $k = 3$, substitute x = 5 into $y = kx^2$ to find y.

$$y = 3 \cdot 25 = 75.$$

Numeric Entry Problem

If y is directly proportional to x and $y = 20$ when $x = 4$, find x when $y = 22$.

$$\boxed{4.4}$$

Use the equation $y = kx$ and substitute $x = 4$ and $y = 20$ to find that $k = 5$. Then use the equation $y = 5x$ and substitute $y = 22$. Divide by 5 to find that $x = 4.4$.

Quantitative Comparison Problem

Compare Quantity A and Quantity B, using the information below. **b) Quantity B is greater.**

Quantity A	Quantity B
The value of x when $y = 1.2$ if x and y are inversely proportional and $x = 4$ when $y = 12$.	**The value of y when $x = 11$ if x and y are directly proportional and $x = 15$ when $y = 60$.**

Substitute. Quantity A is equal to 40 and Quantity B is equal to 44.

CORE CONCEPT 44 SOLUTIONS: Simplifying Algebraic Fractions

Fill in the Blanks

If the denominator of a fraction is equal to 0, we say the fraction is **undefined**. For all values for which the fraction is defined, you can simplify by dividing the **numerator** and the **denominator** by a **common factor**.

Basic Problem

Express $\dfrac{x^2-49}{5x+35}$ in simplest form.   **a)** $\dfrac{x-7}{5}$

Factor the numerator and the denominator to get $\dfrac{(x-7)(x+7)}{5(x+7)}$ and "cancel" out the common factor $(x + 7)$.

Intermediate Problem

Express $\frac{7y-21x}{14x+7k}$ in simplest form.   **b)** $\frac{y-3x}{2x+k}$

Factor the numerator and the denominator to get $\frac{7(y-3x))}{7(2x+k)}$ and "cancel" out the common factor 7.

Challenging Problem

Express $\frac{2x^2-10x-12}{x^2+11x+10}$ in simplest form.   **d)** $\frac{2(x-6)}{(x+10)}$

Factor the numerator and the denominator to get $\frac{2(x-6)(x+1)}{(x+10)(x+1)}$ and "cancel" out the common factor $(x + 1)$.

Numeric Entry Problem

The following fraction is undefined for two values of y. What is the product of those two values?

$$\frac{y^2 - 8y + 20}{y^2 - 11y + 10}$$

$$\boxed{10}$$

The fraction is undefined when the denominator is equal to 0. The denominator $y^2 - 11y + 10$ factors into $(y - 1)(y - 10)$. When $y = 1$ or $y = 10$, the denominator is 0. The product of 1 and 10 is 10.

Multiple Choice with Multiple Answers Problem

Which of the following simplify to $\frac{x-1}{x+2}$?   **[a]** $\frac{x^2-6x-7}{x^2+9x+14}$ **[c]** $\frac{x^2-2x-3}{x^2+5x+6}$

Factor the numerator and the denominator and "cancel" out the common factors:

For choice [a]: $\dfrac{x^2+6x-7}{x^2+9x+14} = \dfrac{(x+7)(x-1)}{(x+2)(x+7)} = \dfrac{x-1}{x+2}$.

For choice [b]: $\dfrac{7x-1}{7(x+2)}$ is in simplest form — there are no common factors.

For choice [c]: $\dfrac{x^2+2x-3}{x^2+5x+6} = \dfrac{(x+3)(x-1)}{(x+2)(x+3)} = \dfrac{x-1}{x+2}$.

For choice [d]: $\dfrac{x^2-4}{x^2+4x+4} = \dfrac{(x-2)(x+2)}{(x+2)(x+2)} = \dfrac{x-2}{x+2}$.

CORE CONCEPT 45 SOLUTIONS: Multiplying and Dividing Algebraic Fractions

Fill in the Blanks

Multiplying algebraic fractions is much like **multiplying** numeric fractions. The gist is to **factor** each numerator and denominator, cancel out the **common** factors to simplify, then multiply the **numerators** and multiply the denominators. Division problems can be changed to **multiplication** problems using "keep-change-flip" and the multiplication steps.

Basic Problem

Find the product of $\dfrac{x^2-49}{x^2+2x+1}$ and $\dfrac{x^2-1}{2x-14}$.

a) $\dfrac{x^2+6x-7}{2x+2}$

This factors to $\dfrac{(x-7)(x+7)}{(x+1)(x+1)} \cdot \dfrac{(x-1)(x+1)}{2(x-7)}$ and common factors are cancelled. The remaining binomials in the numerator, $(x+7)(x-1)$, are multiplied.

Intermediate Problem

What is the quotient when $\dfrac{8x^4y^3}{5x^2-15x}$ is divided by $\dfrac{6x^2y^4}{x^2-9}$?

d) $\dfrac{4x^3+12x^2}{15xy}$

After changing to a multiplication problem and factoring, this becomes $\dfrac{8x^4y^3}{5x(x-3)} \cdot \dfrac{(x-3)(x+3)}{6x^2y^4}$. The common factor $(x-3)$ is cancelled along one diagonal, and the common factor $2x^2y^3$ is cancelled along the other diagonal.

Challenging Problem

Find the product of $\frac{14x^5+7x}{x^2-49}$ and $\frac{(x+7)^2}{14x^2}$.

c) $\frac{(2x^4+1)(x+7)}{2x(x-7)}$

After factoring this becomes $\frac{7x(2x^4+1)}{(x-7)(x+7)}$ and $\frac{(x+7)(x+7)}{14x^2}$. The common factor $(x+7)$ is cancelled along one diagonal, and the common factor $7x$ is cancelled along the other diagonal.

Numeric Entry Problem

For what value of x does the product $\frac{5x}{7y} \cdot \frac{21y}{x^2}$ equal 3?

After simplifying, the product becomes $\frac{15}{x}$. Solve the equation $\frac{15}{x} = 3$ to get $x = 5$.

Quantitative Comparison Problem

Compare Quantity A and Quantity B, using the information below. **a) Quantity A is greater.**

Quantity A	Quantity B
The reciprocal of $\frac{5x}{y}$ when $x = 4$ when $y = 12$.	**The quotient $\frac{x}{3y} \div \frac{21x}{y}$.**

Quantity A becomes $\frac{y}{5x} = \frac{12}{20} = \frac{3}{5}$. Quantity B becomes $\frac{x}{3y} \div \frac{21x}{y} = \frac{x}{3y} \cdot \frac{y}{21x} = \frac{1}{63}$.

CORE CONCEPT 46 SOLUTIONS: Adding and Subtracting Algebraic Fractions

---

Fill in the Blanks

The answer to an addition problem is called the **sum** and the answer to a subtraction problem is called the **difference**. To add or subtract fractions with unlike denominators, you need to find the **least common denominator** before you can add or subtract. To find the LCD, you need to multiply each fraction by **1** in a form that will create equivalent fractions that have the same **denominator**.

Basic Problem

Find the sum of $\frac{13}{12y^5}$ and $\frac{7-y}{4y^2}$.   **a)** $\frac{-3y^4+21y^3+13}{12y^5}$

The LCD is $12y^5$ so multiply the second fraction by $\frac{3y^3}{3y^3}$.
Be sure to distribute $3y^3$ over $(7 - y)$ when you multiply.

Intermediate Problem

Subtract $\frac{x-1}{2x+10}$ from $\frac{6}{x^2-25}$.   **c)** $\frac{-x^2+6x+7}{2x^2-50}$

The common denominator is $2(x-5)(x+5) = 2x^2 - 50$. Multiply $\frac{6}{x^2-25}$ by $\frac{2}{2}$ and multiply $\frac{x-1}{2x+10}$ by $\frac{x-5}{x-5}$ and then subtract.

Challenging Problem

What is the product of the solutions to the equation $\frac{5}{p} - \frac{6}{p^2} = 1$?   **a) 6**

The common denominator is p^2. The fractions on the left add to $\frac{5p-6}{p^2}$. The equation becomes $\frac{5p-6}{p^2} = 1$. Cross multiply to get $p^2 - 5p + 6 = 0$, which has solutions 2 and 3, so the product is 6.

Numeric Entry Problem

What is the coefficient of c in the lowest common denominator used to subtract $\frac{5}{36c}$ from $\frac{y^2}{24c}$?

$$\boxed{72}$$

The LCD is $72c$ since $36c$ and $24c$ divide evenly into $72c$.

Multiple Choice with Multiple Answers Problem

Which of the following fraction problems have a least common denominator of

$$2(x - 2)(x - 3)?$$

[b] $\dfrac{8x}{2x-4} - \dfrac{9}{2x-6} =$
  [c] $\dfrac{5x-1}{x-3} - \dfrac{17}{2x^2-10x+12} =$
  [d] $\dfrac{19x^2}{2} + \dfrac{55}{x^2-5x+6} =$

Factor each denominator to find the LCD. You don't need to actually "do" the addition or subtraction problems. The common denominator for choice [a] is $(x - 2)(x - 3)$.

CORE CONCEPT 47 SOLUTIONS: Distance Problems

Fill in the Blanks

The distance formula relates distance, rate, and **time** to each other using the equation $\boldsymbol{R \cdot T = D}$. Distance divided by rate equals **time** and distance divided by time equals **rate**. There is another distance formula that relates distance, miles per gallon, and **gallons**. With either distance formula, if you have expressions for two of the variables, you can create an expression for the third variable using **algebra**.

Basic Problem

Two trains at stations 440 miles apart leave at the same time and travel towards each other on parallel tracks. The faster train traveled an average of 20 mph faster than the slower train. They met each other after 4 hours. What was the speed of the faster train?   **c) 65**

First set up a table.

	Rate (mph)	Time (hours)	Distance (miles)
Fast train	$x + 20$	4	$4(x + 20)$
Slow train	x	4	$4x$

The total distance traveled by both trains is 440 miles, so set up an equation showing that both distance expressions add to 440.

$$4(x + 20) + 4x = 440$$

Distribute and solve for x to get that $x = 45$. That is the speed, in mph, of the slower train as you can see from the table. The faster train travels at a speed 20 mph faster, so its speed is 65 mph.

Intermediate Problem

Jordan left his home and walked on a hike and bike path to Sunken Meadow Park, at an average rate of 4 mph. Two hours later Cameron left to bike to the park on the same path, at a speed of 9 mph. How much time did it take for Cameron to overtake Jordan?

b) 96 minutes

Set up a table.

	Rate (mph)	Time (hours)	Distance (miles)
Jordan (walks)	4	$x + 2$	$4(x + 2)$
Cameron (bikes)	9	x	$9x$

Notice that Jordan's time is 2 more than Cameron's since he started earlier. When Cameron overtakes Jordan, they have traveled the same distance, so set the distances equal to each other.

$$4(x + 2) = 9x$$

Distribute and solve to get that $x = \frac{8}{5} = 1\frac{3}{5}$. Convert $1\frac{3}{5}$ hours to minutes by multiplying it by 60, to get 96 minutes.

Challenging Problem

Two planes left from the same airport. They flew in opposite directions. One left an hour later than the other, but flew 50 mph faster than the first plane. Four hours after the second plane left, they were 2900 miles apart. Find the speed of the faster plane.

c) 350 mph

Set up a table.

	Rate (mph)	Time (hours)	Distance (miles)
Faster plane (later)	$x + 50$	4	$4(x + 50)$
Slower plane (earlier)	x	5	$5x$

The distances they traveled sum to 2900, so set up an equation.

$$4(x + 50) + 5x = 2900$$

Distribute and solve to find that $x = 300$, so the faster plane goes 350 mph.

Numeric Entry Problem

A jogger jogs at the rate of 1 mile every 12 minutes. After 5 miles she changes pace to 1 mile every 15 minutes. How many miles does she cover in an hour and a half?

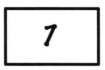

In the first 60 minutes she covers 5 miles, and in the last 30 minutes she covers 2 miles, for a total of 7 miles.

Quantitative Comparison Problem

Compare Quantity A and Quantity B, using the information below. **a) Quantity A is greater.**

<u>Quantity A</u>	<u>Quantity B</u>
The number of miles a car going 45 mph goes in 6 hours.	**The number of miles a car going 42 mph goes in 6 hours and 10 minutes.**

Quantity A is 270 miles, found by multiplying. Quantity B is also found by multiplying. First multiply 6 by 42 to get 252. Since 10 minutes is $\frac{1}{6}$ of an hour, the car travels 7 more miles in those 10 minutes, for a total of 259 miles.

CORE CONCEPT 48 SOLUTIONS: Number Problems

Fill in the Blanks

If two numbers have a sum of 51 and one number is represented by p, the other number can be algebraically represented by **51 - p**. If m represents the smaller of two numbers, and the larger is five less than the triple of m, the larger can be algebraically represented as **3m - 5**. The expression "nine less than y" can be represented algebraically as **y - 9**.

Basic Problem

One integer is 12 less than another. Their sum is 52. What is the smaller of the two numbers?   **d) 20**

The two integers can be represented as x and $x - 12$. The resulting equation is

$$x + x - 12 = 52.$$

Since $x = 32$, the two numbers are 20 and 32, and the smaller is 20.

Intermediate Problem

The larger of two numbers is 15 more than the smaller. If the smaller is tripled, the result is the same as if the larger is increased by 11. What is the larger number?   **c) 28**

The two numbers can be represented as x and $x + 15$. The resulting equation is

$$3x = x + 15 + 11.$$

Since $x = 13$, the two numbers are 13 and 28, and the smaller number tripled (39), is 11 more than the larger (28).

Challenging Problem

Three numbers have a sum of 50. The second is 6 more than the first, and the third is 5 more than the second. What is the largest number?   **b) 22**

The three numbers can be represented as $x, x + 6$, and $x + 11$. The resulting equation is

$$x + x + 6 + x + 11 = 50.$$

Since $x = 11$, the three numbers are 11, 17, and 22, and their sum is 50.

Numeric Entry Problem

One number is three more than twice another number. The sum of the numbers is 45. What is the smaller number?

$$\boxed{14}$$

The numbers can be represented as x and $2x + 3$. Their sum is 45, so set up an equation.

$$x + 2x + 3 = 45 \text{ becomes } 3x + 3 = 45 \text{ so } x = 14.$$

Multiple Choice with Multiple Answers Problem

Which of the following represents "seven more than twice a number"?

[a] 7 + 2x   **[d] 2x + 7**

CORE CONCEPT 49 SOLUTIONS: Consecutive Integer Problems

Fill in the Blanks

If the first integer of a set of consecutive even integers is n, the next consecutive even integer is represented by **$n+2$**. If $y + k$ represents an integer, the next consecutive integer can be represented as **$y + k + 1$**. Since each consecutive odd integer is 2 more than the odd integer before it, the next consecutive odd integer after p is represented as **$p + 2$**.

Basic Problem

The sum of three consecutive odd integers is 69. What is the largest of these three integers?

d) 25

The three consecutive odds are represented as $x, x + 2,$ and $x + 4$. Set up and solve an equation.

$$x + x + 2 + x + 4 = 69$$

Since $x = 21$, the three odd integers are 21, 23, and 25. The largest is 25.

Intermediate Problem

The sum of four consecutive integers is 54. Find the sum of the two even integers in this set of four consecutive integers.　　**a) 26**

The four consecutive integers are represented as $x, x + 1$, and $x + 2$ and $x + 3$. Set up and solve an equation.

$$x + x + 1 + x + 2 + x + 3 = 54 \text{ becomes } 4x + 6 = 54.$$

Since $x = 12$, the four integers are 12, 13, 14, and 15. The sum of the two even numbers, 12 and 14, is 26.

Challenging Problem

In a set of three consecutive even integers, three times the first decreased by twice the second is equal to 14. What is the largest of the three integers? **a) 22**

The three consecutive evens are represented as $x, x + 2$, and $x + 4$. Set up and solve an equation. "Three times the first decreased by twice the second is equal to 14" can be translated to

$$3x - 2(x + 2) = 14.$$

Since $x = 18$, the three integers are 18, 20, and 22. The largest is 22.

Numeric Entry Problem

The sum of two consecutive even integers is 18. What is the product of those two integers?

$$\boxed{80}$$

The two consecutive evens are represented as x and $x + 2$. Set up and solve an equation.

$$x + x + 2 = 18.$$

Since $x = 8$, the two integers are 8 and 10. Their product is 80.

Quantitative Comparison Problem

Compare Quantity A and Quantity B, using the information below. **a) Quantity A is greater.**

Quantity A	Quantity B
The product of two consecutive integers whose sum is 9.	**The average of two consecutive even integers whose sum is 22.**

Quantity A is 20 since the two consecutive integers that add to 9 are 4 and 5. Quantity B is 11 since the two consecutive integers that add to 22 are 10 and 12. The average of 10 and 12 is 11.

CORE CONCEPT 50 SOLUTIONS: Work Problems

Fill in the Blanks

If Paolo can complete a job in y hours, he can complete $\frac{3}{y}$ of the job in **3** hours. If Rashesh can complete a job in 5 hours, he can complete $\frac{2}{5}$ of the job in 2 hours. If a machine can complete a job in m hours, it can complete $\frac{4}{m}$ of the job in **4** hours.

Basic Problem

Machine A can shred a palette of paper in 3 hours. Machine B can shred the same palette of paper in 6 hours. How long will the two machines take, working simultaneously, to shred a palette of paper?   **c) 2 hours**

Let x represent the time they work together. Solve the equation $\frac{x}{3} + \frac{x}{6} = 1$.

Intermediate Problem

Arsh can paint a garage door in 2 hours. His friend Nikki can paint it in 5 hours. Arsh painted alone for 1 hour and then quit. How many hours will it take Nikki to finish the painting job alone?   **d) 2.5 hours**

In one hour, Arsh does $\frac{1}{2}$ of the whole job. In x hours, Nikki will do $\frac{x}{5}$ of the job. Solve the equation $\frac{1}{2} + \frac{x}{5} = 1$.

Challenging Problem

Raoul takes twice as long as his sister Penny to shovel snow off the driveway. They take 2 hours to do the job together. How long would it take Raoul to do it alone?   **d) 3 hours**

Let x be the amount of time it takes Penny alone. Then $2x$ is the amount of time Raoul takes to do the whole job alone. They work for 2 hours. Solve the equation $\frac{2}{2x} + \frac{2}{x} = 1$.

Numeric Entry Problem

If it takes a machine 30 hours to dig a well, what percent of the job can it complete in 6 hours?

$$\boxed{20} \; \%$$

In 6 hours, the machine does $\frac{6}{30} = \frac{1}{5}$ of the job, and $\frac{1}{5} = 20\%$.

Multiple Choice with Multiple Answers Problem

Which of the following are equivalent measures of time?

[a] 50 minutes   **[b] $\frac{5}{6}$ hour**   **[c] 3,000 seconds**

One-sixth of an hour is 10 minutes, so $\frac{5}{6}$ hour is 50 minutes. Since a minute is 60 seconds, 50 minutes is 3,000 seconds.

Review/Renew

How many common prime factors do the numbers 24 and 45 have?   **a) 1**

Since 24 has prime factors 2 and 3, and 45 has prime factors 3 and 5, they share the common prime factor 3 only.

Review Core Concept 3 if necessary.

Fill in the Blanks

A polygon is a closed **plane** figure with **straight** sides. The **perimeter** of a polygon is the sum of the side lengths. If a polygon is a regular polygon, its sides are **congruent**. A regular quadrilateral (4 sides) is commonly known as a **square**. A square with perimeter 32 has side lengths of **8**. The perimeter of an equilateral triangle with side lengths represented by $2x + 5$ can be represented as **$6x + 15$**.

Basic Problem

A triangle has side lengths that are consecutive integers. The perimeter is 36. What is the length of the longest side?   **c) 13**

The three sides, represented by x, $x + 1$, and $x + 2$, should have sum 36, so set up an equation and solve it.

$$x + x + 1 + x + 2 = 36$$

Since $x = 11$, the three sides are 11, 12, and 13. The longest side has length 13.

Intermediate Problem

Which of the following, I, II, III, are true statements about an 8' by 20' rectangle?
c) II and III only

I.	The perimeter is 28'.
II.	The length is four more than twice the width.
III.	The perimeter is the same as the perimeter of a square whose side is 14'.

Since 20 is 4 more than twice 8, statement II is true. The rectangle has a perimeter of 56', as does a square with side 14', so statement III is true and statement I is false.

Challenging Problem

A rectangle has sides 5 and 8. If all sides are increased by the same amount, the new perimeter is 42. What is the width of the rectangle with the increased sides?   **b) 9**

Let x represent the amount of increase. The sides of the larger rectangle can be represented as $x + 5$ and $x + 8$, so set up an equation and solve it.

$$2(x + 5) + 2(x + 8) = 42$$

Since $x = 4$, the sides of the larger rectangle are 9 and 12. The width is 9.

Numeric Entry Problem

The perimeter of a rectangle is 39. Its length is 15. What is its width?

$$\boxed{4.5}$$

The two lengths of 15 add to 30. The two widths must add to 9. Divide 9 by 2 to get that the width is 4.5.

Quantitative Comparison Problem

Compare Quantity A and Quantity B, using the information below. **a) Quantity A is greater.**

Quantity A	Quantity B
The perimeter of a 12' by 20' rectangle.	**The side of a regular pentagon with perimeter 300'.**

Quantity A is 64', found by adding all four sides of the rectangle. Quantity B is 60', found by dividing 300 by 5.

Review/Renew

What is the value of $100 - 6(1 + 3^2) \div 4$?   **a) 85**

Use the order of operations.

$$100 - 6(1 + 3^2) \div 4$$
$$100 - 6(1 + 9) \div 4$$
$$100 - 6(10) \div 4$$
$$100 - 60 \div 4$$
$$100 - 15 = 85.$$

Review Core Concept 7 if necessary.

Fill in the Blanks

The line segment that connects the center of a circle to the circle is called a **radius**. The length of a diameter is twice the length of a **radius**. The length of the circle itself is called its **circumference**, and the formula to find this length uses the Greek letter π which is approximately equal to **3.14**. If a circle's diameter is 40, its radius is **20**.

Basic Problem

The circumference of a circle, in terms of π, is 17π. What is the radius of the circle?   **b) 8.5**

Since $C = \pi d$, the diameter of the circle is 17. The radius is half of the diameter, so divide 17 by 2.

Intermediate Problem

A circle with radius 9 is inscribed in a square. What is the perimeter of the square?   **b) 72**

Draw a diagram.

18

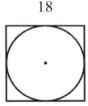

The radius is 9, so the diameter is 18. The side length is the same as the diameter's length. Multiply 18 by 4 to get the perimeter.

Challenging Problem

A string is placed around a semicircle with radius 10, along the diameter from A to B and then around the arc back to A.

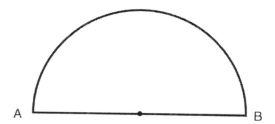

Find the length of the string (the distance all the way around the semicircle) to the nearest tenth of a foot. Use $\pi \approx 3.14$. **c) 51.4**

The radius is 10, so the circumference, found by substituting into $C = 2\pi r$, is 20π, which is approximately 62.8. The semicircle's length is half of the circumference, so divide 62.8 by 2 to get 31.4. Then add on the length of the diameter, which is 20, to get 51.4.

Numeric Entry Problem

What is the circumference of a circle whose radius is the product of the two smallest prime numbers? Use $\pi = 3.14$ and round to the nearest tenth.

The two smallest primes are 2 and 3, and their product is 6, so the radius is 6. Substitute into the circumference formula $C = 2\pi r$, to get 37.68, and round to the nearest tenth.

Multiple Choice with Multiple Answers Problem

Which of the following have an arc length of 6π?

[a] A sector with a central angle of 90° in a circle with radius 12.

[b] A sector with a central angle of 60° in a circle with radius 18.

[c] A sector with a central angle of 30° in a circle with diameter 72.

[d] A sector with a central angle of 45° in a circle with diameter 48.

All four answers are correct. Find the circumference using the circumference formula, and then multiply by the fraction of the circle taken up by the sector.

Review/Renew

Find the multiplicative inverse of the least common multiple of 4 and 14.   c) $\frac{1}{28}$

The least common multiple of 4 and 14 is 28, found by listing the multiples of each number. The multiplicative inverse is the reciprocal, found by "flipping" $\frac{28}{1}$.

Review Core Concepts 5 and 8 if necessary.

CORE CONCEPT 53 SOLUTIONS: Areas of Polygons

Fill in the Blanks

The amount of space inside a polygon is called its **area**. Area is measured in **square** units. The area of a triangle with base k and height h is $\frac{1}{2}kh$. The area of a parallelogram with base 10 and height 4 is **40** square units. A rectangle is a special type of parallelogram with angles that measure **90** degrees. The area of a rectangle with length l and width w is lw.

Basic Problem

A rectangle has width represented by the expression $2x^3$ and length represented as $5x^4$. What is the expression for its area?   c) $\mathbf{10x^7}$

Multiply length times width using the laws of exponents.

$$2x^3 \cdot 5x^4 = 10x^7.$$

Intermediate Problem

What is the perimeter of a square whose area is 196 square feet?   d) 56'

If the area is 196, you can take the square root to find the length of a side, since a square is a rectangle with congruent sides.

$$\sqrt{196} = 14$$

The perimeter is 4(14) = 56'.

Challenging Problem

A regular heptagon (7 sides) has an inscribed circle with radius 5. Its perimeter is 33.6. What is its area? **a) 84**

Since its perimeter is 33.6, each side can be found by dividing 33.6 by 7. The sides have length 4.8. What might seem like a daunting problem can now be simplified using a diagram.

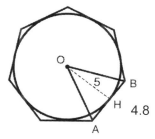

Look at triangle AOB. The radius of the inscribed circle is the altitude of triangle AOB. The area of triangle AOB is $\frac{1}{2}bh$. Substitute $b = 4.8$ and $h = 5$ to get that the area of the triangle is 12. Since the heptagon contains 7 triangles congruent to triangle AOB, multiply 12 by 7 to get that the area of the heptagon is 84.

Numeric Entry Problem

What is the length of a rectangle with area 50 square units and width 4?

$$\boxed{12.5}$$

Since $A = lw$, divide 50 by 4.

Quantitative Comparison Problem

Compare Quantity A and Quantity B, using the information below.
c) The two quantities are equal.

Quantity A	Quantity B
A side of a square with area 169 square feet.	The diameter of a circle with circumference 13π feet.

Quantity A is 13 feet, found by taking the square root of 169. Quantity B is 13 found by looking at the circumference formula $C = \pi d$.

Review/Renew

The ratio of bicyclists to joggers at a local charity event is 7:5. If there are 240 people in the event, how many joggers are there?   **c) 100**

You can represent the number of bicyclists as $7x$, and the number of joggers as $5x$. Set up an equation.

$$7x + 5x = 240$$

Since $x = 20$, and $5x$ represents the number of joggers, there are $5(20) = 100$ joggers.

Review Core Concept 18 if necessary.

CORE CONCEPT 54 SOLUTIONS: Areas of Circles and Sectors

Fill in the Blanks

If a circle has radius k, the area of the circle is $A = \pi k^2$. Since the circle's area formula requires inputting the radius, if you are given the diameter, you can find the radius by **dividing by 2**. If you are given the circle's area in terms of π, you can find the radius by taking the **square root** of the coefficient of π.

Basic Problem

A circle has diameter 40. Find its area in terms of π.   **d) 400π**

Divide by 2 to get that the radius is 20. Substitute 20 for r into $A = \pi r^2$.

Intermediate Problem

A circle is inscribed in a square whose area is 100. Find the area of the circle to the nearest tenth.   **b) 78.5**

Draw a diagram. It will help you notice that the sides of the square are 10, so the radius of the circle is 5.

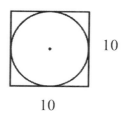

10

10

Substitute 5 for r into $A = \pi r^2$ to get 78.5.

Challenging Problem

A sector of a circle has a 60° central angle, and its area is 13.5π. What is the length of its diameter?   **a) 18**

The sector's area is $\frac{60}{360}$ of the circle's area. This fraction simplifies to $\frac{1}{6}$. Multiply 13.5π by 6 to get the area of the circle, which is 81π. The square root of 81 is 9, and that is the radius. Multiply 9 by 2 to get the diameter.

Numeric Entry Problem

A circle has area, in terms of π, of 49π. What is the diameter of the circle?

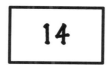

The square root of 49 is 7 and that is the radius. Double 7 to get the diameter, 14.

Multiple Choice with Multiple Answers Problem

Which of the following have equivalent areas?

[a] a circle with radius 4   **[b] a circle with circumference 8π**

[c] a circle with diameter 8

The circles in choices [a] , [b], and [c] have a radius of 4, and area 16π. The circle in choice [d] has diameter 4, radius 2, and area 4π.

Review/Renew

Convert $\frac{5}{8}$ to an equivalent percent.   **b) 62.5%**

Change $\frac{5}{8}$ to and equivalent decimal by dividing 5 by 8. The answer is 0.625. Move the decimal two places to the right and add a percent sign.

Review Core Concept 17 if necessary.

CORE CONCEPT 55 SOLUTIONS: Shaded Area

Fill in the Blanks

The area of a semicircle can be found by using the circle area formula and dividing by **2**. If any polygon is dissected and a new region is formed using all of the original dissected regions from the polygon, the area of the newly formed figure is **equal to** the area of the original figure. You can use the diagram to determine if the shaded area problem involves addition or **subtraction**.

Basic Problem

A rectangular plaza 200' by 80' is being constructed in a town square, as shown in the diagram below. It will be covered with sod except for the area occupied by three circular fountains. The larger fountain has a diameter of 40' and the smaller fountains have diameters of 22'. How many square feet of sod are necessary to cover the sodded area? Round to the nearest square foot.   **a) 13,984**

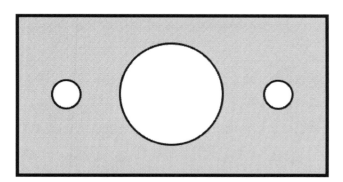

The area of the rectangle is found by multiplying the length by the width.

$$200 \cdot 80 = 16,000$$

The area of the large circle is found by substituting 20 for r, since the diameter is 40, into the formula for the area of a circle.

$$A = \pi r^2$$

$$A = \pi \cdot 20^2 = 400\pi \approx 1,256$$

The total area of the two smaller circles is found by substituting 11 for r, since the diameter is 22, into the formula for the area of a circle.

$$A = \pi r^2$$

$$A = \pi \cdot 11^2 = 121\pi \approx 379.94$$

Since there are two small circles, multiply by 2.

$$379.94 \cdot 2 = 759.88 \approx 760.$$

Subtract 1,256 and 760 from 16,000 to get that the sodded area is 13,984 to the nearest integer.

Intermediate Problem

An 8" by 10" photo is going to have a border (called a matte) around it. The matte is 2" in width. What is the area of the matte?   **b) 88 sq. in.**

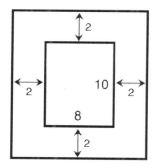

Add two sets of 2" to each dimension of the photo, since the matte is 2" thick on *both* sides. The outside rectangle has dimensions 12 by 14 and it has area 168 square inches. The photo has area 80 square inches. Subtract to find that the area of the matte is 88 square inches.

Challenging Problem

A circle with radius 20 is inscribed in a square. Find the area of the shaded region shown in the figure. Round to the nearest integer.   **a) 86**

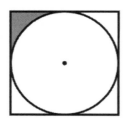

The radius is 20 so the diameter, which is the same length as a side of the square, is 40. The square has area 1,600.

The circle has area

$$A = \pi r^2.$$

$$A = \pi \cdot 20^2 = 400\pi \approx 1,256.$$

Subtract 1,256 from 1,600 to get 344. Divide that by 4 to get 86.

Numeric Entry Problem

What is the "perimeter" (distance around the outside) of the school track from Example 1? Round to the nearest integer.

The two semicircles create one full circle.

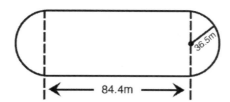

Use the circumference formula $C = 2\pi r$. Substitute 36.5 for r.

$$C = 2\pi \cdot 36.5 \approx 229.22$$

The two sides from the rectangle total 168.8 m. Add 229.22 m to 168.8 m to get 398.02, which is 398 m to the nearest integer.

Quantitative Comparison Problem

Compare Quantity A and Quantity B, using the information below. **a) Quantity A is greater.**

Quantity A	Quantity B
The remaining area of a 14 x 20 rectangle with a 4 x 4 square inside of it removed.	**The remaining area of a circle with radius 8 with a 4 x 3 rectangle inside of it removed.**

Quantity A has area 280 - 16 = 264 square units. Quantity B has area $64\pi - 12 \approx 189$ square units.

Review/Renew

What is the solution set for the absolute value equation $|x + 7| = 17$? **c) {-24, 10}**

Create two equations and solve each.

$$x + 7 = 17 \qquad\qquad x + 7 = -17$$

Subtract 7 from both sides.

$$x = 10 \qquad\qquad x = -24$$

Review Core Concept 38 if necessary.

CORE CONCEPT 56 SOLUTIONS: Volume

Fill in the Blanks

The amount of space inside of a three-dimensional solid is called its **volume**. While area is measured in **square** units, volume is measured in **cubic** units. A cube is a rectangular solid with six congruent square faces. If a cube has side length 7, its volume is **343** cubic units. The volume formula for a **sphere** is $V = \frac{4}{3}\pi r^3$.

Basic Problem

The Great Pyramid of Giza in Egypt has a square base, with sides 755.75'. Its height is 481.4'. What is the volume of this pyramid, in cubic feet? Round to the nearest thousand cubic feet.   **a) 91,652,000**

Substitute into the formula.

$$V = \frac{1}{3}lwh = \frac{1}{3}755.75 \cdot 755.75 \cdot 481.4 \approx 91{,}651{,}830.4 \approx 91{,}652{,}000.$$

Intermediate Problem

What is the diameter of a sphere whose volume, in terms of π, is $7{,}776\pi$?   **b) 36**

The volume, V, is already given. Substitute into the formula $V = \frac{4}{3}\pi r^3$.

$$7{,}776\pi = \frac{4}{3}\pi r^3$$

Divide both sides by π to get $7{,}776 = \frac{4}{3}r^3$. Multiply both sides by $\frac{3}{4}$ to get $5{,}832 = r^3$. Use a calculator or trial and error to get 18 as the radius. The diameter is twice that, or 36.

Challenging Problem

An industrial funnel filter is in the shape of an inverted cone at the bottom of a right circular cylinder. The cylinder gets filled with solid material which is collected as fluid drips out through the filter.

The height of the cylinder is 10' and the height of the cone is 6'. The diameter of the cylinder is 8'. What is the volume of this filter? Round to the nearest integer. **a) 603 cu. ft.**

The volume of the cylinder formula is $V = \pi r^2 h$. The radius is 4. Substitute.

$$V = \pi r^2 h = \pi \cdot 4^2 \cdot 10 \approx 502.4.$$

The volume of a cone formula is $V = \frac{1}{3}\pi r^2 h$. Substitute.

$$V = \frac{1}{3}\pi \cdot 4^2 \cdot 6 = \frac{1}{3}\pi \cdot 16 \cdot 6 = 32\pi \approx 100.48.$$

Add 502.4 to 100.48 and round to the nearest integer. The volume of the filter is 603.

Numeric Entry Problem

Find the volume of a right circular cone with height 7, whose base has diameter 13. Round to the nearest integer.

$$\boxed{310}$$

The radius is 6.5 since the diameter is 13. Substitute into the volume of a cone formula
$$V = \frac{1}{3}\pi r^2 h.$$

$$V = \frac{1}{3}\pi r^2 h = \frac{1}{3}\pi \cdot 6.5^2 \cdot 7 \approx 310.$$

Multiple Choice with Multiple Answers Problem

Which of the following right circular cylinders have a volume greater than 50?

[b] $r = 2$; $h = 4$ [c] $r = 4$; $h = 2$ [d] $r = 3$; $h = 3$

Use the formula $V = \pi r^2 h$ and substitute. Rounded to the nearest integer, choice [a] is about 9, choice [b] is just over 50, choice [c] is about 100, and choice [d] is about 85.

Review/Renew

Joelle got a new job with a starting salary of $52,500. Her salary increases 3% each year. What will her salary be in her fourth year? Round to the nearest dollar.   **d) $57,368**

The first-year salary is $52,500, so there are three subsequent pay increases.

$$52,500(1.03)^3 = 57,368.1675 \approx \$57,368.$$

Review Core Concept 41 if necessary.

Fill in the Blanks

The triangle **inequality** theorem says that the **sum** of any two sides of a triangle must be **greater** than the third side. As a result of this, the third side must be greater than the **difference** between the other two sides. If two sides of a triangle measure 11 and 30, the remaining side must have measure between **19** and **41**.

Basic Problem

A triangle has sides 7 and 8. Which of the following could be the third side of the triangle?
a) 14.9

The sum of the two sides is 15 and the difference is 1. The third side must have length in between these numbers.

Intermediate Problem

Two side lengths of a triangle are $x + y$ and y, where x and y are natural numbers. The third side is p. Which inequality represents possible values for p?   **d) $x < p < x + 2y$**

The sum of the two sides is $x + y + y = x + 2y$ and the difference is $x + y - y = x$. The third side must have length in between these numbers.

Challenging Problem

A triangle has side lengths 6, 8, and x. Which of the following, I, II, III, are true statements about x?   **c) III only**

$$
\begin{array}{lll}
\text{I.} & & x < 8 \\
\text{II.} & & x < 13.9 \\
\text{III.} & & x > 2
\end{array}
$$

The sum of the two sides is 14 and the difference is 2. The third side must have length in between 2 and 14. Statement I is not true since x can be greater than 8. Statement II is not true because x can be greater than 13.9, while still being less than 14. Statement III is true.

Numeric Entry Problem

Two sides of a triangle are the two largest prime numbers less than 20. The third side is the average of these two side lengths. What is the length of the third side?

$$\boxed{18}$$

The two largest primes less than 20 are 17 and 19. Add them and divide by 2 to get the average, which is 18.

Quantitative Comparison Problem

Compare Quantity A and Quantity B, using the information below.

d) The relationship cannot be determined from the information given.

Quantity A	Quantity B
The perimeter of a triangle with sides 4, 5, and 6.	**The perimeter of a triangle with two sides measuring 4 and 5.**

Quantity A is 15, found by adding the three sides. The third side in the Quantity B triangle is between 1 and 9, so its perimeter can be smaller or greater than 15.

Review/Renew

Find the value of x in the following proportion.   **b) 35**

$$\frac{19}{7} = \frac{95}{x}$$

Cross multiply to get $19x = 665$ and then divide both sides by 19.

Review Core Concept 18 if necessary.

CORE CONCEPT 58 SOLUTIONS: The Pythagorean Theorem

Fill in the Blanks

If one of the angles in a triangle measures 90 degrees, the triangle is called a **right** triangle. The two adjacent legs in a right triangle are **perpendicular** to each other. The **hypotenuse** is the longest side and it is across from the right angle. The **Pythagorean** theorem says that in a right triangle with legs x and y, and hypotenuse p, $x^2 + y^2 = p^2$.

Basic Problem

A rectangle has length 15 and width 8. What is the length of the diagonal of the rectangle?

a) 17

The diagonal creates a right triangle, and the diagonal is the hypotenuse. Substitute into

$$a^2 + b^2 = c^2.$$

$8^2 + 15^2 = c^2$ becomes $64 + 225 = 289 = c^2$ and $c = \sqrt{289} = 17.$

Intermediate Problem

A right triangle has a hypotenuse with length 41 and a leg with length 9. What is the perimeter of the right triangle?   **d) 90**

Substitute into

$$a^2 + b^2 = c^2.$$

$$9^2 + b^2 = 41^2$$

$$81 + b^2 = 1,681 \text{ so } b^2 = 1,600 \text{ and } b = 40.$$

The three sides measure 9, 40, and 41, so the perimeter is 90.

Challenging Problem

An isosceles triangle has base 10. The two congruent sides each have measure 14. What is the area of the triangle, in square units, to the nearest tenth?   **c) 65.4**

The altitude of an isosceles triangle bisects the base as shown in the figure.

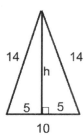

Substitute into $a^2 + b^2 = c^2$ to get the height h.

$$5^2 + h^2 = 14^2 \text{ becomes } h^2 = 171 \text{ so } h = \sqrt{171} \approx 13.08.$$

The area of a triangle is $\frac{1}{2}bh$. Substitute $b = 10$ and $h = 13.08$ and round to the nearest tenth to get 65.4.

Numeric Entry Problem

A right angle with segments 5 and 11 is inscribed in a semicircle as shown. Find, to the nearest hundredth, the radius of the circle.

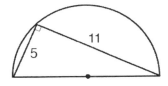

6.04

Substitute into $a^2 + b^2 = c^2$ to get the hypotenuse.

$$5^2 + 11^2 = c^2 \text{ becomes } c^2 = 146 \text{ so } c = \sqrt{146} \approx 12.083.$$

The hypotenuse is also the diameter, so divide by 2 to get that the radius is 6.04.

Multiple Choice with Multiple Answers Problem

Legs a and b are given for four right triangles. Which of the following right triangles has a perimeter less than 30?

[a] $a = 4$; $b = 3$ **[c]** $a = 6$; $b = 8$ **[d]** $a = 12$; $b = 4$

Use the Pythagorean theorem for each to get the hypotenuse. Add the three sides to get the perimeter. The hypotenuse in choice [a] is 5. The hypotenuse in choice [b] is 13, so the perimeter is 30, which is not less than 30. The hypotenuse in choice [c] is 10. The hypotenuse in choice [d] is just under 13, so the perimeter is under 30.

Review/Renew

The function ♦ is defined as $x ♦ y = 4x + y^2$. What is the value of 6 ♦ 3?   **a) 33**

Substitute into $x ♦ y = 4x + y^2$.

$$x ♦ y = 4x + y^2.$$

$$6 ♦ 3 = 4 \cdot 6 + 3^2 = 24 + 9 = 33.$$

Review Core Concept 23 if necessary.

CORE CONCEPT 59 SOLUTIONS: Angles in Triangles

Fill in the Blanks

The sum of the interior angles of a triangle is **180** degrees. An exterior angle to a triangle is equal to the sum of the two **non-adjacent** interior angles. If two angles add up to 180 degrees, we say they are **supplementary** angles. An obtuse angle is greater than **90** degrees but less than **180** degrees. Consequently, a triangle can have at most **one** obtuse angle(s). A triangle can have at most **three** acute angles.

Basic Problem

One of the acute angles in a right triangle is five times the measure of the other. What is the measure of the larger angle?   **b) 75**

The acute angles in a right triangle add up to 90 degrees. Represent the two angles as x and $5x$. Set up the equation $x + 5x = 90$ and solve it to find that $x = 15$. The larger angle is $5x$, so substitute 15 for x to find that the larger angle is 75 degrees.

Intermediate Problem

In triangle RST, an exterior angle at T measures 123 degrees. Angle R is twice the measure of angle S. Find the measure of angle R.   **d) 82**

Draw a diagram.

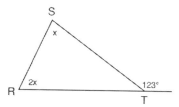

The exterior angle is the sum of the two remote interior angles. Set up an equation.

$$x + 2x = 123 \text{ becomes } 3x = 123 \text{ so } x = 41.$$

Substitute 41 for x in the expression $2x$ to get that angle R measures 82 degrees.

Challenging Problem

The angle measures of a triangle are consecutive even integers. What is the measure of the largest angle?   **b) 62**

The angle measures can be represented as x, $x + 2$, and $x + 4$. Set up an equation since their sum is 180.

$$x + x + 2 + x + 4 = 180 \text{ becomes } 3x + 6 = 180 \text{ so } x = 58.$$

The largest angle is represented by $x + 4$ so substitute 58 for x to find that the largest angle is 62 degrees.

Numeric Entry Problem

The three angles of a triangle are in the ratio 2:3:5. Find the number of degrees in the smallest angle.

$$\boxed{36}$$

The angle measures can be represented as $2x$, $3x$, and $5x$. Set up an equation since their sum is 180.

$$2x + 3x + 5x = 180 \text{ becomes } 10x = 180 \text{ so } x = 18.$$

The smallest angle is represented by $2x$ so substitute 18 for x to find that the smallest angle is 36 degrees.

Quantitative Comparison Problem

Compare Quantity A and Quantity B, using the information below.
c) The two quantities are equal.

Quantity A	Quantity B
The largest angle in a triangle whose angles are in the ratio 1:4:5.	**The measure of the largest angle in a right triangle.**

Quantity A is 90 degrees, found by using the equation $x + 4x + 5x = 180$. Since $x = 18$, the largest angle measure, $5x$, is 90. Quantity B is 90 degrees.

Review/Renew

Simplify the following rational expression $\frac{8w^5 + 12w^3 - 10w^2 - 2w^{12}}{2w^2}$.   **a) $4w^3 + 6w - 5 - w^{10}$**

Use the laws of exponents and divide each monomial in the numerator by the denominator. Remember that when you divide you subtract the exponents. Review Core Concept 30 if necessary.

CORE CONCEPT 60 SOLUTIONS: Angles in Polygons

Fill in the Blanks

The sum of the interior angles of an n-sided polygon can be found using the formula **$180(n - 2)$**. The number of degrees in an interior angle of a regular n-sided polygon is $\frac{180(n-2)}{n}$. The number of degrees in an exterior angle of a regular n-sided polygon is $\frac{360}{n}$. All of these formulas are based on the fact that the sum of the measures of the angles in a **triangle** is 180 degrees.

Basic Problem

What is the measure of an interior angle of a regular nonagon (9 sides)?   **d) $140°$**

Substitute 9 for n in the formula $\frac{180(n-2)}{n}$ to get 140.

Intermediate Problem

An exterior angle of a certain regular n-sided polygon measures 30 degrees. How many sides does this polygon have?   **a) 12**

Set $\frac{360}{n}$ equal to 30 to get that n = 12.

Challenging Problem

An interior angle of a regular n-sided polygon measures 156 degrees. If each side measures 10 inches, what is the perimeter of the polygon?   **a) 150"**

Set $\frac{180(n-2)}{n}$ equal to 156 and solve for n to get that n = 15. Multiply 15 by 10 to get the perimeter.

Numeric Entry Problem

What is the sum of the interior angles of a heptagon (7 sides)?

$$\boxed{900}$$

Substitute 7 for n in the formula $180(n - 2)$ to get $180(7 - 2) = 180(5) = 900$.

Multiple Choice with Multiple Answers Problem

Which angles equal 20 degrees?

[a] The exterior angle of an 18-sided regular polygon.

[b] The smallest angle in a triangle whose angles are in the ratio 2:7:9.

Choice [a] uses the formula $\frac{360}{n}$ where n = 18. Choice [b] uses the equation $2x + 7x + 9x = 180$ to get $x = 10$ and the smallest angle is $2x = 20$. Since the acute angles in a right triangle add to 90 degrees, the other acute angle in choice [c] is 40 degrees, but the largest is 50. Choice [d] is 45 degrees, found by dividing 360 by 8.

Review/Renew

An inch is equivalent to approximately 2.54 centimeters. How many inches are equivalent to 77 centimeters? Round to the nearest hundredth.   **a) 30.31**

Set up a proportion. Put centimeters in the numerator and inches in the denominator.

$$\frac{2.54}{1} = \frac{77}{x}$$

Cross multiply to get $2.54x = 77$ and divide both sides by 2.54. Round to two decimal places. Review Core Concept 22 if necessary.

CORE CONCEPT 61 SOLUTIONS: Similar Polygons

Fill in the Blanks

Corresponding sides of **similar** triangles are in proportion, and corresponding angles of similar triangles are **congruent**. The ratio between any pair of corresponding sides is called the **ratio** of **similitude**. The ratio of areas between two similar polygons is the **square** of their ratio of similitude.

Basic Problem

Triangles *LMN* and *HJK*, shown below, are similar.

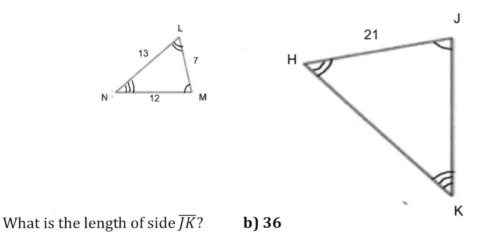

What is the length of side $\overline{JK}$?   **b) 36**

Let the length of $\overline{JK}$ be *y*. Set up a proportion to find *y*.

$$\frac{7}{21} = \frac{12}{y}$$

Cross multiply and solve.

$$12 \cdot 21 = 7y \text{ so } 252 = 7y \text{ and } y = 36.$$

Intermediate Problem

The ratio of similitude between two similar pentagons is 3:4. If the area of the smaller pentagon is 90, what is the area of the larger pentagon?　　**b) 160**

The ratio of the areas is the square of the ratio of similitude, so it is $\frac{9}{16}$. Set up a proportion to find p, the area of the larger pentagon, and solve.

$$\frac{9}{16} = \frac{90}{p} \text{ so } 9p = 1{,}440 \text{ and } p = 160.$$

Challenging Problem

Two hexagons are similar. The area of the larger hexagon is 225 and the area of the smaller hexagon is 81. If the perimeter of the smaller hexagon is 45, what is the perimeter of the larger hexagon?　　**d) 75**

The ratio of the areas is the square of the ratio of similitude, so the ratio of similitude is the square root, which is $\frac{9}{15}$ and this simplifies to $\frac{3}{5}$. This is the ratio of the perimeters. Set up a proportion to find h, the area of the larger pentagon, and solve.

$$\frac{3}{5} = \frac{45}{h} \text{ so } 3h = 225 \text{ and } h = 75.$$

Numeric Entry Problem

The ratio of similitude between two rectangles is 3:7. If the area of the smaller rectangle is 54, what is the area of the larger rectangle?

$$\boxed{294}$$

The ratio of the areas is the square of the ratio of similitude, so it is $\frac{9}{49}$. Set up a proportion to find r, the area of the larger rectangle, and solve.

$$\frac{9}{49} = \frac{54}{r}$$ so $9r = 2{,}646$ and $r = 294$.

Quantitative Comparison Problem

Compare Quantity A and Quantity B, using the information below. **a) Quantity A is greater.**

<u>Quantity A</u>

The ratio of the perimeters of two triangles if the ratio of their sides is 2:5.

<u>Quantity B</u>

The ratio of the areas of two triangles if the ratio of their perimeters is 2:5.

Quantity A is $\frac{2}{5}$ since the perimeter has the same ratio as the sides. Quantity B is $\frac{4}{25}$ since the area ratio is the square of the perimeter ratio. Note that $\frac{4}{25} < \frac{2}{5}$.

Review/Renew

What is the value of $8y^{-2}$ when $y = -6$?   **b)** $\frac{2}{9}$

Using the laws of exponents, $8y^{-2} = \frac{8}{y^2} = \frac{8}{36} = \frac{2}{9}$. Review Core Concept 35 if necessary.

CORE CONCEPT 62 SOLUTIONS: The 30-60-90 Special Right Triangle

---

Fill in the Blanks

If one acute angle of a right triangle measures 60 degrees, the other acute angle measures **30** degrees. A triangle with these three angle measures is called a **30-60-90** triangle. The shortest leg is opposite the **30**-degree angle, and the hypotenuse is opposite the **90**-degree angle. The hypotenuse measures **twice** the length of the shortest leg. The shortest leg measures **half** the length of the hypotenuse.

Basic Problem

In right triangle LMN, the right angle is at M and $\angle L = 30°$. If the hypotenuse measures 52, find the length of leg MN.   **a) 26**

Draw a diagram. Let x be the length of MN.

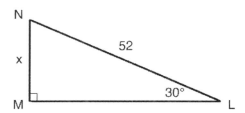

The side opposite the 30-degree angle is half of the hypotenuse. Half of 52 is 26.

Intermediate Problem

Right triangle XYZ has a right angle at Y. Leg XY measures 7 meters. Angle X measures 60 degrees. Find, to the nearest tenth, the perimeter of the triangle.   **c) 33.1 m**

Draw a diagram. Label the lengths of all of the sides using the 30-60-90 triangle.

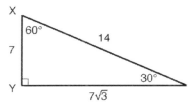

Add: $7 + 14 + 7\sqrt{3} = 21 + 7\sqrt{3}$. Enter this on your calculator and round.

Challenging Problem

What is the area, in square feet, of an equilateral triangle with perimeter 15 feet? Round to the nearest tenth.   **b) 10.8 sq. ft.**

Draw a diagram.

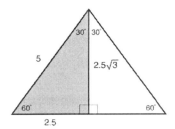

Divide 15 by 3 to get each side equal to 5. Use the 30-60-90 triangle to get the height. The area is $\frac{1}{2}bh$. The base b is 5 and the height h is $2.5\sqrt{3}$. Substitute and round.

Numeric Entry Problem

The hypotenuse of a 30-60-90 triangle has length 75. Express the length of the side opposite the 30-degree angle as a decimal. Round to the nearest tenth.

$$\boxed{37.5}$$

The side opposite the 30-degree angle is half of the hypotenuse. Divide 75 by 2 to get 37.5.

Multiple Choice with Multiple Answers Problem

Side lengths are given below for four 30-60-90 right triangles. Which of the following right triangles has a perimeter less than 24?   **[a] short side = 5**   **[d] hypotenuse = 10**

Choice [a] has sides of 5, $5\sqrt{3}$, and 10 so its perimeter is less than 24. Choice [b] has sides of 8, $8\sqrt{3}$, and 16 so its perimeter is greater than 24. Choice [c] has sides of 6, $6\sqrt{3}$, and 12 so its perimeter is greater than 24. Choice [d] has sides of 5, $5\sqrt{3}$, and 10 so its perimeter is less than 24.

Review/Renew

A rectangle has a length that is 10 more than its width. Its perimeter is 180. What is its length?   **b) 50**

Let x represent the width and let $x + 10$ represent the length. Remember to add two lengths and two widths. Create an equation.

$$x + x + x + 10 + x + 10 = 4x + 20 = 180 \text{ so } x = 40.$$

The width is 40 and the length is 50. Review Core Concept 51 if necessary.

Fill in the Blanks

The 45-45-90 triangle is often called the **isosceles right** triangle. Since the two legs have the same length, we say they are **congruent**. If you are given the length of the legs, you can find the hypotenuse by multiplying the leg length by $\sqrt{2}$. If you are given the length of the hypotenuse, you can find the length of each leg by **dividing** by $\sqrt{2}$.

Basic Problem

An isosceles right triangle has legs with length 20. What is the exact length of the hypotenuse? **c) $20\sqrt{2}$**

Draw a diagram.

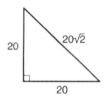

The hypotenuse is found by multiplying the side length by $\sqrt{2}$.

Intermediate Problem

What is the exact length of the diagonal of a square with perimeter 64?   **d) $16\sqrt{2}$**

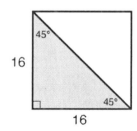

Draw a diagram. If the perimeter is 64, you can divide by 4 to find that each side measures 16. Therefore, the diagonal, which is the hypotenuse, measures $16\sqrt{2}$.

Challenging Problem

A square has diagonal 10. What is its area?   **b) 50**

Draw a diagram.

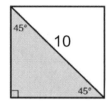

The sides are found by dividing the hypotenuse by $\sqrt{2}$. Each side has length $\frac{10}{\sqrt{2}}$. Multiply $\frac{10}{\sqrt{2}}$ by $\frac{10}{\sqrt{2}}$ to get the area.

$$\frac{10}{\sqrt{2}} \cdot \frac{10}{\sqrt{2}} = \frac{100}{2} = 50.$$

Numeric Entry Problem

An isosceles right triangle has a hypotenuse with length 20. What is the length of one of the legs? Round to the nearest tenth.

$$\boxed{\mathbf{14.1}}$$

The legs are found by dividing the hypotenuse by $\sqrt{2}$.

$$\frac{20}{\sqrt{2}} \approx 14.14 \approx 14.1$$

Quantitative Comparison Problem

Compare Quantity A and Quantity B, using the information below. **b) Quantity B is greater.**

<u>Quantity A</u>	<u>Quantity B</u>
The hypotenuse of a 45-45-90 triangle with area 8.	**The perimeter of a 45-45-90 triangle whose legs have length 2.**

Quantity A's triangle has area 8, which means $\frac{1}{2}bh = 8$, and since the base and height are the same, $\frac{1}{2}x^2 = 8$. Solve to get $x = 4$, so the hypotenuse is $4\sqrt{2} \approx 5.7$. The sides of the triangle in Quantity B are 2, 2, and $2\sqrt{2}$, so the perimeter is about 6.8.

Review/Renew

Simplify $\sqrt{48}$ into simplest radical form.   **a) $4\sqrt{3}$**

Separate $\sqrt{48}$ into the product of two radicals, one of which is the largest perfect square factor of 48, and simplify.

$$\sqrt{48} = \sqrt{16} \cdot \sqrt{3} = 4\sqrt{3}.$$

Review Core Concept 34 if necessary.

CORE CONCEPT 64 SOLUTIONS: Parallel Lines

Fill in the Blanks

If two parallel lines are cut by a transversal, **alternate** interior angles are congruent. This can be shown by superimposing a juxtaposition of the letter **Z** over the diagram. If two lines are cut by a transversal and the alternate interior angles are not congruent, the lines are not **parallel**. If two parallel lines are cut by a transversal, interior angles on the same side of the transversal are **supplementary**.

Basic Problem

Two parallel lines are cut by a transversal, and interior angles on the same side of the transversal have measures represented by $x + 11$ and $4x + 24$. Find the number of degrees in the smaller angle.   **c) 40**

Interior angles on the same side of the transversal are supplementary so set up an equation.

$$x + 11 + 4x + 24 = 180 \text{ becomes } 5x = 145 \text{ so } x = 29 \text{ and } x + 11 = 40.$$

Intermediate Problem

If lines m and n are parallel, which of the following, I, II, III, are true statements?
c) II only

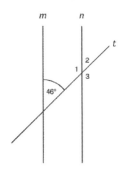

I. ∡1 is complementary to ∡2.
II. ∡1 is congruent to ∡3.
III. ∡2 measures 134°.

Statement I is false since ∡1 is supplementary to ∡2. Statement II is true due to vertical angles. Statement III is false since ∡2 = 46° due to corresponding angles.

Challenging Problem

If $x, y, z,$ and w are degree measures of the angles shown in the figure below, find the value of $x + y + z + w$. **a) 293**

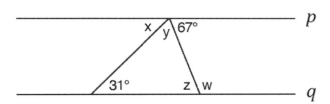

Due to alternate interior angles, $z = 67°$. Due to the angle sum in a triangle being 180 degrees, $y = 82°$. Due to alternate interior angles, $x = 31°$. Due to linear pair with $z, w = 113°$.

$$x + y + z + w = 31 + 82 + 67 + 113 = 293.$$

Numeric Entry Problem

Two interior angles on the same side of a transversal are consecutive odd integers. Find the number of degrees in the smaller angle.

The angles are supplementary and the consecutive odd integers can be represented by x and $x + 2$. Set up the equation $x + x + 2 = 180$ and solve for x, which is the smaller angle.

Multiple Choice with Multiple Answers Problem

If $x = 4$, which could represent the degree measures of a pair of alternate interior angles for a set of parallel lines?

[a] $2x$ and $x + 4$ **[c] $5x + 20$ and $10x$**

The alternate interior angles must have equal measure. Substitute 4 for x.

Review/Renew

Simplify $\frac{x^2 - 25}{2x - 10}$.   **a)** $\frac{x+5}{2}$

Factor the numerator to $(x - 5)(x + 5)$ and the denominator to $2(x - 5)$. Cancel the common factor $(x - 5)$. Review Core Concept 44 if necessary.

CORE CONCEPT 65 SOLUTIONS: Proportions and Multiple Transversals

---

Fill in the Blanks

There are many relationships between angles when two **parallel** lines are cut by a **transversal**. For example, when parallel lines are cut by a transversal, **alternate** exterior angles are congruent. If two or more parallel lines are cut by two transversals, there are some additional segment relationships. The **segments** on the transversals created by the parallel lines are in proportion.

Basic Problem

If lines m, n, and p are parallel, and they are cut by transversals a and b, find the value of the line segment with length y.   **d) 15**

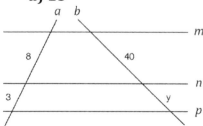

Set up the proportion $\frac{8}{3} = \frac{40}{y}$. Cross multiply and solve to get $8y = 120$ and $y = 15$.

Intermediate Problem

If lines a, b, and c are parallel, and they are cut by transversals t and s, find the value of the line segment with length x. **b) 28**

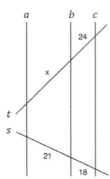

Set up the proportion $\frac{21}{18} = \frac{x}{24}$. Cross multiply and solve to get $18x = 504$ and $x = 28$.

Challenging Problem

Lines m, n, and p are parallel, and they are cut by transversals t and w. Transversal w is perpendicular to the parallel lines, and both transversals intersect line m at point K. Lengths of segments are given. What is the value of x? **b) 2.5**

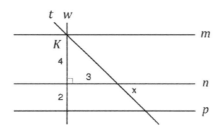

Use the Pythagorean theorem and leg lengths 3 and 4 to find the hypotenuse segment between m and n is 5. Set up the proportion $\frac{4}{2} = \frac{5}{x}$. Cross multiply and solve to get $4x = 10$ and $x = 2.5$.

Numeric Entry Problem

Three parallel lines are cut by a transversal, and the segments yield the following proportion.

$$\frac{5}{8} = \frac{p}{20}$$

What is the value of p?

$$\boxed{12.5}$$

Cross multiply and solve to get $8p = 100$ and $p = 12.5$.

Quantitative Comparison Problem

Compare Quantity A and Quantity B, using the information below.
c) The two quantities are equal.

Quantity A	Quantity B
The value of y in the proportion $\frac{6}{y} = \frac{54}{45}$.	**The value of k in the proportion $\frac{1}{17} = \frac{k}{85}$.**

Cross multiply and solve. Both y and k are equal to 5.

Review/Renew

An arithmetic sequence has first term 3 and common difference 6. Find the 16th term.
c) 93

Use the formula to find the nth term: $a_n = a_1 + (n - 1)d$

Substitute and solve: $a_{16} = 3 + (16 - 1)6$ so $a_{16} = 93$.

Review Core Concept 39 if necessary.

CORE CONCEPT 66 SOLUTIONS: Special Angles in Circles

Fill in the Blanks

A central angle's degree measure is equal to the degree measure of its **intercepted arc**. An inscribed angle's degree measure is equal to **half** its intercepted arc. If an angle is inscribed in a semicircle, it is a **right** angle. Arcs and angles can be measured in **degrees**.

Basic Problem

Inscribed angle *XYZ* in circle *O* has vertex *Y*, and it intercepts an arc that measures 47 degrees. What is the measure of ∢*XYZ*?   **c) 23.5°**

An inscribed angle is half the measure of its intercepted arc.

Intermediate Problem

Quadrilateral *ABCD* is inscribed in a circle. Angle *DAB* measures 80 degrees. What is the measure of angle *DCB*?   **d) 100**

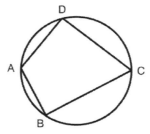

Arc *DCB* is twice the measure of angle *DAB*, so arc *DCB* measures 160 degrees. Arc *DAB* takes up the remainder of the circle, so subtract 160 from 360 to find that arc *DAB* measures 200 degrees. Angle *DCB* intercepts arc *DAB*, so it is half of 200.

Challenging Problem

Triangle *ABC* in circle *O* has diameter *AC* and side lengths as labelled in the diagram below. What is the area of circle O? Leave answer in terms of π.   **a) 25π**

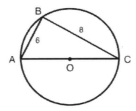

An angle inscribed in a semicircle is a right angle, so triangle *ABC* is a right triangle, and the diameter is the hypotenuse. Use the Pythagorean theorem, and substitute 6 and 8 for the leg lengths.

$$a^2 + b^2 = c^2 \text{ becomes } 6^2 + 8 = c^2, \text{so } c = 10.$$

If the diameter is 10, the radius is 5. Use the area of a circle formula $A = \pi r^2$.

Numeric Entry Problem

Central angle *DOF* in circle *O* measures 79 degrees. Find the degree measure of angle *DEF*.

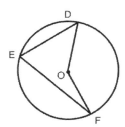

$$\boxed{39.5}$$

Arc *DF* is also 79 degrees since *DOF* is a central angle. Angle *DEF* is an inscribed angle, so measures half of 79, which is 39.5 degrees.

Multiple Choice with Multiple Answers Problem

In circle *O*, minor arc *AB* measures 60 degrees. Which of the following also measure 60 degrees?

[b] central angle *AOB*.   [c] angle *OAB* in triangle *AOB*.   [d] angle *OBA* in triangle *AOB*

Choice [a] is 30 degrees since an inscribed angle is half of its intercepted arc. Choice [b] has a central angle, whose measure is equal to its intercepted arc. Choices [c] and [d] involve the base angles of an isosceles triangle. Triangle *AOB* is at least isosceles since the sides that are the two radii are congruent. Central angle *AOB* is 60, so angles *ABO* and *OAB* evenly split the remaining 120 degrees. The triangle is actually equilateral.

Review/Renew

What is the solution set for the equation $|2x - 10| = 72$?   **a) {41, -31}**

Set up two equations and solve each.

$$2x - 10 = 72 \qquad\qquad 2x - 10 = -72$$

$$2x = 82 \qquad\qquad\qquad 2x = -62$$

$$x = 41 \qquad\qquad\qquad x = -31$$

Review Core Concept 38 if necessary.

Fill in the Blanks

Since a picture is a thousand words, graphs can be very useful to display information. A pie chart, also called a **circle graph**, uses **sectors** of a circle to show a percent breakdown of data. If two sectors of a circle are close in size, it is harder to rank the data than if it was presented in a **bar** graph, which uses parallel, horizontal or vertical **bars** to display data. Displaying changes over time is best accomplished using a **line** graph, and because of their artistic qualities, **pictographs** are often used in magazines.

Basic Problem

In the bar graph above, what is the difference between the most popular and least popular colors of guitars sold?   **c) 65**

The most popular guitar sold, white, recorded 80 sales. The least popular, woodgrain, recorded 15 sales.

Intermediate Problem

In the line graph above, approximately how much larger was the temperature differential between the two cities in January than in June?   **a) 55**

The January difference was approximately 75 degrees. The June difference was approximately 20 degrees. The approximate difference is 55 degrees.

Challenging Problem

The bar graph in the Introduction shows sales of different color Stratosphere guitars at Smash Music Stores last year. If a pie chart was made out of this data, representing all of the Stratosphere guitar sales there, approximately how many degrees would be in the central angle of the sector for White guitars?   **b) 111**

There were 260 Stratosphere guitars sold, and 80 were white.

Color	Number of Guitars Sold
Black	60
Blue	30
Red	75
White	80
Woodgrain	15

$$60 + 30 + 75 + 80 + 15 = 260.$$

Use the percent proportion to find the percent of white guitars sold.

$$\frac{x}{100} = \frac{80}{260}$$

Cross multiply and solve for x.

$$260x = 8{,}000 \text{ so } x \approx 30.8\%.$$

Use the percent proportion again to find the percent of 360 degrees needed for that sector of the circle graph.

$$\frac{30.8}{100} = \frac{x}{360}$$

Cross multiply and solve for x.

$$100x = 11{,}088 \text{ so } x \approx 111°.$$

Note that the problem asked for an approximation, since two steps in this solution had rounding, so 111 degrees is the best answer.

Numeric Entry Problem

If a sector of a circle graph is supposed to represent 15%, how many degrees would be in the central angle of that sector?

$$\boxed{54}$$

Take 15% of 360 degrees using the percent proportion.

$$\frac{15}{100} = \frac{x}{360}$$

Cross multiply and solve for x.

$$100x = 5{,}400 \text{ so } x = 54.$$

Quantitative Comparison Problem

Compare Quantity A and Quantity B, using the information below.
c) The two quantities are equal.

<u>Quantity A</u>   <u>Quantity B</u>

The number of ♦ symbols   **The number of π symbols**
it would take to represent   **it would take to represent**
550 diamonds if each ♦   **275 pizza pies sold if each**
represented 20 diamonds.   **π represented 10 pizzas.**

Divide 550 by 20 and 275 by 10. Both quantities equal 27.5.

Review/Renew

Using factoring, find the solution set for the quadratic equation $x^2 - 9x - 10 = 0$.
b) {10, -1}

Factor and then set each factor equal to 0 and solve.

$$x^2 - 9x - 10 = 0$$

$$(x - 10)(x + 1) = 0, \text{ so } x = 10 \text{ or } x = -1.$$

Review Core Concept 36 if necessary.

CORE CONCEPT 68 SOLUTIONS: Graphing Lines in the Coordinate Plane

---

Fill in the Blanks

A linear equation with two variables has infinitely many solutions, so you cannot put all of the solutions in a **list**. If the coordinates (2, 5) are substituted in the equation $Ax + By = C$ and make it true, the point with those coordinates is on the **graph** of the **line** with that equation. If the coordinates do not satisfy the **equation**, then the point with those coordinates is not on the **graph** of the line.

Basic Problem

Which of the following points is not on the line with equation $5y - x = 1$?   **b) (4, 19)**

Substitute to show that $5(19) - 4 \neq 1$.

Intermediate Problem

The sum of two numbers is 16. Chiara creates a linear graph to model this scenario. What quadrant will the line not pass through?   **c) III**

In Quadrant III both coordinates are negative, and two negative numbers cannot add to 16.

Challenging Problem

The product of the two coordinates of point Q is 72. The x-coordinate is the additive inverse of the smallest prime number. What quadrant is the point in?   **c) III**

The smallest prime is 2. Its additive inverse is -2. If the product of -2 and another number is 72, that other number is also negative. Points with two negative coordinates get plotted in Quadrant III.

Numeric Entry Problem

What is the x-coordinate of the point on the line whose graph is $2y = 3x - 7$ where $y = 4$?

$$\boxed{5}$$

Substitute 4 for y and solve for x.

$$2(4) = 3x - 7$$

$$8 = 3x - 7 \text{ becomes } 3x = 15 \text{ so } x = 5.$$

Multiple Choice with Multiple Answers Problem

Which if the following equations describe lines that go through the point (-7, 3)?
[a] $x + y = -4$ **[b]** $y = x + 10$

Substitute x = -7 and y = 3 into each equation.

Review/Renew

Find the sum of the roots for the quadratic equation $x^2 + 4x - 21 = 0$.   **b) -4**

The two roots, -7 and 3, are found by factoring. Their sum is -4.
Review Core Concept 36 if necessary.

Answers to Quizzes 1-25 with Core Concept Cross References

Fill in the Blanks

The **slope** of a line describes how steep the line is. The slope of a line can be found by dividing the rise by the **run**. Slopes can be any real number, and lines parallel to the y-axis have a slope of 0. Lines **parallel** to the x-axis have an undefined **slope**. The slope-intercept form of the equation of a line is $y = mx + b$.

Basic Problem

What is the slope of the line that passes through $(5, 7)$ and $(6, 11)$?   **a) 4**

Substitute into the slope formula.

$$m = \frac{\Delta y}{\Delta x} = \frac{y_2 - y_1}{x_2 - x_1} = \frac{11 - 7}{6 - 5} = \frac{4}{1} = 4.$$

Intermediate Problem

What is the equation of the line $2x - 3y = 24$ in slope-intercept form?
d) $y = \frac{2}{3}x - 8$

Subtract $2x$ from both sides to get $-3y = -2x + 24$. Divide both sides by -3 to get $y = \frac{2}{3}x - 8$.

Challenging Problem

Which of the following lines has the same slope as the line with equation $4y - 3x = 12$?

d) $y = \frac{3}{4}x + 11$

Convert $4y - 3x = 12$ into slope-intercept form. Add $3x$ to both sides to get $4y = 3x + 12$. Divide both sides by 4 to get $y = \frac{3}{4}x + 3$. The slope is $\frac{3}{4}$, which is the slope of the line $y = \frac{3}{4}x + 11$.

Numeric Entry Problem

What is the y-intercept of the line with equation $5x + 2y = 12$?

Quantitative Comparison Problem

Compare Quantity A and Quantity B, using the information below.
c) The two quantities are equal.

Quantity A	Quantity B
The slope of the line whose equation is $y = 7 - 6x$.	**The y-intercept of the line whose equation is $y = 9x - 6$.**

Quantity A is -6 and Quantity B is -6.

Review/Renew

Which of the following is equivalent to $\frac{17}{85}$?   **a) 20%**

The fraction $\frac{17}{85}$ simplifies to $\frac{1}{5}$, which is equivalent to 20%. Review Core Concepts 15 and 17 if necessary.

> **CORE CONCEPT 70 SOLUTIONS:** Slopes of Parallel and Perpendicular Lines

Fill in the Blanks

If two lines are perpendicular, their slopes are **negative reciprocals**. The product of any number and its reciprocal is **1**, and the product of any number and its negative reciprocal is **-1**. When two lines are **parallel**, they have the same **slope**.

Basic Problem

Which of the following equations describes a line perpendicular to $5x = 3y + 13$?
a) $y = -\frac{3}{5}x + 2$

Convert $5x = 3y + 13$ to slope-intercept form. Subtract 13 from both sides.

$$3y = 5x - 13$$

Divide by 3.

$$y = \frac{5}{3}x - \frac{13}{3}$$

The slope is $\frac{5}{3}$. The slope of a line perpendicular to this line is the negative reciprocal, $-\frac{3}{5}$. Only choice a) satisfies this.

Intermediate Problem

$\overleftrightarrow{AB}$ passes through the points (1, 4) and (7, 16). A line parallel to $\overleftrightarrow{AB}$, named $\overleftrightarrow{KL}$, passes through (10, 1). What is the equation of $\overleftrightarrow{KL}$?   **d) $y = 2x - 19$**

First get the slope of $\overleftrightarrow{AB}$.

$$m = \frac{\Delta y}{\Delta x} = \frac{y_2 - y_1}{x_2 - x_1} = \frac{16 - 4}{7 - 1} = \frac{12}{6} = 2.$$

Substitute to find the y-intercept b.

$$1 = 2(10) + b$$

$$1 = 20 + b$$
$$b = -19.$$

Challenging Problem

Two lines, $\overleftrightarrow{AB}$ and $\overleftrightarrow{CD}$, are perpendicular to the line with equation $y = 5x - 17$. What is the product of the slopes of lines $\overleftrightarrow{AB}$ and $\overleftrightarrow{CD}$?   **c) $\frac{1}{25}$**

The slopes of the perpendicular lines are both $-\frac{1}{5}$. The product of $-\frac{1}{5}$ and $-\frac{1}{5}$ is $\frac{1}{25}$.

Numeric Entry Problem

Find the slope of a line perpendicular to the line with equation $2y = -5x + 10$.

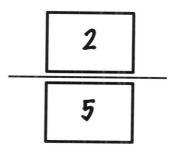

Convert $2y = -5x + 10$ to slope-intercept form. Divide by 2.

$$y = -\frac{5}{2}x + 5.$$

The slope is $= -\frac{5}{2}$ so the slope of a perpendicular line is $\frac{2}{5}$.

Multiple Choice with Multiple Answers Problem

Which of the following equations describe lines that are parallel to $y = 2x + 9$?

[a] $2x - y = 11$ **[b] $y - 2x = 10$**

The slope of $y = 2x + 9$ is 2 and parallel lines have equal slopes. Change choices [a] and [b] to slope-intercept form $y = mx + b$. The slope is 2 in each case. The slope in choice [c] is $-\frac{1}{2}$ and the slope in choice [d] is $\frac{1}{2}$.

Review/Renew

A triangle has side lengths that are consecutive even integers. The perimeter is 66. What is the length of the longest side?   **b) 24**

The sides can be represented by x, $x + 2$, and $x + 4$. They sum to 66.

$$x + x + 2 + x + 4 = 66, \text{ so } 3x + 6 = 66 \text{ and } x = 20.$$

Substitute 20 for x. The longest side, $x + 4$, is 24.
Review Core Concepts 49 and 51 if necessary.

Fill in the Blanks

If you wanted to graph the solution to an inequality in two variables, you should change the inequality to an **equation** and graph the line. If the inequality is a "strict" inequality (< or >), the graph of the line is a **dashed** line. If the graph of the line is not a "strict" inequality (≤ or ≥), the graph is not a **dashed** line. A point is picked to see which side of the line needs to be **shaded**.

Basic Problem

The graph of the solution set of an inequality is shown below.

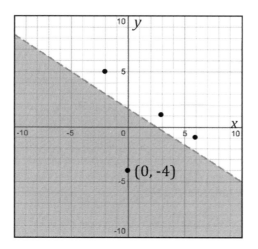

Which of the following points is a solution to the inequality?   **a) (0, -4)**

This is the only point in the shaded area, as shown with its coordinates labelled on the graph. The other three points, from choices b), c), and d), are also shown on the graph.

Intermediate Problem

The graph of a system of linear inequalities is shown below.

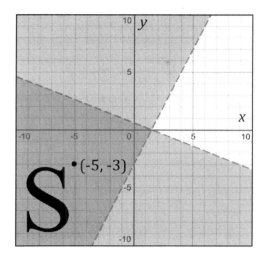

Which of the following points is in the solution set of the system?   **d) (-5, -3)**

This is the only point in the shaded areas for both inequalities. Check out the location in the graph above.

Challenging Problem

The graph of a system of linear inequalities is shown on the right.

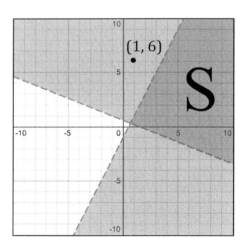

Which of the following points is not a solution to the system of inequalities shown in the graph, but is a solution to one of the inequalities?   **c) (1, 6)**

The points (5, 0) and (6, 1) are in the solution set for the system of inequalities. The point (-5, 1) isn't in the solution set for either inequality.

Look where (1, 6) lies.

Numeric Entry Problem

If the point $(3, k)$ is in the solution set for the inequality $x + y \leq 7$, what is the maximum possible value of k?

Substitute $x = 3$ and $y = k$ into $x + y \leq 7$ to get $3 + k \leq 7$.
Subtract 3 from both sides to see that k is at most 4.

Quantitative Comparison Problem

Compare Quantity A and Quantity B, using the information below. **a) Quantity A is greater.**

Quantity A	Quantity B
The number of solutions to the inequality $y < x + 1$.	**The number of solutions to the inequality $|x + y| < -5$.**

Quantity A is an inequality that has infinitely many solutions. Imagine the graph of the dashed line with one side shaded. Quantity B has no solutions. The absolute value makes the left side of the inequality positive or 0, and neither can be less than -5.

Review/Renew

Twelve is 60% of what number?   **a) 20**

Set up the percent proportion $\frac{12}{x} = \frac{60}{100}$. Cross multiply and solve to get $x = 20$.

Review Core Concept 19 if necessary.

CORE CONCEPT 72 SOLUTIONS: The Midpoint and Distance Formulas

---

Fill in the Blanks

The distance and midpoint formulas are **not** given on the GRE so they have to be memorized. The midpoint between two points (a, k) and (f, h) is $\left(\frac{a+f}{2}, \frac{k+h}{2}\right)$. The distance between these two points is $\sqrt{(f - a)^2 + (h - k)^2}$. If M is the midpoint of the segment PQ, then segment PM is **congruent** to segment MQ.

Basic Problem

What is the length of line segment KL if K has coordinates $(3, 7)$ and L has coordinates $(5, -9)$? Round to the nearest tenth.   **d) 16.1**
Substitute into the distance formula to find the length of KL.

$$d = \sqrt{(5-3)^2 + (-9-7)^2}$$

$$d = \sqrt{(2)^2 + (-16)^2} = \sqrt{4 + 256} = \sqrt{260} \approx 16.1.$$

Intermediate Problem

Point X has coordinates (-2, 10) and point Y has coordinates (10, 26). Find the distance between the midpoint of segment XY and point Y.   **c) 10**

Substitute into the midpoint formula.

$$\left(\frac{x_1 + x_2}{2}, \frac{y_1 + y_2}{2}\right) = \left(\frac{-2 + 10}{2}, \frac{10 + 26}{2}\right) = \left(\frac{8}{2}, \frac{36}{2}\right) = (4, 18).$$

Substitute into the distance formula to find the length of YM.

$$d = \sqrt{(10 - 4)^2 + (26 - 18)^2}$$

$$d = \sqrt{(6)^2 + (8)^2} = \sqrt{36 + 64} = \sqrt{100} = 10.$$

Challenging Problem

The midpoint of segment AB is (8, 29). Point A has coordinates (9, 42). What are the coordinates of point B?   **b) (7, 16)**

Substitute, cross multiply, and solve for x_2.

$$\frac{9 + x_2}{2} = 8$$

$$9 + x_2 = 16$$

$$x_2 = 7.$$

Substitute, cross multiply, and solve for y_2.

$$\frac{42 + y_2}{2} = 29$$

$$42 + y_2 = 58 \text{ so } y_2 = 16.$$

Numeric Entry Problem

Find the distance between the points $(13, 7)$ and $(15, 21)$. Round to the nearest tenth. Use the distance formula and substitute.

$$d = \sqrt{(x_2 - x_1)^2 + (y_2 - y_1)^2}$$

$$d = \sqrt{(15 - 13)^2 + (21 - 7)^2}$$

$$d = \sqrt{(2)^2 + (14)^2} = \sqrt{200} \approx 14.1.$$

14.1

Multiple Choice with Multiple Answers Problem

Which of the following points are located 5 units from $(1, 7)$?
[b] $(4, 11)$ **[c] $(-2, 3)$**   **[d] $(6, 7)$**

Substitute each choice, along with the other point $(1, 7)$, into the distance formula $d = \sqrt{(x_2 - x_1)^2 + (y_2 - y_1)^2}$.

Review/Renew

Find the 5th term of a geometric sequence whose 7th term is 12,288 and whose 8th term is 49,152.   **a) 768**

Divide 49,152 by 12,288 to get the common ratio r.

$$49{,}152 \div 12{,}288 = 4.$$

Divide 12,288 by 4 to get the 6th term, which is $3{,}072$. Divide 3,072 by 4 to get the 5th term, which is 768. Review Core Concept 44 if necessary.

CORE CONCEPT 73 SOLUTIONS: Equations of Circles

Fill in the Blanks

The standard form of the equation of a circle with center (d, k) and radius p is $(x - d)^2 + (y - k)^2 = p^2$. The standard form can be changed to the **general** form by expanding the squared binomials, combining like terms, and setting the equation equal to **0**. If you wanted to change the general form to the standard form, you would have to **complete the square**.

Basic Problem

What is the equation of a circle with center (-5, 1) and radius 10?
a) $(x + 5)^2 + (y - 1)^2 = 100$

Substitute into the standard form of the equation of a circle $(x - h)^2 + (y - k)^2 = r^2$.

Intermediate Problem

The center of a circle is (-3, 11). If the circle has circumference 12π, what is the equation of the circle?　　**a)** $(x + 3)^2 + (y - 11)^2 = 36$

The circumference formula is $C = \pi d$, so the diameter is 12. This makes the radius 6.

Challenging Problem

The point (12, 20) is on the circle with center (4, 5). Find the area of this circle in terms of π. **c)** 289π

Use the distance formula to find the length of the radius.

$$d = \sqrt{(x_2 - x_1)^2 + (y_2 - y_1)^2}$$

$$d = \sqrt{(12 - 4)^2 + (20 - 5)^2}$$

$$d = \sqrt{(8)^2 + (15)^2} = \sqrt{64 + 225} = \sqrt{289} = 17.$$

The area of a circle formula is $A = \pi r^2$ so substitute $r = 17$.

Numeric Entry Problem

What is the diameter of a circle whose equation is $(x - 7)^2 + (y + 18)^2 = 40$? Round to the nearest tenth.

$$\boxed{12.6}$$

The radius is $\sqrt{40} \approx 6.3245$. Since the diameter is twice the radius, multiply by 2 and round to the nearest tenth to get 12.6.

Quantitative Comparison Problem

Compare Quantity A and Quantity B, using the information below. **a) Quantity A is greater.**

Quantity A	Quantity B
The number of points 5 units from (3, 14).	**The number of solutions to the inequality $\lvert x + y - 17 \rvert < -99$.**

Quantity A describes a circle, and there are infinitely many points on a circle. Quantity B has no solutions. The absolute value makes the left side of the inequality positive or 0, and neither can be less than -99.

Review/Renew

What is the greatest integer between -18.4 and -6.5?   **d) -7**

We are looking for the rightmost integer less than -6.5. Think of the number line. The next integer to the left of -6.5 is -7, and that is the greatest integer in the interval. Review Core Concept 1 if necessary.

CORE CONCEPT 74 SOLUTIONS: Graphing a Parabola

Fill in the Blanks

The equation of the axis of symmetry for the parabola $y = kx^2 + nx + h$ is $x = -\frac{n}{2k}$. The y-intercept for this parabola is **h**. Once you know the x-coordinate of the **turning point**, you can write the equation of the axis of symmetry, since the turning point is on the **axis of symmetry**. If k is a prime number, the parabola $y = kx^2 + nx + h$ faces concave **up**, since prime numbers are always **positive** numbers.

Basic Problem

What is the turning point of a parabola whose equation is $y = (x - 3)^2 - 2$?   **d) (3, -2)**
Since this is already in vertex form, the turning point, (vertex), is (3, -2).

Intermediate Problem

A parabola has axis of symmetry $x = -4$, and y-intercept 15. Which of the following could be its equation?   **d) $y = x^2 + 8x + 15$**

The equation of the axis of symmetry is $x = -\frac{b}{2a}$, which must equal -4. The y-intercept is 15, since, when $x = 0$, $y = 15$. Only choice d) works.

Challenging Problem

A parabola has equation $y = x^2 + kx + j$. The y-axis is its axis of symmetry. Its turning point is $(p, 19)$. What is the sum of k, j, and p?   **b) 19**

The parabola can only hit the y-axis once. Where the parabola intercepts the y-axis is the turning point, $(p, 19)$. Therefore, $j = 19$. The x-coordinate for any point on the y-axis is 0, so $p = 0$. The axis of symmetry is $x = 0$, which is the y-axis, so $-\frac{k}{2a} = 0$ so $k = 0$.

Numeric Entry Problem

What is the y-intercept for the parabola whose equation is $2y = x^2 - 8x + 22$?

$$\boxed{11}$$

Divide both sides by 2 to get standard form.

$$y = \frac{1}{2}x^2 - 4x + 11,$$ so the y-intercept is 11.

Multiple Choice with Multiple Answers Problem

Which of the following points are located on the axis of symmetry for the parabola whose equation is $y = x^2 - 8x + 16$?   **[b] (4, 7)**   **[d] (4, -17)**

The axis of symmetry is the vertical line $x = \frac{-b}{2a} = \frac{8}{2} = 4$. For a point to be on this line, its x-coordinate must be 4.

Review/Renew

What is $\frac{3}{7}$ of 280?   **b) 120**

Multiply. Simplify using the common factor 7.

$$\frac{3}{7} \cdot \frac{280}{1} = \frac{3}{1} \cdot \frac{40}{1} = 120.$$

Review Core Concept 12 if necessary.

CORE CONCEPT 75 SOLUTIONS: Transformations

Fill in the Blanks

If, in a function $f(x)$, x is replaced with $-x$, the graph is reflected in the **y**-axis. If x is replaced with $(x + 9)$, the graph translates 9 units to the **left**. If x is replaced with $(x - 11)$, the graph translates 11 units to the **right**. If $g(x) = f(x - 14) + 3$, the graph of $g(x)$ is a **translation** of the graph of $f(x)$.

Basic Problem

The function $f(x)$ is graphed. The function $g(x)$ is a translation of $f(x)$ on the same axes, 9 units to the right of, and 11 units higher than, the graph of $f(x)$. Which of the following is the function $g(x)$?   **a)** $g(x) = f(x - 9) + 11$

The $(x - 9)$ replacing x signifies a translation 9 units to the right. The '+11' signifies a vertical shift up 11 units.

Intermediate Problem

The function $f(x)$ is graphed. The function $g(x)$ is graphed on the same axes, where $g(x) = f(x + 7) - 8$. Describe the position of $g(x)$ compared to $f(x)$.

b) $g(x)$ is 7 units to the left of, and 8 units down from, the graph of $f(x)$.

The $(x + 7)$ replacing x signifies a translation 7 units to the left. The '-8' signifies a vertical shift down 8 units.

Challenging Problem

The following figure has the graph of $f(x)$, and two transformations of $f(x)$, labelled $g(x)$ and $h(x)$.

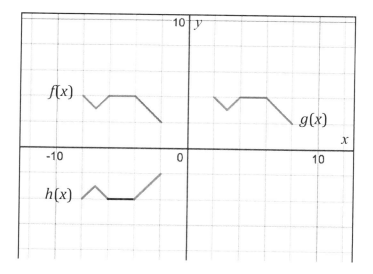

Which of the following statements correctly describes the transformations?

a) $g(x)$ is a translation of $f(x)$, and $h(x)$ is a reflection of $f(x)$

Notice that $g(x)$ looks like a slide of $f(x)$ to the right, and slides indicate translations. If the x-axis was a mirror, the reflection of $f(x)$ would be $h(x)$.

Numeric Entry Problem

The function $p(x)$ is graphed. The function $r(x)$ is graphed on the same axes, where $r(x) = p(x+7) + 19$. Which number represents the amount of the vertical translation?

$$\boxed{19}$$

The '+19' indicates a vertical translation. The replacement of $(x + 7)$ for x in $p(x)$ indicates a horizontal translation to the left.

Quantitative Comparison Problem

Compare Quantity A and Quantity B, using the information below. **b) Quantity B is greater.**

<table>
<tr><td><u>Quantity A</u></td><td><u>Quantity B</u></td></tr>
<tr><td>**The value of k if the graph of $f(x - k)$ is 7 units to the left of the graph of $f(x)$.**</td><td>**The value of h if the graph of $f(x) + h$ is 7 units higher than the graph of $f(x)$.**</td></tr>
</table>

In Quantity A, $k = -7$ since $f(x + 7)$ represents a movement of $f(x)$ to the left 7 units. In Quantity B, $h = 7$.

Review/Renew

The circumference of a circle, in terms of π, is 27π. What is the radius of the circle?
b) 13.5

The circumference formula is $C = \pi d$, so the diameter of the circle is 27. Divide by 2 to get that the radius is 13.5. Review Core Concept 53 if necessary.

CORE CONCEPT 76 SOLUTIONS: Permutations

Fill in the Blanks

An arrangement in which order matters is called **permutation**. The **multiplication** principle is helpful when computing the number of different arrangements. The importance of repeated multiplications in descending order, like $5 \cdot 4 \cdot 3 \cdot 2 \cdot 1$, all the way down to 1, can be shortened by using **factorial** notation, which is an exclamation point after the original number.

Basic Problem

A class has 27 students in it. How many different slates of a President, Vice-President, Secretary and Treasurer can be created? (A student can hold only one office).
b) 421,200

Use the formula $27P4$, or set up four slots and fill in $27 \cdot 26 \cdot 25 \cdot 24 = 421{,}200$.

Intermediate Problem

Ken and Kerry's Ice Cream Parlor sells 22 flavors of ice cream, and offers 12 different toppings. Their sundaes come in 2 sizes. A sundae has one flavor and one topping. How many different sundaes can be created at Ken and Kerry's?   **a) 528**

Set up three slots; for size, flavor, and one topping.

$$2 \cdot 22 \cdot 12 = 528.$$

Challenging Problem

The chess club has 15 members. How many different groups of 2 chess players can be created from the 15 members?   **d) 105**

You can set up two slots, for the two people, or use the formula to compute $15P2$.

$$15 \cdot 14 = 210.$$

However, there is no "order" to the choice of players that will play against each other. So, the choice of Janice first and Craig second provides the same chess contest as Craig first and Janice second. As a result, we need to divide 210 by 2 to get 105 possible groups of 2.

Numeric Entry Problem

The Park Bake Shop has five different shapes of cookie cutters, two different kinds of sprinkles, and three different types of frosting. How many different kinds of cookies can they create if each cookie has one flavor of frosting and one type of sprinkles?

Set up three slots; for cookie shape, frosting, and sprinkles.

$$5 \cdot 2 \cdot 3 = 30.$$

$$\boxed{\textbf{30}}$$

Multiple Choice with Multiple Answers Problem

Which of the following numbers of permutations are multiples of 10?
[b] $6P3$ **[c] $5P3$**

Choice [a] is 3,024. Choice [b] is 120. Choice [c] is 60. Choice [d] is 504.

Review/Renew

If y is inversely proportional to x and $y = 2$ when $x = 36$, find x when $y = 12$.   **c) 6**

The equation for inverse variation is $xy = k$. Substitute $x = 36$ and $y = 2$ to find that $k = 72$. Substitute $k = 72$ and $y = 12$ into $xy = k$, and solve for x. Review Core Concept 46 if necessary.

CORE CONCEPT 77 SOLUTIONS: Combinations

Fill in the Blanks

An arrangement in which order matters is called a **permutation** while an arrangement in which order does not matter is called a **combination**. Both concepts have formulas which rely on **factorials**, which are indicated by the exclamation point notation. The numerical difference between $12P5$ and $12C5$ is **94,248**.

Basic Problem

The Kings Park Ice King sells 52 flavors of Italian ices. A Supreme cup consists of 4 different flavors. How many different groups of 4 flavors can be made from the 52 available flavors?
d) 270,725

$$52C4 = \frac{52!}{4! \cdot 48!} = \frac{52 \cdot 51 \cdot 50 \cdot 49 \cdot 48!}{4! \cdot 48!} = \frac{52 \cdot 51 \cdot 50 \cdot 49}{4 \cdot 3 \cdot 2 \cdot 1} = 270{,}725$$

Intermediate Problem

Simran is getting a Super Mega cup of ice cream from Marvel Ice Cream. They offer 31 flavors, and a Super Mega cup has scoops of 5 different flavors. Simran wants one of the scoops to be chocolate. How many different combinations of the Super Mega cup with chocolate can be created?   **c) 27,405**

Since 1 of the scoops is already spoken for (chocolate), Simran needs to compute the number of groups of 4 flavors that can be made from 30 flavors (we need to exclude one of the flavors, chocolate).

$$30C4 = \frac{30!}{4! \cdot 26!} = \frac{30 \cdot 29 \cdot 28 \cdot 27 \cdot 26!}{4! \cdot 26!} = \frac{30 \cdot 29 \cdot 28 \cdot 27}{4 \cdot 3 \cdot 2 \cdot 1} = 27{,}405.$$

Challenging Problem

Miguel is buying a lottery ticket. The ticket has 52 numbers on it and you need to pick 6 different numbers. If he buys one ticket, how many groups of 6 numbers will not match his?
d) $(52C6) - 1$

There are $52C6$ different possible number combinations, of which Miguel has one, which must be subtracted.

Numeric Entry Problem

What is the value of r if $10Cr = 10$, and r is a positive integer less than 9?

$$\boxed{1}$$

Try it by substituting positive integers for r. It makes sense since there 10 groups of 1 object you can make from 10 objects--each object from the original group of 10 objects. Note that $10C9$ also equals 10, but the problem asked for a number *less* than 9.

Quantitative Comparison Problem

Compare Quantity A and Quantity B, using the information below. **a) Quantity A is greater.**

<u>Quantity A</u>   <u>Quantity B</u>

The number of permutations you can make if you take 4 students from a group of 13 students.

The number of combinations you can make if you take 4 students from a group of 25 students.

Quantity A is $13P4 = 17,160$ and Quantity B is $25C4 = 12,650$.

Review/Renew

What is the perimeter of a square whose diagonal is $10\sqrt{2}$?   **b) 40**

Draw a diagram to help you. Look at the shaded right triangle. The square's diagonal is its hypotenuse. From the 45-45-90 triangle, you know that each side of the square measures 10.

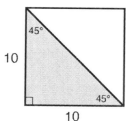

The perimeter, 40, is the sum of all four sides. Review Core Concept 63 if necessary.

CORE CONCEPT 78 SOLUTIONS: Probability

Fill in the Blanks

The probability of an event is a fraction, decimal or percent between the numbers **0** and **1** inclusive. The **complement** of an event K is denoted K' and it is the event that K does not occur. If $P(K)$ represents the probability of event K occurring, then $P(K')$ can be computed by subtracting **$P(K)$** from 1.

Basic Problem

A single die is rolled. What is the probability of it not landing on an even prime number?

d) $\frac{5}{6}$

The die is equally likely to land on any of its 6 faces. The only even prime number is 2, so 5 out of the 6 faces do not show an even prime number.

Intermediate Problem

The following Venn diagram describes the cars on the lot at the Nomad Chevrolet dealership.

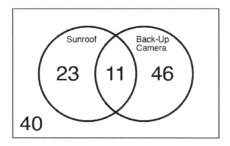

If a car was selected at random, what is the probability that it would have a sunroof?

b) $\frac{17}{60}$

Look at the sunroof circle. You can see that $23 + 11 = 34$ cars had a sunroof. The total number of cars on the lot is $23 + 11 + 46 + 40 = 120$. Note that $\frac{34}{120} = \frac{17}{60}$.

Challenging Problem

The automobile license plate numbers for a certain state are two letters followed by three numbers. If a plate is randomly selected, what is the probably that it will have your initials?

b) $\frac{1}{676}$

Use the slots to compute the total number of different possible plates. Set up five slots; for two letters and three numbers.

$$26 \cdot 26 \cdot 10 \cdot 10 \cdot 10 = 676{,}000$$

Our denominator is 676,000. How many of these plates have your initials? Set up five slots; for two letters and three numbers. Remember that since you want your initials, a '1' is placed in the slots for the letters. You don't care what numbers you get as long as you get your initials.

$$1 \cdot 1 \cdot 10 \cdot 10 \cdot 10 = 1,000$$

Our numerator is 1,000. The probability is $\frac{1,000}{676,000} = \frac{1}{676}$.

Numeric Entry Problem

An urn contains 3 green, 5 red, and 2 blue marbles. A red marble is picked without replacing it, and then another marble is selected. What is the probably that the second marble is blue?

After the red is selected, there are 9 marbles left, 2 of which are blue.

Multiple Choice with Multiple Answers Problem

A die is in the shaped of an **icosahedron**. It has 20 congruent faces, with the numbers 1 - 20 written on it, with one number on each face. What is the probability of the die landing on a prime number?

[a] $\frac{8}{20}$ [c] $\frac{2}{5}$

There are 8 prime numbers on the die faces; 2, 3, 5, 7, 11, 13, 17, 19. The fraction $\frac{8}{20}$ simplfies to $\frac{2}{5}$, so both answers are correct.

Review/Renew

How many kilograms are equivalent to 78,345 grams?   **a) 78.345 kg**

Remember K-H-D-U-D-C-M? Grams are in the units category (U) and you'd have to move 3 places to the left to get to kilograms (K). Move the decimal point on the right of 78,345 three places to the left. Review Core Concept 22 if necessary.

Fill in the Blanks

When you graph numerical quantities, you can put your entries in order, so you can use a graph with labeled axes. However, when you are displaying data about **categorical** variables like color, clothing, food, etc., you cannot order them, so **two-way** tables are an efficient way to show the information. You need to read all questions carefully so you can find the correct row, column, or cell to create the **numerator** and denominator of the fraction required.

Basic Problem

The following two-way table displays how students at Melville Marra Middle School prefer to listen to recorded music.

	CD	Vinyl Record	File Download to MP3 Player	Streaming Service	Totals
Band Member	11	13	45	39	108
Orchestra Member	7	8	11	50	76
Neither Band nor Orchestra	44	23	66	121	254
Totals	62	44	122	210	438

How many more students prefer CDs over vinyl?　　　**c) 18**

There are 438 students at the school, and 62 prefer CDs, while 44 prefer vinyl. Subtract to get 18.

Intermediate Problem

Based on the table from the Basic Problem above, what percent of the students prefer using a streaming service? Round to the nearest percent.　　　**c) 48%**

There are 438 students, and 210 of them prefer a streaming service. Create a fraction, $\frac{210}{438}$, convert it to a percent by dividing, and round.

$$\frac{210}{438} \approx 0.479 \approx 48\%.$$

Challenging Problem

Based on the table from the Basic Problem above, if a student who prefers vinyl was to be selected at random, what is the probability that the person was in the orchestra? Round to the nearest percent.   **c) 18%**

We are given that the student prefers vinyl, so the denominator of the fraction will be 44. Since 8 of these vinyl people are in the orchestra, the fraction is $\frac{8}{44}$. This can be used as an empirical probability. Convert it to a percent by dividing, and round.

$$\frac{8}{44} \approx 0.181 \approx 18\%.$$

Numeric Entry Problem

Based on the table from the Basic Problem above, how many band members do not prefer streaming services?

$$\boxed{69}$$

There are 108 band members, and 39 of them prefer streaming services. The rest, 69 of them, do not.

Quantitative Comparison Problem

Compare Quantity A and Quantity B, using the information below and the table from the Basic Problem above. **b) Quantity B is greater.**

<u>Quantity A</u>	<u>Quantity B</u>
The number of students at Melville Marra Middle School who prefer vinyl records.	**The number of Band members at Melville Marra Middle School who prefer file downloads to MP3 players.**

Quantity A is 44 and Quantity B is 45, from the table.

Review/Renew

What is the additive inverse of $-|2 - 9|$?   **a) 7**

First work inside the absolute value bars.

$$-|2 - 9| = -|-7| = -7.$$

The additive inverse of -7 is 7. Review Core Concept 4 if necessary.

CORE CONCEPT 80 SOLUTIONS: Independent Events

Fill in the Blanks

If the outcome of event X does not affect the probability of event Y occurring, we say that X and Y are **independent** events. If the events A and B are independent, then $P(A) \cdot P(B)$ is equal to **$P(A$ and $B)$**. So, to determine if two events K and L are independent, you need to compute three probabilities; **$P(K)$, $P(L)$, and $P(K$ and $L)$**.

Basic Problem

A summer baseball/softball camp surveys its 60 attendees to compile information about their meal program. The information appears in the two-way table below.

	Baseball (B)	Softball (S)	Total
Hot Dogs (H)	11	4	15
Chicken Fingers (C)	33	12	45
Total	44	16	60

What is the probability $P(C)$ that a camper prefers chicken fingers?   **b) $\frac{45}{60}$**

Out of the total of 60 campers, 45 prefer chicken.

Intermediate Problem

Using the two-way table from the Basic Problem above, what is the value of $P(C) \cdot P(B)$?

c) $\frac{11}{20}$

We know from the Basic Problem above that $P(C) = \frac{45}{60} = \frac{3}{4}$. Out of a total of 60 campers, 44 prefer baseball, so $P(B) = \frac{44}{60} = \frac{11}{15}$. The product $\frac{3}{4} \cdot \frac{11}{15}$ is equal to $\frac{11}{20}$ when simplfied.

Challenging Problem

Using the two-way table from the Basic Problem above, what is the probability $P(C$ and $B)$ that a randomly-selected camper prefers baseball as a favorite sport and chicken fingers as a favorite meal?

a) $\frac{11}{20}$

Out of the 60 campers, 33 choose baseballs as their favorite sport and chicken fingers as their favorite food, and $\frac{33}{60}$ simplifies to $\frac{11}{20}$.

Numeric Entry Problem

Using the two-way table from the Basic Problem above, and your answers to the Basic Problem, the Intermediate Problem, and the Challenging Problem, what is the difference between the probability $P(C$ and $B)$ and the probability $P(C) \cdot P(B)$?

The difference is 0 since $P(C) \cdot P(B) = P(C$ and $B)$, and the events C and B are independent.

Multiple Choice with Multiple Answers Problem

If R and T are independent events, and $P(R) = \frac{45}{60}$ and $P(T) = \frac{44}{60}$, which of the following expressions are equivalent to $P(R$ and $T)$?

[a] 0.55   **[b]** $\frac{33}{60}$ **[c]** 55%   **[d]** $\frac{11}{20}$

All four choices are correct.

Review/Renew

When written in scientific notation, how many significant digits does the number 4,071,000 have?   **b) 4**

The number is equal to 4.071×10^6 in scientific notation, so there are 4 significant digits, and they are 4, 0, 7, and 1. Review Core Concept 33 if necessary.

CORE CONCEPT 81 SOLUTIONS: Mean, Median, Mode

Fill in the Blanks

The mean of a set of numbers is the **arithmetic** average and it can be found using addition and **division**. The **median** is the middle value once the numbers are put in ascending or descending order. This statistic is not numerically affected much by extremely high or low values. The case that occurs the most is called the **mode**.

Basic Problem

Find the mean of the following set of numbers:

$$25, 37, 3, 40, 65$$

a) 34

The sum of these five numbers is 170. Divide by 5 to get 34.

Intermediate Problem

Find the mean of the first eight prime numbers.   **b) 9.625**

The first eight prime numbers are 2, 3, 5, 7, 11, 13, 17, 19. Their sum is 77. Divide 77 by 8 to get 9.625.

Challenging Problem

Find the mean of the median and the mode for this set of data:

$$12, 12, 12, 13, 14, 17, 17, 21, 23,$$

d) 13

The mode, seen by inspection, is 12. The median is 14. The mean of 12 and 14 is

$$\frac{12 + 14}{2} = 13.$$

Numeric Entry Problem

Find the product of the median and the mode for the following set of numbers:

6, 3, 2, 8, 7, 8, 9, 8, 1, 1, 12, 4, 11.

$$\boxed{56}$$

Arrange the numbers in order first, and look for the middle value.

$$1, 1, 2, 3, 4, 6, \textcircled{7}\ 8, 8, 8, 9, 11, 12$$

The median is 7. By inspection, we can see that the mode is 8. The product is 56.

Quantitative Comparison Problem

Compare Quantity A and Quantity B, using the information below. **b) Quantity B is greater.**

Quantity A	Quantity B
The mean of the first five prime numbers.	**The median of the first five composite numbers.**

In Quantity A, the first five prime numbers are 2, 3, 5, 7, 11, and their mean is 5.6. In Quantity B, the first five composite numbers are 4, 6, 8, 9, 10, and their median is 8. Remember that the number 1 is neither prime nor composite.

Review/Renew

What is the product of $5 - 2x$ and $5 + 2x$?   **a) $25 - 4x^2$**

This is the difference of two perfect squares, so you can multiply mentally. (If you forgot that, use "FOIL" to multiply).

$$(5 - 2x)(5 + 2x) = 25 - 4x^2.$$

Review Core Concept 37 if necessary.

Fill in the Blanks

A **frequency distribution** is a table or graph that is useful in displaying frequencies of outcomes when there is a large amount of data. The **total** frequency can be found by adding up all of the individual frequencies for each category. The mean, the **median**, and the **mode** can be computed using the information from a frequency distribution.

Basic Problem

Jordan's probability class is testing a typical six-sided die to see if it is fair. They record 500 rolls of the die, and display the results in the frequency distribution table below. Fill in the blank entries in the table.

Score	Frequency	(Score)·(Frequency)
1	82	82
2	84	168
3	83	249
4	81	324
5	85	425
6	85	510
	Total = 500	Total = 1,758

What is the exact mean for this frequency distribution?   **d) 3.516**

Divide the total points, 1,758, by the total frequency, 500.

Intermediate Problem

A baseball scout rated the arm accuracy of kids on a travel team and filed this frequency distribution in bar graph form as part of his report. The vertical axis gives the frequency of each rating.

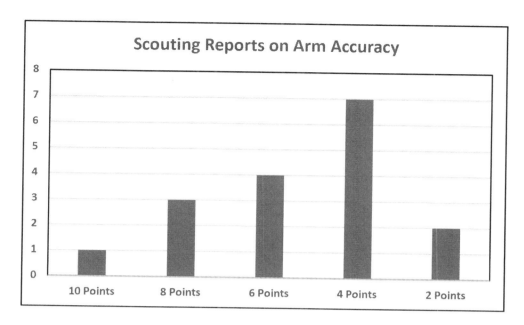

Scouting Reports on Arm Accuracy

What is the mean rating, to the nearest tenth?   **c) 5.3**

Add to find the total frequency.

$$1 + 3 + 4 + 7 + 2 = 17$$

Multiply the frequencies by the ratings, and divide by 17.

$$\frac{1(10) + 3(8) + 4(6) + 7(4) + 2(2)}{17} \approx 5.2941 \approx 5.3.$$

Challenging Problem

An elementary school nurse weighs 253 students and gets an average weight of 66 pounds. After all of that work, she finds out that the scale she was using under-weighed each person by 2 pounds. What is the correct mean?   **c) 68**

You might realize that you can just add 2 to the mean of 66 to get 68. If not, figure out the total number of pounds by multiplying 253 by 66.

$$253 \cdot 66 = 16,698.$$

Add the extra pounds originally not counted by multiplying 253 by 2.

$$253 \cdot 2 = 506.$$

Add 506 to 16,698 to get the total pounds, and divide by 253 to get 68.

Numeric Entry Problem

If 14 students score 80 on a test and 11 score 90, what is the mean score, to the nearest tenth, of all 25 students?

$$\boxed{84.4}$$

Get the total points by multiplying, and then divide by 25:

$$\frac{14(80) + 11(90)}{25} = 84.4.$$

Multiple Choice with Multiple Answers Problem

Look at the table from Example 1. What fraction of the students scored 30?

[b] $\frac{8}{23}$ **[d]** $\frac{16}{46}$

The table shows that 16 out of the 46 students scored 30. The fraction $\frac{16}{46}$ simplifies to $\frac{8}{23}$.

Review/Renew

Inscribed angle XYZ in circle O has vertex Y, and it intercepts an arc that measures 98 degrees. What is the measure of $\angle XYZ$?   **a) 49°**

An inscribed angle has measure equal to half its intercepted arc's measure. Half of 98 is 49.

Review Core Concept 66 if necessary.

CORE CONCEPT 83 SOLUTIONS: Relative Frequency

Fill in the Blanks

If a frequency distribution has a relative frequency column, the sum of all the entries in that column must be **1**. This is because that sum represents 100% of the **total** frequency. A relative frequency can also act as a **probability** to assess how probable certain outcomes are.

Basic Problem

At Baldwinsville High School, 456 of the 611 students have a pet. What is the relative frequency of students who have a pet?   **c)** $\frac{456}{611}$

Intermediate Problem

Using the table from Example 1, what is the relative frequency of students who did not score 5 on the quiz?   **b)** $\frac{16}{17}$

Ten out of the 170 students did score a five. Subtract to find that 160 students didn't score a 5. The relative frequency $\frac{160}{170}$ simplifies to $\frac{16}{17}$.

Challenging Problem

The Venn diagram below shows how many children at Camp Camo visited the Baseball Hall of Fame (B), or Football Hall of Fame (F), both, or neither.

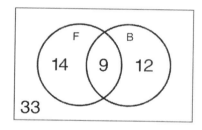

What is the relative frequency of children from the camp who attended exactly one of those Halls of Fame?   **a)** $\frac{13}{34}$

The area with the 9 represents students who visited both Halls of Fame, and we exclude that. Add 14 and 12 to get 26. The total frequency, 68, is found by adding 14, 9, 12, and 33. The relative frequency is $\frac{26}{68}$, which simplifies to $\frac{13}{34}$.

Numeric Entry Problem

Fifteen of the 144 members of the Hillside Middle School Honor Society missed the induction ceremony. What is the relative frequency of students who did attend the induction ceremony?

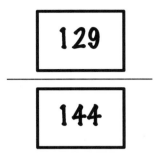

$$\frac{129}{144}$$

Subtract from 144 to find that 129 members missed the ceremony. Note that this fraction can be simplified to $\frac{43}{48}$, so that answer is also correct.

Quantitative Comparison Problem

Compare Quantity A and Quantity B, using the information below.

d) The relationship cannot be determined from the information given.

Quantity A	Quantity B
The relative frequency of students who take instrumental music courses at Elmira High School, if the frequency of students who take instrumental music is 177.	**The relative frequency of students who do not take instrumental music courses at Elmira High School, if the frequency of students who take instrumental music is 177.**

Without knowing the total frequency, or the number of students who don't take instrumental music, you cannot create a relative frequency.

Review/Renew

A right triangle has a leg that measures 12 feet and a hypotenuse that measures 13 feet. What is the area of the triangle?   **d) 30 sq. ft.**

The two legs form the base and the height since they are at right angles. Substitute into the Pythagorean theorem, $a^2 + b^2 = c^2$, to get the other leg, which has length 5 feet. Substitute 5 and 12 for b and h in the area of a triangle formula $A = \frac{1}{2}bh$ to get 30 square feet.

Fill in the Blanks

The **expected value** can be thought of as the average of a series of outcomes from an experiment. The sum of the probabilities in a table set up to compute expected value is **1**. The Geek letter **sigma** is used in the expected value formula to indicate that the products of the outcomes and their probabilities must be added.

Basic Problem

A high-priced charity dinner is raising money using a carnival spinning wheel. Based on the table below, what is the expected value? Round to the nearest cent.   **d) $10.94**

Payout (x)	$5	$10	$20	$50
Probability $P(x)$	$\frac{9}{16}$	$\frac{1}{4}$	$\frac{1}{8}$	$\frac{1}{16}$

$$E(X) = 5\left(\frac{9}{16}\right) + 10\left(\frac{1}{4}\right) + 20\left(\frac{1}{8}\right) + 50\left(\frac{1}{16}\right) \approx 10.94.$$

Intermediate Problem

The following table shows all five possible outcomes of a certain experiment, along with the probability of each outcome. What is the value of k?   **c) 0.05**

Number Selected (x)	8	4	2	1	0
Probability $P(x)$	0.4	0.3	0.2	0.05	k

Since the table includes all possible outcomes of the experiment, the probabilities add to 1.

$$0.4 + 0.3 + 0.2 + 0.05 + k = 1, \text{ so } k = 0.05.$$

Challenging Problem

In Example 2 above, how much profit will the carnival company make if they charge $4 to play a game and 1,250 games are played during the carnival? Round to the nearest dollar.
a) $1,500

In Example 2, the expected payout per game is $2.80. If $4 is charged to play, the expected profit per game is 4 - 2.80 = $1.20. Multiply 1.20 by 1,250 games.

Numeric Entry Problem

What is the expected value for rolling a typical, fair, six-sided die?

Set up a table with values 1, 2, 3, 4, 5, 6 and note that each has probability $\frac{1}{6}$. Use the formula, multiply and add, to get 3.5. If you were to roll a die many, many times, the average of all of your rolls would be near 3.5.

Multiple Choice with Multiple Answers Problem

What is the sum of the probabilities in the following table?   **[c]** $\frac{16}{16}$ **[d] 1**

Payout (x)	$2	$4	$6	$25
Probability $P(x)$	$\frac{9}{16}$	$\frac{1}{4}$	$\frac{1}{8}$	$\frac{1}{16}$

The sum of the probabilities is 1, and $\frac{16}{16} = 1$.

Review/Renew

What is the value of $\left(\sqrt[5]{32}\right)^3$?   **c) 8**

The fifth root of 32 is 2, and 2 to the third power is 8. Review Core Concept 32 if necessary.

CORE CONCEPT 85 SOLUTIONS: Box and Whisker Plots

Fill in the Blanks

A boxplot divides 100% of the data into four sections separated by **quartiles**. The fourth quartile is also the **maximum** and the second quartile is also the **median**. Q_1 denotes the first quartile, which is the 25th **percentile**. The key numbers in a box and whisker plot make up its **five-number summary**.

Basic Problem

A box and whisker plot has a five-number summary of 11, 21, 25, 32, 55. What is its interquartile range?   **a) 11**

The interquartile range, or IQR, is $Q_3 - Q_1$. Substitute 32 for Q_3 and 21 for Q_1 to get 11.

Intermediate Problem

A box and whisker plot has a five-number summary of 21, 28, 35, 52, 65. What is its 75th percentile?   **d) 52**
The 75th percentile is Q_3, which is 52 in this five-number summary.

Challenging Problem

A box and whisker plot has a five-number summary of 21, 28, 35, 52, 65. Which of the following numbers could not be the mean of the data set?   **b) 19**

The minimum is 21. All of the scores are greater than 19, so the mean cannot be 19.

Numeric Entry Problem

A teacher gave an easy 5-point quiz to help boost grades at the end of a marking period. Every student in the class scored a 5 on the quiz. What is the interquartile range for this distribution of scores?

$$\boxed{0}$$

If all of the scores are 5, Q_1 and Q_3 are each 5, and the IQR = $Q_3 - Q_1 = 0$.

Quantitative Comparison Problem

Compare Quantity A and Quantity B, using the information below. **b) Quantity B is greater.**

Quantity A	Quantity B
The mean of the data from a boxplot with this five-number summary: 10, 14, 16, 21, 23.	**The value of Q_2 from a boxplot with this five-number summary: 13, 17, 28, 32, 41.**

Although you cannot determine the mean from a boxplot's five-number summary, notice that Quantity B is 28 since Q_2 is the median. Also notice that all of the scores from Quantity A are below 28, so, whatever the mean is, it is less than 28.

Review/Renew

A circle has circumference 20π. What is the area of a sector of the circle whose central angle measures 72 degrees? Round your answer to the nearest tenth.   **b) 62.8**

From the circumference formula, $C = \pi d$, you can see that the diameter is 20, so the radius is 10. Substitute into the area formula $A = \pi r^2$ to get that the area of the full circle is 100π. Substitute 3.14 for π and divide by 5 since 72 degrees represents one-fifth of the circle. Review Core Concepts 52 and 54 if necessary.

CORE CONCEPT 86 SOLUTIONS: Measures of Spread

Fill in the Blanks

The mean, median, and mode are measures of **central tendency**. The range, interquartile range, and **standard deviation** are measures of dispersion, or spread. They show how much the scores in the distribution are spread out around the **mean**.

Basic Problem

What is the population standard deviation for a distribution composed of the scores 5, 8, 10, 15, 22? Round to the nearest hundredth.   **c) 5.97**

The mean, μ, is 12. Use a table to get the population standard deviation.
- Find the difference between μ and each of the scores.
- Square each of the differences.
- Add up all of the squared amounts to get 178.
- Divide by n, which is 5, to get the average of the squared differences.
- Take the square root of the quotient, 35.6.

Score (x_i)	$(x_i - \mu)$	$(x_i - \mu)^2$
5	-7	49
8	-4	16
10	-2	4
15	3	9
22	10	100
Total = 60		**Total = 178**

Intermediate Problem

Distribution R has mean 230 and standard deviation 1.5. Which of the following scores is least likely to be in the distribution?   **d) 278**

The standard deviation of 1.5 shows that these scores are pretty close to the mean of 230.

Challenging Problem

A distribution has mean 61 and range 20. Which of the following scores cannot be in the distribution?   **a) 82**

The mean has scores above it and below it. So, there are scores lower than 61. If the range is 20, no score can be 21 points higher, which 82 is.

Numeric Entry Problem

Compute the sample standard deviation for the distribution composed of the scores 2, 4, 6, 8. Round to the nearest tenth.

$$\boxed{2.6}$$

The mean, $\bar{x}$, is 5. Use a table to get the sample standard deviation.

- Find the difference between $\bar{x}$ and each of the scores.
- Square each of the differences.
- Add up all of the squared amounts to get 20.
- Divide by $(n - 1)$ which is 3.
- Take the square root of the quotient you just computed to get 2.582. Round.

Score (x_i)	$(x_i - \bar{x})$	$(x_i - \bar{x})^2$
2	-3	9
4	-1	1
6	1	1
8	3	9
Total = 20		Total = 20

Multiple Choice with Multiple Answers Problem

Which of the following data sets has a range of 18?　　[d] **5, 18, 18, 21, 23**

The range is the difference between the highest and lowest scores. *Be careful to not assume that the scores are given in ascending or descending order!* Look at all of the scores, and notice that 23 - 5 = 18. Keep in mind that the "Multiple Choice with Multiple Correct Answers" questions on the GRE *can* have only one correct answer.

Review/Renew

If 15% of a number is 135, what is 80% of that number?　　**c) 720**

Use the percent proportion $\frac{15}{100} = \frac{135}{x}$ to get that $x = 900$.

Use the percent proportion $\frac{80}{100} = \frac{y}{900}$ to get that $y = 720$.

Review Core Concept 19 if necessary.

CORE CONCEPT 87 SOLUTIONS: The Normal Distribution

Fill in the Blanks

The normal curve is often called the **bell** curve because of its shape. The area under the curve represents **100**% of the data, and **99.7**% of the scores occur within 3 standard deviations of the mean. The curve looks the same on both sides, which means it is **symmetric** with respect to the mean.

Basic Problem

A normal distribution has mean 54 and standard deviation 6. Which of the following scores has a percentile rank closest to 84?　　**c) 60**

The score of 60 is 1 standard deviation above the mean, because 54 + 6 = 60. You can see in the diagram from Example 2 in Core Concept 87 that this is the 84th percentile.

Intermediate Problem

Distribution X is normal, with mean 64 and standard deviation 5.2. Distribution Y is also normal, with mean 64 and standard deviation 7.1. Distribution Z is normal, with mean 24 and standard deviation 5.2. Distribution W is normal, with mean 24 and standard deviation 4. In which distribution are you most likely to find the score of 76?   **b) Distribution Y**

Distribution Y has a mean of 64, and a standard deviation of 7.1, so a score of 76 is within 2 standard deviations of the mean. In the other three distributions, the score of 76 is more standard deviations away from the mean.

Challenging Problem

The mean and standard deviation of four normal distributions are given below. Which of the distributions is most likely to have a range of 20?   **b) $\mu = 90$; $\sigma = 3$**

Since 99.7% of the data occurs within 3 standard deviations of the mean, we need to look at $\mu \pm 3\sigma$ for each choice to get the scores 3 standard deviations below and above the mean., and see which is nearest a range of 20. Remember the range is the difference between the highest and lowest scores. In choice b), 3 standard deviations below the mean is 81, and three above is 99, for a range of 18, which is the closest of the choices.

Numeric Entry Problem

A normal distribution has mean 54 and standard deviation 6. What score has a percentile rank closest to 16%? Round to the nearest integer.

$$\boxed{48}$$

A score of 48 is 1 standard deviation below the mean (54 - 6 = 48), which means it is the 16th percentile.

Quantitative Comparison Problem

Compare Quantity A and Quantity B, using the information below. **b) Quantity B is greater.**

<u>Quantity A</u>	<u>Quantity B</u>
The percentile rank of the third quartile Q₃.	**The percentile rank of a score in a normal distribution that is one standard deviation above the mean.**

Quantity A is 75% by definition of the third quartile. Quantity B is 84% since 50% of the area under the curve is below the mean, and 34% of it is between the mean and 1 standard deviation above the mean. Adding 50% to 34% give us 84%.

Review/Renew

Find the number of degrees in an interior angle of a regular octagon.   **c) 135°**

The formula is $\frac{180(n-2)}{n}$ where n is the number of sides. Substitute 8 to get $\frac{180(8-2)}{8} = 135$.

Review Core Concept 60 if necessary.

> **CORE CONCEPT 88 SOLUTIONS: Scatterplots and Trend Lines**

Fill in the Blanks

When two pieces of numerical data are collected from subjects participating in an experiment, the data is called **bivariate** and it can be graphed on the **coordinate** axes using a **scatterplot**. If the scatterplot shows that, as x increases, y increases, we say there is a **positive** association between the variables. If the scatterplot shows that, as x increases, y decreases, we say there is a **negative** association between the variables. In both cases, there is no **causation** implied by the association. That is something that would have to be investigated. However, a trend line might help us **predict** y-values for new x-values.

Example 1 Scatterplot	Example 2 Scatterplot
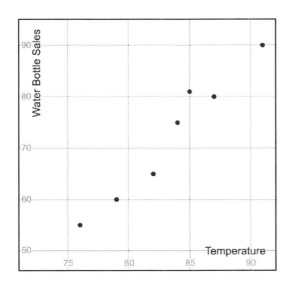	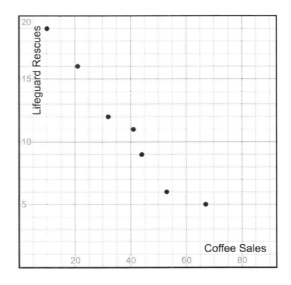

Basic Problem

Using the data from the scatterplot in Example 1, if the trend shown continued into the following week, what would be the best prediction for the number of water bottles sold if the temperature was 90 degrees? **a) 88**

The point (90, 88) would continue the trend of positive association established by the other points on the scatterplot.

Intermediate Problem

Using the data from the scatterplot in Example 2, if the trend shown continued into the following week, what would be the best prediction for the number of lifeguard rescues if that day's coffee sales was 80? **b) 3**

The point (80, 3) would continue the trend of negative association established by the other points on the scatterplot.

Challenging Problem

Dobby did research on the reading level of elementary school students. It turned out that there was a high positive association between reading level and the shoe size of these students. As shoe size increased, reading level generally increased. This was not causal--the researcher did not claim that bigger feet made somebody read better! Which of the following variables was likely "behind the scenes" of why these two variables had a positive association? **b) age**

As age increases during elementary school, reading level increases and shoe size increases. The positive associations between age and shoe size and age and reading level create the positive association between shoe size and reading level.

Numeric Entry Problem

Using the data from the scatterplot in Example 2, what is the number of lifeguard rescues associated with 10 coffees sold?

$$\boxed{19}$$

The point (10, 19) is one of the scatterplot points.

Multiple Choice with Multiple Answers Problem

Which of the following regression lines depict a negative association between the two variables?   [a] $y = 21 - 4x$ [c] $y = -5x + 21.6$

A negative slope indicates a negative association. Recall that the slope is the coefficient of x.

Review/Renew

Which of the following is equivalent to -3^{-4} ?   c) $-\frac{1}{81}$

The negative exponent tells us to put 3^4 in the denominator of a fraction.

$$-3^{-4} = -\frac{1}{3^4} = -\frac{1}{81}.$$

Note that you are raising '3' to the 4th power, not '-3' to the fourth power. Review Core Concept 31 if necessary.

PART 6

ANSWERS TO QUIZZES 1 - 25

Answers to Quizzes 1-25 with Core Concept Cross References

Quiz Number	Question Number	Answer	Core Concept Reference
1	1.	c) -8.2	CC 1
	2.	a) $-\lvert 5 - 8 \rvert$	CC 2
	3.	b) 5	CC 3
	4.	a) 5.66	CC 4
	5.	d) $\frac{13}{22}$	CC 5
2	1.	b) 11	CC 6
	2.	b) 20	CC 7
	3.	b) $\frac{7}{37}$	CC 10
	4.	a) 66	CC 18
	5.	c) 20%	CC 19
3	1.	a) 586	CC 20
	2.	a) 6.78 L	CC 22
	3.	c) 44	CC 23
	4.	b) $5 + 9x^5$	CC 30
	5.	c) $21x^6$	CC 29
4	1.	b) 135°	CC 60
	2.	d) 16	CC 61
	3.	d) 48 degrees	CC 59
	4.	a) $16y^8$	CC 29
	5.	a) 90	CC 8
5	1.	a) $\frac{2\sqrt{5}}{5}$	CC 34
	2.	a) 55	CC 49
	3.	c) 19	CC 48
	4.	a) 18	CC 53
	5.	c) 41	CC 58
6	1.	b) $\frac{3}{5}$	CC 11
	2.	b) 23	CC 49
	3.	b) 72	CC 59
	4.	a) 225π	CC 54
	5.	d) 48'	CC 53

Quiz Number	Question Number	Answer	Core Concept Reference
7	1.	a) -10	CC 1
	2.	b) 25°	CC 66
	3.	b) {30, -41}	CC 38
	4.	d) 92	CC 39
	5.	b) 5	CC 43
8	1.	a) $3x^2k - 6xk^2$	CC 24
	2.	c) 12	CC 59
	3.	b) 0.875	CC 15
	4.	a) $11\frac{2}{3}$	CC 32
	5.	c) 40	CC 58
9	1.	b) 29,760	CC 76
	2.	b) $y = 4^x$	CC 41
	3.	c) $y - 3x = 7$	CC 69
	4.	b) 36	CC 12
	5.	b) $\frac{68}{75}$	CC 14
10	1.	c) 126	CC 67
	2.	d) -49	CC 37
	3.	b) 28	CC 7
	4.	a) 26	CC 51
	5.	c) 16	CC 54
11	1.	c) $\frac{1}{2}$	CC 70
	2.	b) 4	CC 3
	3.	a) $-\frac{3}{7}$	CC 4
	4.	c) 8	CC 9
	5.	d) $\frac{39}{7}$	CC 10
12	1.	c) 8	CC 29
	2.	b) $\frac{7}{12}$	CC 78
	3.	d) $4\sqrt{3}$	CC 34
	4.	b) 10	CC 36
	5.	c) $-\frac{1}{17}$	CC 5
13	1.	b) 7	CC 23
	2.	b) 70	CC 27
	3.	b) $30x^7$	CC 29
	4.	c) $9 - 4x^2$	CC 37
	5.	a) $2\frac{16}{25}$	CC 12

Quiz Number	Question Number	Answer	Core Concept Reference
14	1.	b) 20	CC 61
	2.	a) 540°	CC 60
	3.	b) 80	CC 59
	4.	b) $20\sqrt{3}$	CC 62
	5.	a) 8	CC 58
15	1.	b) $\{-15 < x < 10\}$	CC 38
	2.	a) 512	CC 40
	3.	b) 3	CC 81
	4.	d) $3\frac{1}{3}$	CC 13
	5.	c) 45.17	CC 16
16	1.	b) 13.5	CC 81
	2.	c) 65	CC 51
	3.	c) 240	CC 51
	4.	d) 55	CC 18
	5.	c) 12%	CC 20
17	1.	b) 78°	CC 59
	2.	a) $y = -\frac{2}{7}x + 2$	CC 70
	3.	a) 8.1	CC 72
	4.	b) $(5, 13)$	CC 74
	5.	c) $(x + 4)^2 + (y - 3)^2 = 144$	CC 73
18	1.	b) $\frac{x^2+5x-14}{3x+6}$	CC 45
	2.	c) $(5, 7)$	CC 72
	3.	b) -13	CC 4
	4.	b) -16	CC 23
	5.	d) $24ab$	CC 25
19	1.	b) $y = x^2 - 4$	CC 74
	2.	a) $\frac{4b^2}{9a^3c^7}$	CC 31
	3.	b) 128	CC 32
	4.	c) $(x - 5)(x - 4)$	CC 35
	5.	a) $\{1.4, -4.4\}$	CC 36
20	1.	c) 24	CC 58
	2.	b) $(4, 5)$	CC 68
	3.	c) -1	CC 70
	4.	a) $(0, 4)$	CC 71
	5.	c) 16π	CC 73